THE HISTORICAL BACKGROUND
OF CHEMISTRY

THE HISTORICAL

Henry M. Leicester

. . . .

BACKGROUND

OF CHEMISTRY

New York · John Wiley & Sons, Inc.

London · Chapman & Hall, Limited

PREFACE

In the present book I have attempted to follow the development of chemistry through the thoughts and ideas of chemists rather than through the details of their lives. Historians of science now generally recognize that scientific discoveries, great or small, are almost never spontaneous and original contributions of one man. Even the most revolutionary theories are the result of a long, slow evolution. Basic ideas arise in various places. Gradually these are united, modified, supplemented, and at last announced in what appears to be a new concept. This concept in turn influences and alters subsequent theories, and so the potentially endless progress of science results.

It is clear that the full story of such developments involves not only the personalities and intellects of the scientists themselves, but also the social and economic conditions which surround them and the philosophical ideas to which they are exposed. The complete evaluation of all these factors for any one science would require a massive volume which should be the joint work of many men with different training and viewpoints. As yet, such a volume is lacking for the history of chemistry.

There is also a place for a less extensive work, in which some of these influences are indicated as the story of scientific development is told. In writing this book I have placed the main emphasis on the development and interrelation of chemical concepts. The relative brevity of the treatment has prevented any detailed consideration of other factors, but where possible I have tried to indicate some of the more important areas in which chemistry has had an influence on world history, and others in which the conditions of the world have influenced the chemist himself.

To trace the interrelationships of chemical concepts I have had to devote considerable attention to the earlier periods when chemistry was not recognized as a science in its own right. Many historians of chemistry, especially in earlier days, have felt that only after the time of Boyle and Lavoisier could chemistry have a real history. This does not seem to me to be true. The germ of many modern theories is to be found among the ancient Greeks or even earlier. Fortunately it is becoming possible to consider these early years in more detail than could have been done some time ago. There has been a rather large amount of recent research into the pre-alchemical and alchemical periods, and the position of many renaissance and post-renaissance scientists has been reevaluated. This has made easier the task of following the influences which led to modern chemistry, in spite of the many gaps which still remain. If my attempt can show the modern chemist something of what he owes to his predecessors, I shall be satisfied.

I wish to express my deep thanks to Herbert S. Klickstein who has read and discussed the entire manuscript of this book with me and to whom I am indebted for many stimulating ideas. I am most grateful to the late Clara de Milt for criticisms of the earlier chapters, and to Rudolf Hirsch, Claude K. Deischer, Frederick O. Koenig, and Henry J. Ralston, who have helped me with various parts of the work. I am especially grateful to Denis I. Duveen for the previously unpublished photograph of a page from Lavoisier's notebook. Martin Levey has supplied me with photographs of early Babylonian and Assyrian apparatus, and the *Journal of Chemical Education* has allowed me to reprint these and pictures of Chinese chemical apparatus. I owe my thanks to them. I am most grateful for the indispensable aid of Eva V. Armstrong and Robert F. Sutton of the Edgar Fahs Smith Memorial Library at the University of Pennsylvania; for the valuable assistance of Mrs. Arline Robinson, Librarian of the College of Physicians and Surgeons of San Francisco; and for help from the Libraries of Stanford University and the University of California. Thanks are due to the Oxford University Press for permission to quote individual passages from their editions of the works of Plato and Aristotle.

HENRY M. LEICESTER

San Francisco, Calif.
June, 1956

Contents

CHAPTER I

INTRODUCTION

Chemistry as a science can hardly be said to have begun much before the sixteenth century. Only then did men begin to distinguish the study of individual substances and their changes under the influence of heat, solvents, or reagents from the other changes that went on in the world. Only then did the idea arise that such changes could be considered as much a subject of special study as the behavior of the stars, the nature of numbers, or the illnesses and injuries of the human body.

This does not mean, however, that chemistry had no history prior to that time. In fact, in its technological branches chemistry goes back to prehistoric times. The discovery of fire offered the first opportunity to carry on chemical operations, and early man learned to prepare objects of copper, bronze, and other easily available materials by its aid. There are no written records of this period. Only by the analysis of the weapons and utensils that primitive man manufactured can we gain an idea of the methods and materials which he used.

It might be supposed that the introduction of writing would lead to the preservation of more definite accounts of chemical processes. A few such accounts exist, but it is clear that their authors did not consider these processes as we would today. As civilization developed, as arts and crafts were discovered and improved, many chemical substances were employed but interest lay always in the final product and its use. Only the artisans themselves were concerned with the method by which the product was obtained. With an instinct that seems almost innate in human nature, most of these artisans preserved their trade secrets for themselves and their own descendants. Written records of their processes were seldom kept, for they depended on oral tradition to train their successors. Therefore, again, our knowledge of their methods depends on analyses of objects made and used in ancient civilizations. Everything we know of the subject implies that chemistry, as it would be called today, is as old as man, but it also indicates that in prehistoric times and in early civilizations it was purely empirical and could in no sense be considered a science.

Man has always sought to make tools and objects to add to his comfort or please his decorative instincts, but he has also shown a different side to his nature. He has sought to understand the world around him and the forces that act upon him. Unless he can account for these in a way that seems logical to him, he does not rest content. In earliest times, he peopled his world with gods and demons. Every object, animate or inanimate, was governed by a purposeful being, and these beings kept a watchful eye on each man, at least in his own estimation.

In almost every society, the desire to propitiate these beings, whose attentions were more often malevolent than kindly, led to the separation of a special group in the tribe whose business it was to learn the nature of these supernaturals and to control them. Thus arose the witch doctors, the medicine men, the priests. As the state of civilization advanced, the priestly class was more and more set apart, became more and more specialized. Its members had leisure to think of the forces around them, to organize and systematize the tribal myths, and eventually to establish the accepted version of such legends. Of necessity, these myths in their final form had to be sufficiently plausible to give to the people at large an answer they could accept to the basic questions which occur to everyone: How did the world begin; where did man come from; what are these great forces that surround us, the sun, the moon, the storms, the sea?

In every civilization with which we are acquainted, the answers to these questions were woven into the myths of gods and heroes. Underlying the different accounts in different mythologies, there are often basic similarities, which may represent borrowings from other tribes, but may sometimes represent fundamental methods of human thought. Such ideas were passed on from generation to generation, forming the basis upon which men's minds functioned. As technologies developed, as philosophies evolved, some of these ideas were adapted and used in increasingly involved ways to explain the nature of the visible world. They formed the basis of primitive science, if we consider science to be a system of observation and explanation of the natural world. Beyond this, primitive science did not go. There was no attempt to test ideas by experiment, nor to check hypotheses by predicted facts. Such a stage was not reached until nearly modern times. Yet from this fundamental, primitive science all our modern sciences have come.

Although it is possible to trace these ideas and their developments through the history of any science, historians of general science have seldom attempted to use the history of chemistry for this purpose. Since chemistry evolved late, and sprang from physics, technology, and alchemy, these scholars have turned their attention almost entirely to the sciences that did arise early in history. These were pre-eminently astronomy and mathematics. Astronomy naturally appeared early, for the sun, moon, and stars were clearly visible and impressive. The regularity of their movements must have struck even primitive man and given him a sense of order which was probably his first realization of the regularity of nature. The astrological ideas, which attained great importance in the Mesopotamian cultures and spread from this center over the whole civilized world, also led to an intensive study of the stars. Astronomy as a science thus existed from very early times. Mathematics arose from the need for practical measurements and computations, and when, as was especially so in Greece, it expanded into a science in its own right, it demanded no manual work, and so fitted into the pattern of pure reasoning which was so characteristic of Greek science.

Therefore, historians of the development of human thought as revealed in the history of science have stressed the evolution of these sciences and have tended to neglect the trends and developments which led eventually to a science of chemistry. The historians of chemistry, on the other hand, have too often concerned themselves only with strictly chemical laws and processes, without realizing the wider forces which have affected their development. The history of chemistry should trace the factors in early philosophy and technology which slowly led to an independent science if it is to give a true picture of how this science developed into the giant which modern chemistry has become.

Modern science is western science. The scientific age came into being in western Europe. This is as true for chemistry as it is for any other science of today. The development of western science can be traced back to two civilizations, the Mesopotamian and the Egyptian. From these it can be followed through Greece, Syria, and Arabia to medieval Europe, and thence directly to the present day. This is not to say that the scientific ideas and methods of other civilizations such as India or China were without influence. They have added their contributions as side streams, which have flowed into the main current without greatly altering its general direction. Their study has another value for modern science. Since in these countries science followed its own pattern, and that pattern differed from the pattern of western science, the results were different. These results may serve to show us today what might be the consequence of tendencies that exist in contemporary science. This may guide us in planning our future path. For this reason, these side streams call for consideration in the general history of any science.

As indicated above, chemistry has always consisted of two parts, a practical or technological, and a theoretical. Sometimes one of these branches has been dominant, sometimes the other. At certain noteworthy periods, both have flourished together. The history of chemistry shows that, when this condition prevails, the greatest advances are made.

The problem of studying the history of chemistry in its earliest stages therefore resolves itself into a consideration of the practical developments of the artisans on the one hand, and the speculations of the philosophers on the other. It is necessary to trace the activities of the workers in metal, glass, dyes, and the other substances we now consider to be chemical, and to follow the ideas of the cosmologists and philosophers, the earliest scientists. Eventually the two streams unite to produce a true science, a blend of theory and experiment, which we call alchemy. This degenerated into a pseudoscience in many places and under various conditions, but the thread of a true chemistry was always visible and must be followed to the more open path of a genuine science once more. Then the steps which lead to modern theories and their enormous number of applications can be traced in greater detail from the large amount of available source material. Such is the path which the historian of chemistry must attempt to follow.

CHAPTER II

EARLY PRACTICAL CHEMISTRY

The first discovery that permitted primitive man to carry on chemical reactions on any extensive scale was fire.[1] This discovery was made in the earliest times and has always been associated with remains that can be classed as human. Through the millennia, as prehistoric man slowly developed his cultural patterns, fire gradually made possible an increasing number of weapons and implements with which new advances could be made. When early civilizations began to leave the remains that have been found in graves or on the sites of cities, these objects took the form of metal articles and pottery. The stage of cultural development reached by the makers can usually be determined by these objects. It is only from their examination and analysis that any picture of the earliest developments of chemistry can be formed, since the processes employed in making them were almost never described in any written records that have been found. The ancient craftsman did not think of the act of smelting a metal as a chemical operation, or distinguish it from any other act of his life. Yet, as discoveries were made, they were incorporated in the technical processes of the culture and, in time, some were fitted into the cosmological patterns from which ancient science finally evolved.

A good illustration of this is found in the history of iron. Analytical data indicate that the first iron used in both Mesopotamia and Egypt was probably of meteoric origin. This metal, called by the

Egyptians *baa-en-pet,* iron of heaven, gave rise, perhaps in the Hyksos period (1680–1580 B.C.), to the idea that the sky from which the iron came was composed of an iron plate.[2] Thus can be seen the expansion and cosmological development of what must have originally been the discovery and speculation of a simple metal worker who probably worked in or near a temple where his discovery could be passed on to the priests who formulated the cosmology of Egypt.

The best-preserved objects that have come down to us from ancient civilizations have been metallic. This is so much the case that it has become customary to date the periods of man's development after the stone age in terms of copper, bronze, or iron. Even the ancients had similar ideas, although they usually thought of civilization as degenerating from an original golden age through ages of copper and iron. Among the Babylonians both the gods and the planets were associated with different metals.[3]

Archaeological discoveries have shown that the earliest metals used by man were those that occur in native form. Thus copper and gold are found in the most ancient graves of Egypt and Mesopotamia. Although probably the discovery and utilization of these metals occurred independently in many different areas, trade routes between different peoples were established even before there were written records, and so the transport of various metals between the different civilizations no doubt played an important part in the diffusion of cultures in the ancient world.[1]

Following the utilization of native metals, the next great advance was the discovery of methods of obtaining metals from their ores. Smelting of copper by heat in the presence of wood was probably discovered very early by the Sumerians in their prehistoric home in southern Iran.[4] Since no attempt would be made to purify the ores used, the discovery of bronze by smelting a mixture of copper and tin ores no doubt soon followed. The greater hardness and lower melting point of bronze as compared with copper would account for its widespread use once it had been discovered. In Egypt bronze has been found as early as Dynasties III or IV (about 2500 B.C.),[5] whereas at Ur and Eridu in Mesopotamia bronzes were known in the most ancient period, 3500–3000 B.C.[6] Copper continued to be used even after bronze was known, and remains found at sites on the Sinai peninsula where it was mined by the Egyptians show that the chief ore, malachite, was reduced by wood or perhaps charcoal.[7]

Among the Egyptians, most of the gold originally used contained varying amounts of silver. When the silver content was high, a white gold resulted which was at first considered to be a separate metal, asem (called electrum by the Greeks and Romans).[8] The possibility of combining gold and silver to produce an artificial asem was later recognized, but it is very doubtful whether this was considered a sufficient reason for denying its essential individuality. The concept of alloys did not exist in ancient times. Egyptian gold, which itself probably came from Nubia, was later exported to Mesopotamia where the metal was very scarce. Methods for purifying and assaying gold and silver were developed in both areas.

Lead, tin, and iron were used in the ancient civilizations at later periods than copper, bronze, and gold. After their introduction, the metal workers and smiths became a recognized class of artisans. They occupied a special place in all early cultures.[9] Most of the metallurgical work was done in compounds attached to the temples, and, though the priests themselves probably did not do the actual work,[10] the association of metals with the gods became clearly established.

This was particularly true in Mesopotamia. The earliest Sumerians had worshiped gods who were occupied with metallurgy. In later Babylon, Marduk was "Lord of Gold," Ea of Eridu was the protector of the smiths, and the fire god, Gibil, was known as the "divine smith." [11] Thus the metallurgical arts were a very important part of the culture of the two chief powers of the ancient world, Egypt and Assyrio-Babylonia. The relation of metals to the gods, the temples, and the priests was well established. The significance of metal working throughout the world and over long periods of time is reflected even in language. For example, the Sumerian word for a melting furnace, *udun,* through the Babylonian *utunu* and the Arabic *tannur* became, with the inclusion of the Arabic article *al,* the medieval Latin *Athanor,* a standard type of furnace used by the later alchemists.[12] The traditions of the Mesopotamian metal workers traveled very far.

Besides the metals, a great number of other chemical substances were used by the ancients. Glazes were prepared at a very early period and later were developed into true glass. Lapis lazuli, which probably originated in Babylon, was a much-valued article of commerce and was imported freely into Egypt, where it was classed with the metals. Artificial lapis lazuli was made in Babylon, and "Egyptian Blue," a complex silicate of calcium and copper, was famous throughout the ancient world even down to Roman times, when the architect Vitruvius described its preparation.[13]

An interesting example of the two tendencies that seem always to have been present among technologists is given by two types of recipes for making glazes that have been found in Assyria. The first of these dates from not later than the seventeenth century B.C. and was found at or near Tall 'Umar (Seleucia) on the Tigris. It was the "property of Liballit-Marduk, son of Uššur-an-Marduk, priest of Marduk, a man of Babylon." It describes the making of green glazes by the addition of copper to a simple glaze. It is written in a deliberately obscure and confusing style. It uses the cuneiform signs with their most unusual meanings, and is full of puns and abbreviations that render its translation very difficult.[14]   In contrast, the other recipes are very clear.

Fig. 1.   Drawings from seals showing Babylonian and Assyrian furnaces.   (Courtesy of Martin Levey.)

They were found in the ruins of the Royal Library of Assur-banipal at Nineveh, which dates from the seventh century B.C., although they are probably copies of much earlier recipes. The instructions they contain are given clearly, without any attempt to confuse or mystify the reader.[15]   It is evident that the older tablet was written with the intention of preserving the secret of the process described in it in case the tablet should fall into the hands of an unauthorized person. It implies the existence of a secret guild of glaze makers who kept their processes from the public and used a special terminology to set themselves apart. The later tablets, on the other hand, were probably technical recipes which were not expected to pass outside the hands of the guild members and so did not require precautions for secrecy. Many examples of each of these types of records exist in later years.

It is significant that both these recipes involve, in addition to the description of the technical processes, directions for propitiating the spirits that might interfere with the process. In the older text such spirits take the form of a "dead man"; in the later one, of "embryos." The latter may be incomplete and developing spirits which watch over the developing glaze.[16] There are also directions for the proper days on which the work should be done. All of this indicates the powerful influence of the magical practices of the Assyrians. Even technical works could not be carried on unless the proper astrological and demonic aspects of the work were considered. This magical phase of technology finds its counterpart in many of the later processes that eventually led to chemistry as a science.

Fig. 2. Men stirring a commercial-sized vessel. From Tepe Gawra. (Courtesy of Martin Levey.)

It can be seen that the civilizations of Egypt and Mesopotamia had developed a high degree of technical skill in metallurgy and glass making. These skills were in all probability originally developed for the benefit of the king and the temples. The common people also had simpler, practical chemical methods for preparing foods and liquors, weaving and dyeing cloth, and otherwise filling their daily needs. There are numerous references in the texts to various detergent agents used for washing clothes and the body.[17] Illustrations of apparatus that might have been employed in distillations, and even some of the distilling pots themselves, have been found.[18]

However, the more skillful artisans probably were those in the temples. Most of their discoveries were handed down orally, although occasionally, as in the glazing texts, they were recorded on tablets. The close association between the artisans and the temple priests probably led to a considerable theoretical knowledge of the processes used by the artisans on the part of some of the priests.

Such processes were at first, perhaps, chiefly devoted to working up valuable substances. Very early, however, the artisans must have begun to seek cheaper materials and methods for preparing imitations of the precious substances with which they worked. Methods for gilding cheaper metals to resemble gold, or for preparing artificial gems from glass, soon became part of the trade secrets, and were handed down from father to son for generations. These secrets in time would become part of the lore of the temples. Thus, when the priests, and later the philosophers who studied with them, used their knowledge of physical substances and their changes to build up a picture of the "nature of things," their theories could not help but be influenced by all types of the process with which they were acquainted.

Egyptian and Mesopotamian civilizations had thus developed a practical technology utilizing many chemical processes and methods, which was handed down to later generations. It was this technical civilization and these technical processes that probably had a great influence on the thinking of the men who afterward began to speculate on why these changes occurred. As far as we know, the artisans never did this. The priests of Egypt and Mesopotamia, however, did develop a basic pattern of thinking which strongly influenced the later western world.

REFERENCES

1. E. Pietsch, *Atti X⁰ congr. intern. chim.*, **2**, 32–60 (1938).

2. J. R. Partington, *Origins and Development of Applied Chemistry*, Longmans, Green and Co., London, 1935, pp. 86–87.

3. *Ibid.*, pp. 216, 273.

4. R. J. Forbes, *Metallurgy in Antiquity*, Brill, Leiden, 1950, p. 22.

5. Partington, *op. cit.*, pp. 60–70.

6. *Ibid.*, pp. 245–246.

7. *Ibid.*, pp. 60–62.

8. *Ibid.*, p. 39.

9. Forbes, *op. cit.*, pp. 62–101.

10. Partington, *op. cit.*, pp. 15–18.

11. *Ibid.*, p. 216.

12. *Ibid.*, p. 228.

13. *Ibid.*, p. 118; J. M. Stillman, *The Story of Early Chemistry*, D. Appleton and Co., New York, 1924, p. 24.

14. C. J. Gadd and R. Campbell Thompson, *Iraq*, **3**, 87–96 (1936).

15. R. Campbell Thompson, *A Dictionary of Assyrian Chemistry and Geology*, Clarendon Press, Oxford, 1936, pp. xxiii–xxxvi.

16. R. Eisler, *Chem. Ztg.*, **49**, 577–578 (1925).

17. M. Levey, *J. Chem. Educ.*, **31**, 521–524 (1954).

18. M. Levey, *J. Chem. Educ.*, **32**, 180–183 (1955).

SCIENTIFIC IDEAS
OF THE ANCIENT WORLD

Since it was from Mesopotamia and Egypt that the ideas of primitive science reached the Greeks, it is to Mesopotamia and Egypt that we must look for the earliest traces of our science of chemistry. The form of rational thinking assumed in these cultures explains much that we meet later in alchemy and chemistry.

In an attempt to understand the origin of things man is forced to assume a creation, either from nothing or from some primeval substance. The idea of nothingness is difficult to conceive. It is far easier and more comforting to assume some primal material, disorganized and chaotic perhaps, but related in some way to familiar things. Thus the Babylonians pictured the world as created from water. Once the world is organized, however, a most striking feature is the number of contrary factors that it contains. Day and night, or light and darkness, male and female, hot and cold, wet and dry, or, on the moral plane, good and evil: for every quality there is an opposing contrary. We meet them everywhere. Therefore it is easy to conceive of the primal matter splitting into two contrary substances. From these contraries, all else can be formed. This idea, one of the most fundamental concepts of the Mesopotamian and Egyptian minds, tended to become personified in their mythologies, and most often found expression in the ideas of light and darkness, male and female. A god and a goddess personified light and dark, or more often sun and moon, the latter the ruler of the darkness. The deity of the sun was usually male, though sometimes female, but in either case the deity of the moon was of the opposite sex.[1]

To these divine beings, other contrary qualities were often attached. The Babylonians had the sun god, Bel, and the moon goddess, Ishtar (who sometimes also represented the evening star). The Egyptians recognized, at least as their civilization matured, Osiris and Isis. Whether these personified contrary principles were of independent origin is uncertain. Certainly by the second millennium B.C. communication between Mesopotamia and Egypt through Syria was well established. Babylonian became the official language of diplomacy in the whole complex of nations in Asia Minor and around the eastern shores of the Mediterranean Sea. Trade routes flourished. There is no doubt that ideas were exchanged with relative freedom between the two great civilizations of the region. The ideas that developed are clearly shown in the writings of Diodorus Siculus. By the time he wrote, around 50 B.C., the ideas of the Egyptian priests were expressed in terms of Aristotelian philosophy (see p. 27) but the fundamental concepts undoubtedly went back to a far earlier period. In writing of Osiris and Isis, the sun and the moon, he says:

> They say that these gods in their natures do contribute much to the generation of all things, the one being of hot and active nature, the other moist and cold, but both having something of air, and that by these all things are brought forth and nourished, and therefore that every particular being in the universe is perfected and completed by the sun and moon.[2]

Having conceived of the contraries in this way, men seemed to feel an instinctive need for a gap between them, which had to be filled. If there were positive and negative, there must be neutral. Something had to mediate between the contraries. Thus was born the mystic number three, which has had a special significance from the earliest times. These ideas can be developed in great detail to show why number has been so important in man's thinking, why a whole school of philosophy could be founded by Pythagoras to devote itself to the mysteries of numbers, and why even today the devotees of numerology are to be found on all sides. However, the concept of the two contraries and the mediating third will be found to account for much of the thinking of the early chemists.[1]

The Babylonians were keen observers of the stars. Very early in their history they developed the idea that the heavenly bodies were controlled by deities who influenced the lives of men. From this it was but a short step to the concept that the sun, moon, planets, and stars governed every event on earth. The "science" of astrology was born and was carried to an extreme by the Babylonians and Assyrians. No activity of importance could be begun until the stars had been consulted. The casting of horoscopes became one of the most important activities of the priests. When a child was about to be born, an assistant stood by the bed of the mother. At the moment of birth, he clashed his cymbals and the astrologer on the roof immediately noted the position of the stars.[3] The sun, moon, and five planets were the ruling powers of the world. To each was assigned a special function and a set of properties. Each specifically controlled a number of earthly objects, including the metals which played such an important part in the lives of the people. The sun, the brightest and strongest power, naturally controlled the noblest metal, gold. In turn, the moon usually controlled silver, and the planets the other metals. The particular metal that was dominated by each planet varied somewhat from epoch to epoch and from writer to writer. However, by the early alchemical period, Mars was related to iron, Venus to copper, Saturn to lead, Jupiter to electrum, and Mercury to tin.[4] Although in Babylonian times the metals probably had no greater special significance than some other materials, the pattern of control of substances by astral bodies was set and could later be taken over and expanded by the alchemists.

Another consequence of the ideas of astrology also became of great significance to alchemy in later times. To the great and mighty powers in the heavens corresponded the lesser objects on earth which they controlled. A change in one was reflected in a change in the other. The great world could be called the macrocosm; the lesser, the microcosm. Macrocosm and microcosm were inseparable. What happened in one happened in the other. This idea passed through many variations, some of which will be discussed later.

The chief theoretical contributions of the Babylonians to chemistry were of an astrological nature. These ideas spread also to Egypt, but the Egyptian mind had a more practical character. While the Egyptians accepted astrology, they never gave it the importance it assumed among the Babylonians. Egyptian cosmology was largely mythological, but their science tended to be eminently practical. Fragments of their mathematical and medical papyri show us that they could observe objectively and reason acutely.[5] Thus it was their practical arts that contributed most to the development of chemistry. This phase of their contribution will be considered in the discussion of the rise of Greek alchemy.

The streams of cosmological thought and scientific ideas of the two great ancient civilizations, mingling and influencing each other for a period of two thousand years, were eventually focused on a new nation whose intellectual curiosity and speculative thought, fertilized by the older concepts, furnished much of the foundation upon which later science may be said to be based. This new nation was Greece.

REFERENCES

1. T. L. Davis, *J. Chem. Educ.,* **12**, 3–10 (1935).

2. Diodorus the Sicilian, *The Historical Library,* translation of G. Booth, London, 1700, Vol. I, p. 4.

3. Abel Rey, *La science dans l'antiquité,* Vol. I, *La science orientale avant les grecs,* Le Renaissance du Livre, Paris, 1930, p. 159.

4. J. M. Stillman, *The Story of Early Chemistry,* D. Appleton and Co., New York, 1924, p. 9.

5. Rey, *op. cit.,* p. 306.

GREEK SCIENCE

The Greek scientist, at least in the classical period, was the Greek philosopher. Speculation, not experiment, was the formula of the Greek thinker. The names of the philosophers which have come down to us are the names of men who were seeking to explain the nature of the whole universe and to justify it to themselves. They were seldom content to consider minutely a small part of nature. Everything was done upon a grandiose scale, with sweeping generalizations and vast speculations. The only restraint was the intellectual reasonableness of their ideas. They had to justify their ideas to themselves and to a highly critical audience of contemporary philosophers, not in terms of gods and supernatural forces, but in terms of logic.

The chief characteristic that distinguishes them from the modern scientist, who also reasons logically and deduces his ideas from observation, is their tendency to generalize without sufficient data. For the modern scientist, the most natural further step is to check his deductions by actual experiment. This the Greek philosopher almost never did. The society in which he lived prevented him from even thinking of such a procedure. The philosophers were members of a small, elite group, the free citizens. The glories of Greece originated with this small group, but it is often forgotten that this group could never have made the contributions it did had there not been a much larger group of slaves to do the manual work which kept the society running. Work with the hands was for the slave; work with the mind, for the free citizen. Experiments would have been work for the hands. Therefore the philosopher speculated, drew up vast cosmologies, reasoned with the most exacting logic, but never thought of performing the menial labor of practical experiment. This most characteristic feature of Greek science explains to us the almost incomprehensible willingness of the Greeks to accept ideas which held the germ of truth, but which were embellished with what is now seen to be an overlay of fantastic theory. If an idea seemed reasonable, if it fitted into the pattern of a world picture which gradually developed from all the various schools of Greek philosophy, then it was an acceptable idea and needed no further justification. The attitude is perfectly expressed by Plato in the *Timaeus:*

> If then, Socrates, after so many men have said divers things concerning the gods and the generation of the universe, we should not prove able to render an account everywhere and in all respects consistent and accurate, let no one be surprised, but, if we can produce one as probable as any other, we must be content, remembering that I who speak, and you my judges are but men, so that on these subjects we should be satisfied with the probable and seek nothing further. [To which Socrates replies] Excellent, Timaeus. We must by all means accept it as you suggest.[1]

The importance of Greek philosophical speculation to modern science might seem small if this attitude were considered by itself. This, however, cannot be done. The Greek thinkers established generalizations in which lay the seeds of many of our modern concepts, but, what is more important, they established for themselves an authority which was recognized for the next two thousand years. Their ideas formed the basis upon which Alexandrian, medieval, and renaissance science were built and were considered the final answer to all problems by generations which followed them.

In the field of mathematics, a science that requires no experiments, their development of the subject was, on the whole, valid. In the physical and biological sciences this was less often true. Yet their theories form the basis for the story of the intellectual development of western man. Their explanation of Nature (*physis*) affected alchemy and chemistry in every branch. Hence we must follow their ideas to see how they influenced the development of the science of chemistry.

Greek philosophy, and hence Greek science, began in Ionia, in the city of Miletos, in the sixth century B.C. This was not an accident.

Geographically, Ionia lies at the western extremity of Asia Minor, facing Greece proper, but in direct contact with both Babylonia and Egypt. The trade routes through Syria and Lydia led directly to Ionia, and there is little doubt that ideas traveled the same path.[2] It is of interest that Ionia was also the point on the mainland that had the closest contacts with the civilization of Crete. Since we know nothing of ancient Cretan science, this influence cannot be evaluated, but the fact is at least worth noting. Thus Ionia was the spot where the ancient oriental viewpoints met the fresh Greek mind, and Greek philosophy was born.

The first philosopher whose name, though not his writings, has come down to us was Thales (640–546 B.C.). Traditionally, he traveled in Egypt and there learned the foundations of geometry and astronomy. To him is given the credit for first developing a true scientific interest in these subjects. He took the practical land measures of the Egyptians, the astrology of the Babylonians, and generalized them into sciences. Intellectual curiosity rather than practical need guided his activities. He was the first of a long line of Greek thinkers who sought knowledge for its own sake. To him occurred the question which, in, varying forms, occupied the minds of Greek philosophers for generations: Can everything be regarded as a single reality, appearing in different forms?[3] His reply was in the affirmative, and he found the single reality in water. The Babylonians had held that water was the origin of the cosmos, but they made no attempt to remove this concept from the field of mythology. Thales, however, sought to explain his ideas in more physical terms. Water can be converted into air (evaporation); it can be congealed to a solid. It can therefore serve as the origin of all things. The pattern thus set, the attempt to explain the manifold changes in the world around us in purely physical terms became the leading characteristic of the Ionian school of philosophy.

Anaximander (c. 611–545 B.C.), a pupil of Thales, generalized the concept of the first source still further. To him the origin of all things was the *apeiron,* the indefinite and infinite. This undifferentiated mass gave birth to worlds which appeared and disappeared as bubbles in the *apeiron.* These worlds, though emerging from the *apeiron,* were themselves composed of heat and cold. The concept of opposites, so characteristic of primitive science, was here introduced in a cosmological explanation of the world. This idea in one form or another was typical of all later Greek physics.[4]

The idea was expanded by Anaximenes (fl. c. 546, died c. 528), in turn, a pupil of Anaximander. Discarding the vague idea of the *apeiron,* Anaximenes found the primary material in air. Like the water of Thales and the *apeiron* of Anaximander, this original material still bore some resemblance to a primitive chaos from which physical forces produced a visible world. Anaximenes, however, had a clearer explanation of how the world came into being. Air is subject to the reverse processes of condensation and rarefaction. Rarefaction of the air produces fire; condensation leads to formation of water, earth, and stones.[5] These processes are going on continuously in both directions. Everything is in a state of change. It can be seen that there is no idea of elements involved here; rather the concept is of states of matter: gas, liquid, solid.[6] Their interconversions, which are apparent in everyday life, are made the basis for an explanation of the whole system of nature.

In 494 B.C. Miletos was captured by the Persians. The Ionian school of philosophers was driven westward and fertilized the thinking of other parts of Greece. The philosophers found a particularly favorable reception in Sicily and southern Italy where philosophic schools had also been founded. This was the home of Pythagoras and his followers. The man himself is more or less legendary, but his school was well established, a sort of secret brotherhood devoted to a mystical study of numbers. They had discovered the mathematical relationships in musical harmony, and were responsible for the idea that a mixing (*krasis*) of contraries could produce a mean. Applied to music, this led to harmony; applied to medicine it implied that health consisted in the avoidance of extremes, in a balance of opposing forces.[7]

At more or less the same time Parmenides and his followers, especially Zeno, had propounded a theory of unity which denied the existence of motion, separation, or anything else that could imply disunity. This extreme idea did not itself advance Greek thought, but it posed problems, the answer to which led to further developments in the formulation of a cosmological scheme.

Heraklitos, continuing the development of the Ionian school, chose as the origin of all things fire. His concepts were a definite development from those of Anaximenes. He stressed particularly the constancy of change. In fact, it was perhaps the mobility of fire that made it the logical choice for him as the primal matter. Like a river, "everything flows." A world begins when fire, following the "downward path," condenses to water and then to earth. In turn, on the "upward path," it rarefies once more to fire.[8] In addition, his was a "physics of contraries." Night—day, summer—winter, cold—hot, wet—

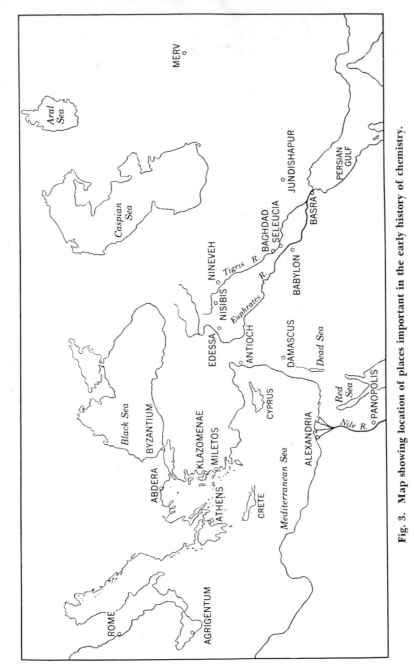

Fig. 3. Map showing location of places important in the early history of chemistry.

dry, these opposites make up the cosmos, the macrocosm. The same set of contraries, the same continual change, occur in the microcosm, man.[9]

Thus, in the Ionian school there was a continuous progression and development of the idea of a primal matter organized into contraries, especially heat and cold, but also stressing moisture and dryness. These are exemplified in the ideas of fire and water, with the related concepts of air and earth. Other factors are also involved, but from the standpoint of later developments of thought these ideas are the most important. The interaction of these principles leads to rarefaction and condensation, to a constant state of movement and change. Ideas of elements, of atoms, and of a vacuum have yet to appear. These concepts emerged as the next step in the development of Greek philosophic thought.

The last philosopher of the Ionian school was Anaxagoras of Klazomenae (c. 499–c. 428 B.C.). Like all the contemporary philosophers, he had to explain the cause of motion. The earlier Ionians had assumed motion to be self-evident, but, after Parmenides denied its existence, it became necessary to account for it in all subsequent theories. Both Parmenides and Anaxagoras came to Athens in about the middle of the fifth century B.C., and from this time Athens became the center of Greek philosophic thought, just as it was the center of art and drama.

Anaxagoras assumed the existence of an infinite number of minute particles which he called "seeds." These were neither created nor destroyed. Change consisted in their mixture and separation, which occurred constantly. These seeds were not atoms in our sense since they contained extremely small portions of everything that exists in the visible world. The amounts of these were variable in an individual seed. On the principle which Anaxagoras introduced, that like attracts like, seeds which contain more flesh, for example, tend to group together to form flesh. To account for separation and motion, Anaxagoras introduced the concept of a guiding intelligence, the *Nous,* mind or reason, which was fundamentally responsible for the constant flux which was part of his picture, as it had been for the other Ionians.[10]

Empedocles of Agrigentum in Sicily (c. 490–c. 435 B.C.), a contemporary of Anaxagoras, was a physician, but also a philosopher in the wide Greek sense. He transformed the older ideas of fire, water, and earth (gas, liquid, solid) into a more precise form, and gave to air a place equal to the other three. There had been a strong tendency to regard air as merely a transition between water and fire. By his acceptance of air as an equal partner, Empedocles gave to fire a place in the material world above that of a mere gas. It was an ethereal substance which by its lightness could well be assigned, as it was by Aristotle, to the heavenly bodies. Empedocles assumed the existence of atoms, not infinite in kind as Anaxagoras had assumed, but of only four different sorts. Now for the first time the theory was clearly stated that there were only four elements, composed of minute, unchanging particles. All visible objects were composed of these elements, or "roots" as Empedocles called them. Instead of assuming an intelligent *Nous* to account for movement, Empedocles further assumed the existence of two additional components of all objects: Love and Strife. Under the influence of Love the elements tended to combine; under the influence of Strife, they separated. This was the first attempt to explain combination in terms of a fixed set of forces, and as such it is the forerunner of the doctrine of affinity which later became so important in chemistry. Empedocles, however, did not think in terms of energy as we do when we use the term affinity. To him Love and Strife were as material as earth, water, air, and fire. The importance of his idea lay in the fact that all changes which the elements underwent under the influence of Love and Strife were mechanical and governed by law. The philosophy of Empedocles was materialistic in the extreme.[11]

Empedocles is also famous for his proof by physical means rather than by intellectual argument that air is a material body. For this he used a *klepsydra,* or water clock. This was a conical object with openings at the base and at the apex. When placed in water, it took a definite time to sink, and thus served as a rough measure of time. Empedocles placed his finger over the opening at the apex and showed that when the cone was immersed water would not fill it completely. When he removed his finger, air rushed out of the opening.[12] This experiment, one of the few that have come down to us from classical times, is noteworthy as showing the beginning of appeal to direct observation. It is far from an experiment in the modern sense, however, since it was not designed to test a theory or serve as a basis for new developments. Rather, it was a lecture demonstration to confirm an idea already established by a process of reasoning.

The atomic theory reached its culmination, so far as the Greeks were concerned, in the ideas developed by Leucippos, of whom almost nothing is known, and by his pupil, Demokritos of Abdera (c. 460–c. 370 B.C.). For the first time, a truly kinetic theory of atoms was expressed. Movement of atoms had been assumed by Anaxagoras and Empedocles, but in what medium the movement occurred was not clear. In the theory of Demokritos the idea of the void, or vacuum, is positively expressed. This concept had been rejected as impossible by Parmenides and his school. Demokritos assumed a void in which the unchangeable atoms of the four elements, earth, air, water, and fire, were in continual random movement. These atoms had physical size and shape, which explained many of their properties. Thus, the atoms of fire were round balls which did not mix with the other elements. The atoms of the latter had geometrical shapes and could become entangled with each other to produce visible substances. The atomic theory of Demokritos was the most completely materialistic that had been developed up to that time.[13] Such atomism was at least partly responsible for the shift of ideas from the path they had followed up to this time.

This shift becomes evident in the ideas of the later Pythagorean school which flourished in Sicily. Preoccupied with number, harmony, and form, the Pythagoreans took over some of the theories of the atomists. They probably first used the word *stoicheion* (letters) to signify elements, and they welcomed the idea of geometrical form as an essential property of atoms. Their ideas of the void were less clear than those of Demokritos. To them it probably resembled air rather than a vacuum. However, they were not ready to go beyond these ideas and accept a completely materialistic cosmos. They concerned themselves more and more with ideas of perfection in the moral sphere.

The reaction from extreme materialism reached almost its highest point in Socrates (c. 470–399 B.C.). After failing to find satisfaction in the theories of the Ionian school while he was young, Socrates turned to the pursuit of an ideal of perfection for man, as opposed to nature. This view Socrates passed on to his great pupil, Plato (c. 428–348 B.C.). It is in Plato that we find to the highest degree a turning away from scientific cosmologies and an attempt to realize the ideal through purely intellectual processes. It has been pointed out that this is an attempt to find the key to nature not in the beginning, but in the end. The cause of things is to be sought not as a mechanical process which drives from behind, but as a final purpose which attracts from ahead.[14] This may seem to be a turning aside from the attempt to explain the universe in what would now be considered scientific terms, but Plato was too much a Greek philosopher not to try to find some sort of physical explanation of the world. Since it was the Platonic idea as modified and developed by Aristotle that governed the thinking of intelligent men for the next two thousand years, the progress of these ideas must be followed, for science during this long period followed the paths that were laid out by the two great philosophers.

Although isolated statements of the scientific ideas of Plato are scattered through a number of his dialogues, they are collected and expressed most clearly in the *Timaeus*. This is also the dialogue that had the greatest influence on medieval thought. Until about 1156 it was the only Platonic dialogue known directly to the West.[15] Much of later chemical thought can be traced to it. Yet the general attitude of Plato to scientific questions held that they were of secondary importance. "A man may sometimes set aside meditation about eternal things, and for recreation turn to consider the truths of generation which are probable only; he will thus gain a pleasure not to be repented of, and secure for himself, while he lives, a wise and moderate pastime." [16]

In the main, the Platonic explanation of nature is Pythagorean and Socratic. All things are combined by the divine Intelligence to produce the best of all possible worlds. Harmony and form are all important. Plato assumes the four elements of Empedocles, but gives to their atoms geometric forms made up of bounding planes. For earth, the planes are squares which can be combined only to give a cube, a stable figure that cannot be rearranged into another form. Thus the solidity and stability of earth are explained. The atoms of the other three elements are made up of enclosing triangles. From such triangles it is possible to construct various regular polyhedra: tetrahedra, octahedra, icosahedra. These are assigned to the different elements on the basis of the properties of the elements themselves. Fire, the most penetrating element, must be composed of tetrahedra, since this figure has the sharpest points and can penetrate best. The octahedron represents air; the icosahedron, water. In this attempt to account for the physical properties of the elements by crude mechanical analogies we see a development of the ideas of Demokritos. Plato, however, unlike Demokritos, did not conceive of the elements as unchanging. The bounding triangles could rearrange themselves into other figures, and thus the elements could be converted into one another. In this way, the concept of the "upward and downward paths," of rarefaction and condensation as explained by the Ionian philosophers, could be accounted for. Obviously, these "elements" of Plato have nothing in common with our idea of elements, but his explanation of their interconvertability was of great significance in the theory of alchemy as it later developed.[17]

The use of mechanical analogies by Plato in explaining chemical changes is clearly shown in the following passage, which also contains the germ of ideas that long prevailed in the minds of chemists of later generations.

> Congealments. Of all the kinds termed fusile, that which is the densest and is formed out of the finest and most uniform parts is that most precious possession called gold, which is hardened by filtration through rocks. This is unique in kind and has both a glittering and yellow color. A shoot of gold which is so dense as to be very hard, and takes a black color, is termed adamant. There is also another kind, which has parts nearly like gold, and of which there are several species; it is denser than gold, and it contains a small and fine proportion of earth, and it is therefore harder, yet also lighter, because of the great interstices which it has within itself; and this substance, which is one of the bright and denser kinds of water, when solidified is called copper. There is an alloy of earth mingled with it which, when the two parts grow old and are disunited, shows itself separately, and is called rust.[18]

In this passage are found a number of ideas that later were expanded by the alchemists. Gold is the most perfect metal; other metals are essentially the same, but contain other admixed substances. Metals, because of their fusibility, partake of the liquid nature of water and are therefore called "waters"; like water, they can be solidified. The formation of "rust" consists in the loss of a part of the whole substance. This, of course, implies a loss of weight.[17] The fuller development of these ideas will be discussed later.

Plato accepted the idea of constant change from the Ionian school. His description of this process gives a clear idea of the feeling of the Greek philosophers.

> We see that what we just now called water, by condensation I suppose becomes stone and earth, and this same element, when melted and dispersed, passes into vapor and air. Air again, when inflamed, becomes fire; and again fire, when condensed and extinguished, passes once more into the form of air; and once more, air, when collected and condensed, produces cloud and mist, and from these, when still more compressed, comes flowing water, and from water comes earth and stones once more; and thus generation appears to be transmitted from one to the other in a circle.[19]

Behind this constant change, Plato felt that there must be something permanent and fixed.

> Suppose a person to make all kinds of figures of gold and to be always transmuting one form into all the rest; somebody points to one of them

and asks what it is. By far the safest and truest answer is, That is gold; and not to call the triangle or any other figures which are formed in the gold "these," as though they had any existence, since they are in the process of change while he is making the assertion.[19]

The matter that lies behind the various forms of the elements Plato considered to be space, which he referred to as the "nurse of generation." On this was impressed the form of the substance that was subject to change, but the nurse of generation itself did not change.

> Wherefore, that which is to receive all forms should have no form; as in making perfumes, they first contrive that the liquid substance which is to receive the scent should be as inodorous as possible; or as those who wish to impress figures on soft substances do not allow any previous impressions to remain, but begin by making the surface as even and smooth as possible. In the same way, that which is to receive perpetually and through its whole extent the resemblances of all external beings ought to be devoid of any particular form.[20]

In the *Timaeus* Plato expands at great length on these ideas and applies them to many common observations from both the mineral and the organic world, but always using his guiding principle of logical deduction without any thought of experimental tests.

Far more directly influential on later generations than the ideas of Plato were those of his pupil, Aristotle (384–323 B.C.). Although his ideas were based on those of Plato, and also, of course, on the whole current of earlier Greek philosophy, Aristotle developed a number of principles of his own. He built up a great body of self-consistent theories that attempted to explain all nature in a more detailed fashion than any of his predecessors had ventured. Aristotle had a more practical and, it can be said, a more scientific mind than Plato. Although his observations in the field of biology were often surprisingly accurate, what is more important is that the picture of nature that he developed became the one and only accepted standard for scientific thought down to the time of the Renaissance. The Hellenistic scientists of Alexandria, the Arabs, and the men of Latin Christendom studied Aristotle so profoundly that his ideas became the unconscious heritage of all thinkers for two thousand years. Every observed fact, every new speculation was automatically fitted into the Aristotelian framework. This gave a unity to men's thinking, no matter how diverse their cultural backgrounds. Eventually, when the fusion of Arabic and western science occurred, there was a common basis from which new advances could come with far less struggle and confusion than might otherwise have been so.

Although Aristotle grew away from Plato as his interest in more practical and less abstract thinking increased, he never abandoned the Platonic idea that the final purpose explains the mechanism of the world.[21] Like all Greek philosophers, Aristotle wished to explain everything. His system of thought was designed to be complete. In consequence he suffered from the same faults as his predecessors. His ideas, derived by deduction or from partial observations, were seldom submitted to any sort of test.[22] Like Plato, the best explanation, to him, was that which seemed most reasonable. Since his explanations were more often of events in the physical than in the spiritual or moral world, his influence on later science was correspondingly greater than that of Plato.

The basis of everything, according to Aristotle, is the first matter (*prote hyle*), on which are impressed the specific qualities that give an individual substance its characteristic form. This first matter obviously corresponds to Plato's nurse of generation. The division into matter and form lies at the basis of all material objects. This first matter is clearly a development of the water, the air, the *apeiron,* the fire of the various Ionian philosophers. However, in the concept of Aristotle there is a more reasonable explanation of the vast differences among the innumerable material objects if we consider that a specific form in each case is impressed on the first matter. It is natural that in later times more attention was devoted to the aspects of the theory which involve form, since by these the practical observations of later workers could be explained,[23] but the concept of the first matter remained basic to all ideas that concerned the transformation of one element into another.

If the first matter was the basis of everything, no room was left for atoms in a void as postulated by Demokritos, and Aristotle was not an atomist. Nevertheless he accepted the idea of the four elements, and, to explain their existence, he assumed the mediation of a set of qualities. These went back to the physics of contraries of Heraklitos. Instead of accepting the large number of contraries which Heraklitos had embodied in his theory, Aristotle confined himself to those that he felt were actually tangible. These were the qualities of heat, cold, dryness, and moisture. The first pair were active qualities; the second, passive. He developed the idea in the following manner:

> The elementary qualities are four, and any four terms can be combined in six couples. Contraries, however, refuse to be coupled: for it is impossible for the same thing to be hot and cold, or moist and dry. Hence it is evident that the couplings of the elementary qualities will

be four: hot with dry, and moist with hot, and again cold with dry and cold with moist, and these four couples have attached themselves to the *apparently* simple bodies (fire, air, water, and earth) in a manner consonant with theory. For fire is hot and dry, whereas air is hot and moist (air being a sort of aqueous vapor), and water is cold and moist, while earth is cold and dry. Thus the differences are reasonably distributed among the primary bodies, and the number of the latter is consonant with theory.[24]

To these four elements which make up all earthly matter, Aristotle felt it necessary to add a fifth element, or essence, the "quintessence," which did not partake of the upward or downward path (rarefaction and condensation) of the earthly elements. This "ether" was an extension of the idea of Heraklitos in making fire the fourth element, but, by Aristotle's time, fire was accepted as equal with the other three elements, and so a fifth element had to be added for the more ideal material which the Greek thinker demanded. The ether had a circular motion, since this was the perfect form, and of it the heavenly bodies were composed. Although this idea continued to influence human thought almost to the present day, it was not of any great importance in explaining the changes that occurred on earth.

It is obvious that Aristotle's elements are not elements in our sense, but merely combinations of qualities. Further, these qualities could be varied in any degree, and so it was possible to transform any element into any other. To convert air into water, it was only necessary that the heat be overcome by the cold, since the moist was common to both. The elements as we know them were not the true elements. Fire as it exists was not the element fire, since its balance of hot and dry was not perfect. It did contain an excess of hotness, however. In later times this concept led to the idealization of certain properties of mercury or sulfur to such an extent that these substances came to represent the qualities themselves.

Combination of qualities to produce elements was the first degree of combination. The elements, however, could combine in any proportion to produce *homoiomeria* which corresponded to the seeds of Anaxagoras. These were the particles out of which blood, stone, flesh were formed. In turn, these combined to produce *anhomoiomeria,* faces, hands, and so on. It is the combination of the elements that is particularly important for the history of chemistry, for by such combinations Aristotle explained all the chemical facts that were known to him.

Aristotle distinguished three types of combination: *synthesis,* which corresponds to our idea of a mechanical mixture; *mixis,* the compounding of solid bodies to produce a new body; and *krasis*, a similar compounding of liquids. The new bodies so produced were absolutely uniform in composition, and no trace of the original components was left. Aristotle thought liquids could combine more readily than solids, and his followers concluded that liquids alone would combine.[25] Actually, the products of *mixis* and *krasis* come closer to our idea of alloys than of compounds.[26] This idea of chemical combination can be recognized even in the early nineteenth century in the theories of Berthollet.

A clear view of Aristotle's ideas of the homogeneity of his *homoiomeria* is found in his explanation of the making of bronze:

> The behavior of the metals is a case in point. For the tin almost vanished, behaving as if it were an immaterial property of the bronze: having been combined, it disappears, leaving no trace except the color it has imparted to the bronze. The same phenomenon occurs in other instances too.[27]

To Aristotle, the individuality of a substance is completely lost when it combines, and the resultant product is something entirely new, although it may show qualities which result from the components. These qualities, however, are a property of the new product, not of the old, and may be immaterial (color) in our concept.

As a further development of his ideas, Aristotle then assumes that two types of "exhalations" can arise from the earth, one vaporous, the other smoky. These exhalations are predominantly moist or dry, respectively. Imprisonment of the exhalations in the earth results in their change into the substances found there. The moist, "vaporous" exhalation gives rise to the metals ("waters"), iron, copper, gold, which are either fusible or malleable. Stones, which come from the dry, "smoky" exhalation, compress the moist exhalation so that it congeals "just as does dew or hoar frost." Hence the metals "are water in a sense, and in a sense not. Their matter was such as might have become water, but it can no longer do so. . . . In every case the evaporation congealed before water was formed. Hence they all (except gold) are affected by fire, and they possess an admixture of earth, for they still contain the dry exhalation." [28]

These ideas are developed at great length in the fourth book of the *Meteorologica*, which has been ascribed to a pupil of Aristotle. A more recent study indicates that it was actually written by Aristotle himself, although it did not form part of the *Meteorologica* as it was originally composed.[25] The fourth book has been called the first textbook of chemistry, for it attempts to explain a bewildering array of facts in terms of the Aristotelian theory. It is a detailed application of this theory in somewhat the manner of an advanced monograph of the present day.

As an example, that solidification can be produced by both heat and cold is explained by the fact that heat acts by drying up moisture, cold by drawing out heat. In either instance, the cold or dry qualities of earth are left predominant. Substances solidified by removal of moisture will dissolve in water, unless the pores left by removal of the moisture are too small to admit water; bodies solidified by removal of heat can be melted by heat. Such bodies are ice, lead, and copper.

These ideas of the variation in proportions of the four qualities occurred in all the explanations of natural phenomena by later Greek and Roman writers, such as Pliny and Vitruvius.[29] They were applied by Galen to medicine in the form of the theory of the four humors, blood, phlegm, black and yellow bile, which had to be balanced in the body if health were to be preserved. This theory was as influential in medicine as was the theory of the four elements in chemistry. The influence of Aristotle cannot be overemphasized in any history of science.

REFERENCES

1. Plato, *Timaeus*, in *The Dialogues of Plato*, translated by B. Jowett, Random House, New York, 1937, Vol. 2, p. 13.

2. Abel Rey, *La science dans l'antiquité*, Vol. II, *La jeunesse de la science grecque*, Le Renaissance du Livre, Paris, 1933, pp. 67–68.

3. J. Burnet, *Greek Philosophy*, Part I, *Thales to Plato*, The Macmillan Co., London, 1914, p. 21.

4. *Ibid.*, p. 22.

5. Rey, *op. cit.*, p. 92.

6. Burnet, *op. cit.*, pp. 26–27.

7. *Ibid.*, pp. 48–50.

8. *Ibid.*, pp. 59–63.

9. Rey, *op. cit.*, p. 316.

10. Abel Rey, *La science dans l'antiquité*, Vol. III, *La maturité de la pensée scientifique en Grèce*, Michel, Paris, 1939, p. 79.

11. *Ibid.*, pp. 94–101; Burnet, *op. cit.*, pp. 69–70.

12. Burnet, *op. cit.*, p. 72.

13. *Ibid.*, pp. 95–98.

14. F. M. Cornford, *Before and after Socrates*, The University Press, Cambridge, 1932, pp. 63–64.

15. G. Sarton, *Introduction to the History of Science*, Vol. I, Williams and Wilkins Co., Baltimore, 1927, p. 113.

16. Plato, *Timaeus, op. cit.*, p. 39.

17. *Ibid.* See also J. M. Stillman, *The Story of Early Chemistry*, D. Appleton and Co., New York, 1924, pp. 120–123, and E. O. v. Lippmann, *Abhandl. Vorträg. Geschicht. Naturwiss.*, **2**, 28–63 (1913).

18. Plato, *Timaeus, op. cit.,* pp. 38–39.

19. *Ibid.,* p. 30.

20. *Ibid.,* p. 31.

21. Cornford, *op. cit.,* p. 90.

22. T. E. Lones, *Aristotle's Researches in Natural Science,* West, Newman and Co., London, 1912, pp. 25–26.

23. v. Lippmann, *op. cit.,* pp. 64–156.

24. Aristotle, *De Generatio et Corruptio,* Book II, c. 2, in *The Basic Works of Aristotle,* ed. by Richard McKeon, Random House, New York, 1941, p. 511.

25. I. Düring, *Aristotle's Chemical Treatise Meteorologica,* Book IV, with introduction and commentary, Elanders boktryckeri, Goteborg, 1944, p. 12.

26. Lones, *op. cit.,* pp. 88–94.

27. Aristotle, *De Generatio et Corruptio,* Book I, c. 10, *op. cit.,* p. 507.

28. Aristotle, *Meteorologica,* Book III, 378, a–b, in *The Works of Aristotle,* ed. by W. D. Ross, Clarendon Press, Oxford, 1931, Vol. III.

29. Stillman, *op. cit.,* pp. 129–133.

CHAPTER V

HELLENISTIC CULTURE
AND THE RISE OF ALCHEMY

With Aristotle, the period of classic Greek philosophy comes to an end. That this is so is largely due to Aristotle's most famous pupil, Alexander the Great (356–323 B.C.). Prior to his conquests, Greece was composed of a number of small city states which constantly struggled with each other for supremacy. Athens held the lead in cultural development, and at times also maintained a political leadership, but conditions were never stable for very long. Alexander changed this. By his conquests he imposed a political stability on Greece that seemed to result in less individuality and originality among Greek thinkers, while it widened tremendously their world outlook.

Alexander was the first world conqueror. From Macedon he led his armies over all the world known to the Greeks and then beyond into lands previously almost unknown to them. When his conquests were complete and he died at Babylon in 323 B.C., he had carried Greek civilization not only into the old centers of culture, Egypt and Mesopotamia, but he also had extended the rule of Macedon across Persia and entered India. For the first time the Indian civilization became generally known to the West. How much Indian thought influenced western thinkers and how much, in turn, India owes to Greek philosophy is still a disputed question. The Indian philosophers did develop theories of atomism which in some respects resemble the atomic theories of the Greeks, but it is almost impossible to date the classical Indian manuscripts. Questions of priority have therefore never been satisfactorily settled. Nevertheless, there seems little doubt that at this time India was not far advanced in chemical development. Aside from the stimulus of a new civilization on general thought in Hellenistic times, the most significant point resulting from the conquest of India was that the way was opened for contacts with the civilization of China, still farther to the East. The importance of this fact will be discussed later.

Not only did Alexander conquer the eastern nations, he made a very definite attempt to fuse the peoples of his empire into one homogeneous whole by encouraging intermarriage between the Greeks and the oriental people among whom they moved. He himself married an eastern princess and at the same time most of his generals took oriental wives. Wherever he went he planned permanent colonies that would bring Greek thought and Greek manners to the conquered people. The most famous of his settlements and the most significant for the future history of chemistry was Alexandria, which he founded at the mouth of the Nile in 332 B.C.

When Alexander died unexpectedly at Babylon, his generals chose a regent to carry on the nominal rule of the Macedonian empire, and then divided the country into satrapies, which were assigned to the various generals. The Satrapy of Egypt was taken by one of the ablest of the generals, Ptolemy. After several years of intrigue, assassination, and open warfare, the Satrapy of Babylon fell to another general, Seleucus. He founded his capital of Seleucia on the Tigris, a city which quickly replaced Babylon as the center of influence in Mesopotamia. Although Seleucus soon moved his capital to Antioch, Seleucia remained a great center of Hellenistic thought until its destruction by the Romans in 164 A.D.

In 305 B.C. the various satraps assumed the titles of King in their own areas. The two kingdoms, which from the first dominated all the others, were Egypt, with its dynasty of the Ptolemies, and the Seleucid Empire, which covered most of Asia Minor, Mesopotamia, and Persia. These kingdoms were the centers of Hellenistic thought for the next three hundred years. This name, Hellenistic, designates the common culture which spread over the whole Near East during this period. Although derived from the Hellenic culture of Greece, it was strongly influenced by the orientals among whom it flourished, and it developed many characteristic features that distinguish it from classical Greek culture.[1]

The greatest center of this Hellenistic culture lay at Alexandria. The Ptolemies were patrons of learning in all forms. The great library and Museum, or university, that they founded attracted scholars and philosophers from all the world. A number of streams of thought met and merged, producing new philosophies and religions. In this great melting pot alchemy arose. Three distinct movements can be traced whose final union led to alchemy. These were Greek philosophy, eastern mysticism, and Egyptian technology.

Even in the days of Plato and Aristotle, Greek philosophy showed two definite tendencies. The mysticism of Pythagoras and some of Plato was opposed by the mechanistic thought of Demokritos and much of Aristotle. The two aspects were often blended in one individual. The Greek desire to explain the entire cosmos in one great scheme encouraged this apparent paradox.

In the Hellenistic culture these tendencies became more sharply separated. Eastern mystical schools abounded, and to those who were mystically inclined they offered a refuge in which scientific thinking was unnecessary. On the other hand, those who were inclined to a more scientific outlook were driven to the mechanical approach by their dislike for the mysticism of their associates. For a time these two schools of thought developed more or less equally. Eventually, as will be seen, the mystical schools became dominant. In the early part of the Hellenistic period, however, this was not true, and as a result there arose throughout the Hellenistic world, and especially in its center, Alexandria, a group of men who approached the modern concept of a scientist more closely than the world had yet known or was to know again for nearly fifteen hundred years.

Such great names as Euclid, Hipparchos, Ptolemy the astronomer, and Archimedes of Sicily attest to the stature of the Hellenistic scientists. These men were not only active in the non-experimental sciences of astronomy and mathematics, but they also turned to actual experiment to support their ideas. We have seen that the Greek philosophers considered that work with their hands was beneath them. The Hellenistic scientists in the earlier periods retained some of this feeling. Archimedes (c. 287–212 B.C.) invented many ingenious mechanisms and performed experiments in the field of hydrostatics, but he considered his purely mathematical work as his only real contribution, worthy of preservation for future generations.[2] Hero of Alexandria, who probably lived between 62 and 150 A.D.,[3] had lost this feeling entirely. His main work, the *Pneumatics,* is devoted to descriptions of mechanical devices such as those that open temple doors when a fire is lighted on the altar, or that deliver holy water when a coin is deposited (a slot machine).

In fact, Hero offers an excellent example of the effect of practical experimental experience on a student of Greek philosophy in Hellenistic times. Like all his contemporaries he was firmly grounded in the principles of Aristotle. When he attempted to explain natural phenomena that did not touch directly on his own work, his explanations were strictly Aristotelian. He wrote of water transformed by fire into air; of the slime and mud formed when water was poured onto earth as the "transformation of water into earth." Yet, when he came to phenomena with which he was actually concerned in his own work, he largely abandoned the ideas of Aristotle. Most of the mechanisms he described were operated by steam (he even described a steam engine). The pressure of gases was the motive power in all cases. Therefore he had a very clear idea of the nature of gases, and in many respects anticipated the kinetic theory. This is clearly shown by the following extract from his book:

> Vessels which seem to most men empty are not empty, as they suppose, but full of air. Now air, as those who have treated of physics are agreed, is composed of particles minute and light, and for the most part invisible. If then, we pour water into an apparently empty vessel, air will leave the vessel proportional in quantity to the water which enters it. [At this point he describes the water clock experiment of Empedocles.] Hence it must be assumed that air is matter. The air when set in motion becomes wind (for wind is nothing else but air in motion) and if, when the bottom of the vessel has been pierced and the water is entering, we place the hand over the hole, we shall feel the wind escaping from the vessel, and this is nothing else but the air which is being driven out by the water. . . . They, then, who assert that there is absolutely no vacuum may invent many arguments on this subject, and perhaps seem to discourse most plausibly though they offer no tangible proof. If, however, it be shown by an appeal to sensible phenomena that there is such a thing as a continuous vacuum, but artificially produced; that a vacuum exists also naturally, but scattered in minute portions; and that by compression bodies fill up these scattered vacua, those who bring forward such plausible arguments in this matter will no longer be able to make good their ground.[4]

He then cites the experiment of blowing air into a globe, proving that compression can occur. When the pressure is released the air rushes out. The particles left behind do not grow in size, and so voids must exist between them. The approach of Hero is very different from that of Plato which was quoted earlier (p. 17). However, he is still not enough of an experimentalist to avoid producing further arguments based on the very plausibility that he had discounted, such as that when the sun's rays penetrate water they do not cause the vessel to overflow, to support his belief in the existence of a vacuum.

The observations of Hero on combustion led him very close to ideas which were not actually accepted until the time of Lavoisier and the beginning of modern chemistry.

> That something is consumed by the action of fire is manifest from coal-cinders, which, preserving the same bulk as they had before combustion, or nearly so, differ very much in weight. The consumed parts pass away with the smoke into a substance of fire, or air, or earth; the subtlest parts pass into the highest region where fire is; the parts somewhat coarser than these into air, and those coarser still, having been borne with the others a certain space by the current, descend again into the lower regions and mingle with earthy substances. Water also, when consumed by the action of fire, is transformed into air; for the vapor arising from cauldrons placed upon flames is nothing but the evaporation of liquid passing into the air. That fire, then, dissolves and transforms all bodies grosser than itself is evident from the above facts.[5]

The main reason that scientists such as Hero did not anticipate the discoveries of the eighteenth century was the tendency, held over from the earlier period of Greek philosophy, to employ experiments to demonstrate a preconceived hypothesis and not to discover a new truth.[6] The theories of Aristotle were used wherever possible to explain new facts, and, when direct observation led to the expression of variant ideas, the Aristotelian ideas were used to strengthen the expression as much as was possible.

The practical interest of Hero in gases was reinforced among the philosophically minded by the physical theories of the Stoics. Stoic philosophy originated in the time of Plato and spread especially in Rome, where it was for a long time the dominant philosophy among the Roman intellectuals. Although it was of smaller importance in Alexandria, its influence was also felt there. The Stoics believed that every phenomenon had a corporeal cause. This took the form of a current of air, or gas, the *pneuma* in Greek, the *spiritus* in Latin. Such a spirit was contained in every object and acted upon every object. It was the cause of growth and decay. In man, air currents discharged from the heart to the various organs brought about life. Thus air came to be regarded as man's soul, though it was a corporeal soul. It is clear that this idea of the *pneuma* could be interpreted in a strictly physical sense, or as a rather metaphysical abstraction, depending upon the individual philosopher. In any case, this philosophical concept supplied a basis for an interest in gases and strengthened the idea that a spirit was an essential part of every material object.[7]

It should be mentioned at this point that, whereas the influence of Aristotle, reinforced by the ideas of most of the philosophers who flourished in Hellenistic times, tended to drive out the atomic ideas of Leucippos and Demokritos, these ideas were not wholly lost. They were taken up by the Epicureans and given their clearest expression in the great poem *De rerum natura* of Lucretius (c. 96–c. 55 B.C.). Although they did not influence scientific thought at this time, nor even for long afterwards, they were not lost, and, as will be seen, their influence was eventually felt once more.

As time passed, an increasing number of mystical religions from the East established themselves in Alexandria, growing up alongside the native Egyptian cults. These religions influenced the Hellenistic philosophies, which grew further and further away from the spirit of the earlier Greek philosophers.

These later philosophies had in common a tendency to turn away from observation and to rely upon mystic revelation for an understanding of nature. In the second century A.D., Gnosticism became prominent. Its adherents believed that they possessed a secret knowledge obtained by revelation alone. Entry into the society of the Gnostics was by a mystical initiation. Like most easterners, Gnostics were not impressed by the Platonic doctrine of the reality only of good. They believed firmly in evil as well, and reverted to the dualism which had been so characteristic of primitive thinking. In the third century, these tendencies were intensified in Neoplatonism. Neoplatonists, who became the dominant philosophers of Alexandria, felt a definite contempt for reason and science. Direct revelation from the Deity was the only source of knowledge. Still later, Manichaeanism, spreading from Persia and Babylonia, brought an uncompromising dualism of good and evil, most often symbolized by light and darkness.

All these sects, which could equally be called mystic philosophies or religions, interacted with one another, with purely magical and astrological practices, and with the Jewish and Christian religions which were an important part of Alexandrian society. It is clear that all these ideas, so widespread in the Hellenistic world, could not fail to influence any contemporary movement that had an intellectual basis.[8]

Apart from the scientific workers of Alexandria, such as Hero, and the mystical philosophers such as the Gnostics and the Neoplatonists, there existed a class of practical artisans who probably at first stood aside from the two groups mentioned. These were the men who prepared the luxuries for the wealthy classes and the temples. As mentioned earlier, Egyptian artisans, working in temple compounds, had been especially skillful in such trades. The processes that they developed have been described by the encyclopedic-minded writers of the Roman period, such as Diodorus Siculus and, above all, Pliny. However, these descriptions are, in the main, second hand. It is obvious that these writers merely copied down what they read or were told, often without any real understanding of the work they were describing. As a result, much fanciful material was mixed with the practical details, and serious errors are often found.

Fortunately, our knowledge of the state of Egyptian practical chemistry has a much firmer basis than these second-hand descriptions. Early in the nineteenth century, Johann d'Anastasy, the Swedish Vice-Consul at Alexandria, acquired a large collection of papyri, written in Greek. Most of these he later sold in the Netherlands, though he distributed some in his native land. Translation and study of these papyri proceeded slowly. In 1885 a papyrus of definitely chemical character was revealed. It was found at Leiden, and is known as the Leiden Papyrus X.[9] In 1913 another papyrus was found at Stockholm [10] and was shown to be written by the same hand as the Leiden Papyrus. It is probable that these two papyri were originally placed together in the tomb of an Egyptian artisan, and that they represent a collection of notes for his own use in his workshop.

These papyri date from the third century A.D., but they are probably compilations of earlier material. They resemble the Assyrian glaze texts in that they are clearly written, with no attempt to deceive the reader. Since they are evidently meant for the use of a skilled workman, they occasionally fail to describe steps that must have been essential, but that were so well understood that it was not considered necessary to write them down. Although no attempt at deception occurs with the use of mystical phrases, the author does use technical terms whose meaning is lost today. Hence we do not understand everything that these papyri contain, but we do obtain a good idea of the state of the chemical arts in the Alexandrian period.

The Stockholm Papyrus contains mostly recipes for mordanting and dyeing and for preparing imitation gems. No theoretical ideas from Greek philosophy appear; the recipes are entirely practical. Magic practices are not suggested, except on a separate leaf that contains an invocation to "Sun, Berbeloch, Chthotho, Miach, Sandum, Echnin, Zaguel." This may have been part of another papyrus, but its existence with that from Stockholm implies that magic practices were found even among the practical artisans, just as they had been among the early Assyrian glaze makers.

While the Stockholm Papyrus contains a few recipes relating to metallurgy, the Leiden Papyrus is almost entirely concerned with the working of metals. From it we gain a picture not only of the methods of the metal worker, but also of some of his purposes. Judging from this papyrus, at least, much of his effort was to produce cheaper imitations of the precious metals, silver and gold. A typical recipe, no. 8, reads as follows:

> Manufacture of Asem [The alloy of silver and gold]. Take soft tin in small pieces, purified four times; take 4 parts of it and 3 parts of pure white copper and 1 part of asem. Melt, and, after casting, clean several times and make with it whatever you wish to. It will be asem of the first quality, which will deceive even the artisans.

Such expressions as the last occur frequently in these recipes: "the product will become as a silver object" (no. 3); and the titles convey a similar idea: "Falsification of Gold" (no. 17), "For Giving Objects of Copper the Appearance of Gold" (no. 38). It is obvious that the artisan who compiled these notes was much occupied with producing imitations of gold and silver that could pass the rough tests applied at that time. Such tests included the use of a touchstone and the behavior on heating. There is no indication that he was attempting to convert base metals into real gold or silver, but there is equally no reason to suppose that, if he happened to produce a substance that resembled gold in all respects known to him, he would not have believed that he had produced gold. No reason was known why any substance might not, under proper conditions, change into any other substance.

Besides working with metals, the artisans used a number of reagents to carry on their processes. Recipe no. 89 describes one of these reagents, sulfur water:

> A handful of lime and another of sulfur in fine powder; place them in a vessel containing vinegar or the urine of a small child. Heat it from below until the supernatant liquid appears like blood. Decant this latter properly in order to separate it from the deposit, and use.

This recipe clearly describes the preparation of a solution of calcium polysulfide that was probably used for changing the surface color of a metal. As will be seen later, such solutions assumed great importance for the alchemists.

The practical recipes of the Leiden and Stockholm Papyri probably represent methods and information assembled over a period of many centuries. The artisans of Egypt had no doubt been preparing similar alloys and dyes since the days of the Pharaohs. Other artisans in other early civilizations probably also had similar recipes at their disposal. So long as these were purely technical in character, their transmission was more or less mechanical. In Alexandria for the first time, the artisans came in contact with the ferment of ideas which has been described. The theories of the philosophers could be applied to the processes carried out by the artisans, and the abstruse speculations could be limited by actual acquaintance with the behavior of matter in many forms. In other words, for the first time occurred a union of theoretical and practical chemistry, and from this union came a totally new growth, alchemy.

The original alchemists must have been men very similar in outlook to Hero. They knew Aristotelian philosophy and applied it wherever they could, but their practical knowledge of the behavior of metals was great enough to cause them to modify the theories or emphasize certain parts whenever this seemed necessary. The exact date at which they worked is not known, but most scholars believe that they were active about the first century A.D. This was a time when scientific philosophy still flourished and mystical ideas had not yet attained the dominance which they later gained. These men did not hesitate to work in the laboratory, to invent new apparatus, and to observe closely the changes that took place in the chemicals they used. Unfortunately, no contemporary record of their work remains. Our knowledge of their activities comes from writings of at least two centuries later, when the intellectual atmosphere was already changing, and even these writings are known only in manuscripts which had been copied and recopied for centuries, and into which many changes must have been introduced. Nevertheless, it is possible to reconstruct much of what the original alchemists did and the theories that guided their work.

This can be done from the fragmentary remains of the earliest alchemical books that have survived. Such books appear under the authorship of a strange list of names, for the true writers attempted to give authority to their works by ascribing them to famous persons of former times. They are said to have been written by gods and goddesses such as Hermes or Isis, by Hebrew leaders such as Moses, by Greek philosophers such as Iamblichos or Demokritos. The works ascribed to the latter were certainly not composed by Demokritos of Abdera, but were probably written by a certain Bolos of Mendes in the first century A.D. They are usually known as the work of the pseudo-Demokritos. The names of women appear among these alchemists, Cleopatra, or Mary the Jewess, who may well have been a real person, and who is said to have invented much apparatus, including the water bath (bain marie).[11]

Since the original alchemists were practical Hellenistic scientists, they possessed a good technical background as Egyptian artisans. They probably resembled the compiler of the Leiden and Stockholm Papyri in experience. Certainly much of their work involved methods he described. At first they attempted to prepare cheaper substitutes for precious metals. Their technical methods made this possible. When they began to speculate about their work, applying the dominant Aristotelian philosophy, they had no reason to doubt that the alloys they produced, which so closely resembled gold, were actually a form of gold, somewhat less perfect than the true metal, perhaps, but only needing a little more effort by the artisans to be transformed into the perfect metal. The Aristotelian idea that all things tend to reach perfection implied that among the metals the less perfect were always striving to reach the perfection of gold. Nature carried out this perfection process deep in the earth and over a long period of time. The artisan in his workshop could repeat much of this process in a relatively short time; therefore it was only necessary to improve his methods somewhat, and he could repeat the natural process completely and make pure gold by his own art. This was the basic idea of alchemy, which represents a logical conclusion from the metallurgical practices of the day. In the application of this idea, a number of other contemporary philosophical ideas were applied, and the discovery of much practical chemistry resulted.

The ancient concept that the changes occurring in the macrocosm, or great world, were repeated in the microcosm, represented by living beings, was fundamental to the thinking of the alchemist. Further, in terms of the Stoic philosophy, a spirit (pneuma) was an essential constituent of all things and acted upon a "body" to produce change. In the microcosm, in plants and animals, the body died, leaving a seed which, impelled by the pneuma, developed through a series of changes to the final perfection of its species. Logically, then, the same course should be followed in the macrocosm. Therefore it was necessary to "kill" the materials with which the alchemist worked. This meant producing a change in their properties that would bring them as nearly as possible into the state of the prime matter. On this, new forms could be impressed. This was done, by analogy with the growing seed, through prolonged treatment with warmth and moisture. The "dead" material could then be expected to develop through a succession of substances to final perfection as gold. It must be remembered that the qualities that were observed by these alchemists were not merely physical states, such as solid or liquid, but also color. To us this is relatively only an incidental quality, but to the Alexandrians it was as fundamental as liquidity or solidity. These qualities became more important in the minds of the Alexandrians than the four Aristotelian elements, for the qualities were actually seen during the work. Although the idea of the four elements was never forgotten, and was used in the more fundamental discussions, most of the explanations of the behavior of physical substances came to be given in terms of the physical properties of solids (earths), liquids (waters), gases (spirits), and color. This method of thinking remained characteristic of chemistry until the time of Robert Boyle.[12]

The Alexandrian technologists were deeply concerned with metals, but they were also practical dyers, as the Stockholm Papyrus shows. They knew how to mordant and to produce a succession of colors. It has been pointed out that their preoccupation with color was also applied to the process of making gold. A succession of colors in the proper order was essential. The colors of silver and gold were among the most characteristic properties of these metals to the alchemist, and by the colors he produced he judged the success of his operations.[13]

On the basis of these ideas, then, the alchemist set about the practical work of transmutation. First he had to produce the "dead" material on which the desired forms could be impressed. The Platonic idea as expressed in the *Timaeus* is here obvious. The "dead" mass should have lost most of its metallic properties and it should be black, that is, lacking in all color. The preparation of this material was called melanosis, or blackening. This was followed by leucosis, or whitening (sometimes called silver-making), then by xanthosis or yellowing (producing gold). In the earliest times a final step, iosis, was often mentioned. This has been interpreted either as producing a violet iridescence on gold [14] or as cleaning off rust,[15] since the Greek word *ios* can mean either violet or rust. At any rate, the product of this step was called "coral of gold" and was regarded as the final step in transmutation. In later times this process was abandoned and the sequence black, white, yellow (or sometimes red) became standard. Thus it can be seen that the chief aim of these alchemists was the production of definite colors on metallic surfaces, and the process of transmutation, both then and later, was often called tingeing.

The dead mass was to be tinged by a process analogous to the growth of a seed. Under the influence of prolonged, gentle heat, the mass was treated with certain spirits and waters which renewed life in it and caused development. Often a small amount of the metal to which it was to be converted was added as a "ferment," or seed in itself. In this case the whole mass was expected to be converted by the "seed of silver" or the "seed of gold" into silver (leucosis) or gold (xanthosis). Although at this time the term philosopher's stone was not used, the basis for this concept was already present.[16]

The reagents that the alchemists used were called "waters" if liquid, and were usually substances that would produce a color on metallic surfaces. Copper could be rendered black either by surface oxidation or by conversion to the sulfide (melanosis), and could be whitened by treatment with arsenic applied as the sulfide, orpiment. Yellowing to gold was usually produced by a solution of polysulfides such as that described in the recipe from the Leiden Papyrus which was quoted earlier. Such solutions were called sulfur water (theion hudor), but in Greek the word for sulfur also means divine. Thus sulfur water was divine water, and it caused the most important transformation in the "divine art." Native sulfur was much used in the preparation of this liquid, although sulfides could also be used as the starting point.[17]

Another important reagent was mercury. Samples of this metal have been found in graves of the sixteenth or fifteenth century B.C., and there are vague references to it in early Greek literature. By the time of Diodorus, Pliny, and Vitruvius, it was a familiar substance, and its preparation by roasting cinnabar was well known. Its peculiar properties aroused much interest. Although it resembled a metal, its liquid nature usually caused it to be classed among the "waters." [18] It was not until comparatively late times (500–700 A.D.) that it was accepted as a metal, and the astrological symbol of mercury that had been assigned to tin [19] was given to it. Nevertheless, the idea that it represented the principle of fluidity which all metals contained, as shown by their fusibility, was in existence early. The ability of mercury to impart a silvery color to other metals also gave it a special position among the alchemists.

Alchemical processes required the construction of much apparatus. Not only was it necessary to treat the metals with various reagents at elevated temperatures, but also the preparation of the reagents themselves often required a number of operations. It might be necessary to extract the "spirits" of materials, such as eggs, which on distillation yielded a fraction containing sulfur that could be used in xanthosis. The Alexandrian chemists showed an astonishing ingenuity in the invention of stills, furnaces, heating baths, beakers, filters, and other pieces of chemical equipment that find their counterparts in use today. In fact, the still was first invented at this time, and for centuries was used only in alchemical operations.[20]

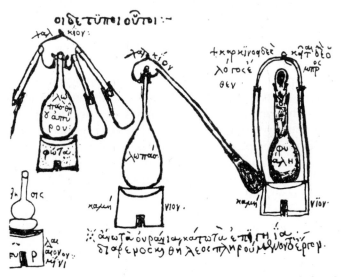

Fig. 4. Greek distillation and digestion apparatus. (From M. Berthelot, *Collection des anciens alchimistes grecs.*)

There is considerable similarity in the alchemical recipes of the earliest period, and these in turn set the pattern for later alchemical writings. The style of these first alchemists is well shown in what is probably among the earliest of the writings, the *Physica et Mystica* of pseudo-Demokritos. The following selection opens the section called Gold-Making, and illustrates the general tone of the work:

Take mercury, fix it with the (metallic) body of magnesia, or the (metallic) body of Italian antimony, or with native sulfur, or with selenite, or burned limestone, or alum of Milos, or arsenic [the sulfide], or what you will. Cast the white earth (so prepared) on copper, and you will have copper without a shadow. Add yellow electron, and you will have gold; with this gold you will obtain the coral of gold reduced to metallic body. The same result will be obtained with yellow arsenic (orpiment) and sandarac (realgar) properly treated or cinnabar wholly transformed. Mercury alone produces copper without a shadow. Nature triumphs over nature.

Treat pyrites of silver, which is also called siderite, according to usage, in a manner to render it fluid. For it is rendered fluid with gray litharge, or white, or by means of Italian antimony. Then sprinkle with lead (I do not say simply lead, so that you may make an error, but lead of Koptos), or with our black litharge, or what you will. Warm, then cast on it a yellow, prepared material, and dye it. Nature rejoices in nature.

Treat the pyrites until they become incombustible, after having lost the black color. Treat with brine, or uncorrupted urine, or with sea water, or oxymel, or what you will, and heat until they become like particles of gold which have not been submitted to the action of fire. This done, mix in native sulfur, or yellow alum, or Attic ochre, or what you will. Then add the silver in order to have gold, and gold to have the coral of gold. Nature dominates nature.[21]

It is almost impossible to follow the details of these recipes because of the vague way in which the various reagents are named. The body of magnesia, for example, might mean any one of a number of metals or alloys obtained by reduction of an earth. However, the general purpose of the recipes seems clear. Thus the first refers to a process for giving copper a gold or silver color with mercury or arsenic alloys.[22] The second describes the treatment of a silver mineral with another metal to get an alloy that is colored yellow by an undescribed reagent. The third concerns the roasting of an argentiferous mineral, followed by treatment with solutions containing sodium chloride. Then a gold-colored alloy is prepared and treated with alloys of silver or gold with baser metals.[21]

The name chemistry first makes its appearance at about the date of these recipes. There has been much discussion of the original meaning of this word. The leading theories derive it either from the Egyptian word *khem*, black, or from the Greek *cheo*, I cast, or pour. Egypt itself was the "black land," and so called from its dark, fertile soil. Chemistry, which originated in Egypt and made melanosis its first step, was thus the "black art." Under the second theory, the name refers to the metallurgical operations of the early chemists. At any rate, the addition of the Arabic definite article *al* gave the word alchemy and recalls the contributions of the Arabs, which will be discussed later. The article was again dropped when the science of chemistry came once more into its own.[23] *

* Mahdihassan [24] has suggested that the term chemistry is derived from the Chinese *chin-i*, gold-making juice (see p. 57), which in the Fukien dialect of southern China is pronounced *kim ya*. He points out that the Arab contact with China was in the Fukien area, and suggests that the term reached the West through the Arab traders.

As can be seen, the Alexandrian chemists were practical men with a high degree of skill. They were active at a time when it almost seemed as if a true science might begin. They carried on numerous chemical reactions guided by a theory that, if erroneous, at least was able to explain results, and was sometimes even able to predict: a yellow substance, sulfur, should under proper conditions give its color to a metal, tingeing it to gold, which was metallic and yellow. As was the case with Hero, their practical knowledge permitted them to modify the Aristotelian theory when necessary. They employed much apparatus and a wide variety of reagents, many prepared by distillation of natural products. It is quite possible that many names that later acquired a symbolic significance, such as "bile of the tortoise," were originally meant literally.[25]

These workers no doubt early developed a technical vocabulary, which not only gave them a quick method of describing the materials they used, but also served to conceal their operations from the general public. It was an obvious step to call the metals by the names of the planets which governed them under the system of astrology which prevailed. Thus gold became the sun; silver, the moon; copper, Venus; lead, Saturn; iron, Mars; and so on. The astrological symbols could also be used instead of the names, as a shorthand system. Other reagents received concealing names, and these differed from place to place, and from period to period. In this way a vast and confused system of names and symbols grew up which has ever since made interpretation of alchemical manuscripts a difficult task.[26] Nevertheless, it is well to remember the practical laboratory skill of the Alexandrians who founded alchemy and influenced the thought of all who studied chemical changes for fifteen hundred years. Even today, alchemical terms, such as hermetic seal, are still used.

By the fourth century, the rising tide of oriental mysticism began to affect alchemy. Astrological and magical practices had probably always been influential among the alchemists, but now these influences began to grow at the expense of the laboratory studies of the Alexandrians. The symbolism of alchemy, if not its practical aspects, appealed greatly to the Gnostics and the Neoplatonists, and, as Jung has shown, to many of the deepest psychological urges of the human mind.[27] The mystics began to interpret the death of the metals and their resurrection and perfection into gold as the symbol of the death, resurrection, and perfection of the human soul. The identity of the macrocosm and the microcosm made this a logical idea in any case, and the mystical philosophies did not hesitate to take over the symbolism divorced from any practical laboratory methods, and to develop it in their own way. To the already confused terminology of alchemy was added a still greater mass of philosophical speculation, using chemical terms, but with almost no chemical content. This served to confuse still further the picture of alchemy that has come down to us, so that it is only in recent years that the origins have become clearer to us. Yet there always remained alchemists who retained their interest in actual laboratory operations. Though the mystically minded referred scornfully to these men as mere "puffers" or "kitchin cooks," [28] it was they who preserved and advanced alchemy as a science until it became chemistry, while the others, lost in a cloud of obscure nomenclature and speculation, contributed nothing further to chemistry.

The practical alchemists must have been very obscure workers at first, for there is no reference to them in the literature of their contemporaries. By the end of the third century, however, their work became better known. The Emperor Diocletian at this time reorganized the political structure and tax system of Egypt. The falsification of gold must have been an important problem by then, for Suidas states that the emperor caused all alchemical books to be burned in 292 A.D.[29] Whether or not this actually occurred, it is indicative of an early and widespread distrust of the alchemists among the general population which continued as long as alchemy itself flourished.

The creative period of Hellenistic alchemy came to a close at about this time. The encyclopedia of alchemy compiled by Zosimos of Panopolis about 300 A.D. already contains much of a mystical and symbolic character. Later writers such as Synesios, Olympiodoros, and others were chiefly copyists and commentators. The theory of alchemy had become standardized, and new apparatus and methods were no longer being discovered. In later Byzantine times alchemy remained static, although many writers continued to transmit the ideas of the earlier alchemists from generation to generation.

If alchemy failed to advance in its technical phases during this period, it underwent a geographical expansion that was of the greatest significance. As the political power of the Roman Empire declined, the Christian Church grew to a dominant position throughout the Hellenistic world. The power of the Neoplatonists and other philosophers was broken, and eventually the learning of Byzantium, Antioch, and Alexandria came to center in the monasteries and schools supported by the Christians.

The early Church grew up in the Hellenistic culture of the eastern Mediterranean, and was itself a powerful agent in spreading this culture. The language of the Church was Greek, and Aristotelian logic was accepted as the method to be used in solving problems. Wherever missionaries wandered, Hellenistic learning and culture accompanied them. Much of the early missionary activity in the East occurred in lands that had been part of the conquests of Alexander the Great and in which a basis of Hellenistic culture already existed, although sometimes overlaid by a strong oriental influence. The spread of Hellenistic thought by the Church was therefore simplified, since it reinforced a pattern already present.[30]

In the fifth century the Church was torn by violent disagreements of a purely theological character. The orthodox position, when finally established, was a moderate compromise, but the more extreme factions refused to accept the settlement. The most influential group of dissidents was led by a Syrian monk named Nestorius, who was excommunicated in 431. Since he had a strong following in Syria, he fled there and established his own church, which became known as Nestorian. It spread rapidly through Syria and Persia, where it became the dominant form of Christianity. The extreme opponents of Nestorianism also refused to be satisfied by compromise, and in 451 they too split from the main body of the orthodox church. Under the name of Monophysites, they obtained their greatest power in Egypt, but they also established churches throughout Syria and Persia.

Although bitterly opposed in theological matters, both Nestorians and Monophysites had the same Hellenistic background. They took with them wherever they went the philosophical and scientific works of Hellenistic culture. They did not lose contact with the Greek-speaking churches of the Eastern Roman Empire, and so they were able to obtain the newer Greek manuscripts as these became available. The Monophysites carried on their studies mostly in monasteries, but the Nestorians founded a number of influential academies and were therefore more effective in spreading Greek culture. Their greatest school was founded at Edessa in Syria, shortly after they organized their church. Edessa, however, was still under the control of the Byzantine emperors, and to avoid persecution the Nestorians were forced to move their school in 489 to Nisibis in Persia. The school of Nisibis became the great central university of the Nestorians. Although the official religion of Persia was Mazdaism, the Persian kings were tolerant of other religions and strongly supported scholars and learning.[31]

The language spoken in Syria was a Semitic tongue called Aramaic. The particular dialect used in the schools of Edessa and Nisibis became the chief literary form of this language under the name of Syriac. Since all instruction in these schools was given in Syriac, it became necessary to have textbooks available in this language. The Nestorians, therefore, made translations of the Greek manuscripts on which their learning was based. These included, besides the purely theological works, books on philosophical, mathematical, astronomical, and medical topics. The number of alchemical manuscripts that exist in Syriac shows that the translators did not overlook this subject. So effective was the work of these translators that many Greek works are known to us only in Syriac translations. Thus Alexandrian alchemy was spread in a new language into Mesopotamia and Persia, the old Seleucid Empire where enough Hellenistic culture remained to assure a ready welcome.

The Persian King, Khusraw I (531–578), was an enthusiastic supporter of Greek learning. Under his patronage a medical school was founded in the city of Jundi-Shapur. The curriculum was that of Alexandria, and was based on the works of Galen. The teaching was in the hands of Nestorian scholars who had been trained at Nisibis. They naturally brought with them the Syriac works that had been prepared at that school, and, to meet the needs of the medical curriculum, they found it necessary to prepare new Syriac translations of Greek medical and scientific texts. It is likely that many alchemical works were translated in this school.[32] It is of interest that Khusraw sent to India to obtain drugs for this institution. Among those obtained was sugar. It had been known in India from 300 A.D., but now was introduced into Persia for the first time. Cultivation of sugar cane began around Jundi-Shapur, but for a long time sugar was used only as a medicine.[33]

In the year 622 occurred the flight of Mohammed (570–632) from Mecca to Medina, the Hegira, from which all Mohammedan events have since been dated. This marks the true birth of Islam, for after that year Mohammed rapidly spread his religion through all Arabia. By the time of his death in 632, most of the previously scattered tribes of Arabs had been united under the banner of the new religion. Then followed rapid subjugation of the non-Arab states. Syria was conquered by 640, Egypt by 641, Persia by 642, and, by the decade from 710 to 720, even remote Spain fell into Muslim hands. Of the important near-by cities, only Byzantium resisted capture and thus was enabled to carry on Greek culture in its original form for seven hundred years longer, a fact of the greatest importance to the cultural history of Europe, though of lesser importance from the standpoint of the history of science.

Meanwhile, the Muslim rulers began to fall out among themselves. The successors of Mohammed had been members of his family, or his immediate followers. They had assumed the title of Khalif, or Successor to the Prophet. In 656 the son-in-law of Mohammed, Ali, was chosen Khalif, but the choice was disputed and civil war followed. In 658 Ali was murdered, and the Khalifate finally passed to Mu'awiya, the founder of the 'Umayyad dynasty. He established his capital at Damascus where his family ruled for about eighty years. These Khalifs did nothing to interfere with the Christians under their rule, and the Nestorian schools of Nisibis and Jundi-Shapur continued to flourish. The Khalifs and their court showed little interest in Greek science, however, and the literary output of this period was confined to traditional Arabic poetry.[34]

Gradually the 'Umayyad dynasty lost popular support. The stricter Muslims were dissatisfied with the lack of religion of the Khalifs, and the Persians grew rebellious. They felt themselves superior to the Arabs who had been desert nomads when Persia was a civilized state. One of the chief centers of Persian dissatisfaction was the city of Merv in Bactria, on the border of Persia and India. Merv was a meeting place of East and West. It had a strong Hellenistic tradition, and Greek learning was highly respected. At the same time, it was a center of Buddhism. Among the most influential citizens were the family of the Barmakids. They had been the hereditary Buddhist abbots of Merv, but shortly before the Arab conquests they had become Mazdeans, and now they became Muslims. They were very much interested in Greek science, and were ardent Persian patriots. They were among the leaders in a plot to dethrone the 'Umayyad dynasty and replace it by one more sympathetic to Persian culture. As a result of this rebellion, the 'Umayyads were overthrown in 750 by Abu'l-Abbas, called the Butcher because of the ferocity with which he sought out and killed all the princes of the 'Umayyads. In fact, only one escaped, fleeing to Spain where he established a separate kingdom that became the rival Khalifate of Cordova.[35]

The newly founded Abbasid dynasty was a strong contrast to its predecessor, the 'Umayyad. It was strongly Persianized and greatly favored Greek learning. For some time the Barmakid family furnished the chief ministers to the Khalifs, and their influence always favored scientific studies. In time the court of the Khalifs became a center for the encouragement of learning, although this was always the activity of a relatively small group in the Arab empire.

The Khalif al-Mansur (ruled 754–775) founded a new capital, Baghdad, in 762. It lay at the point of closest approach between the Tigris and Euphrates rivers, and was not a great distance from Jundi-Shapur. When al-Mansur became ill in 765 he sent for a Nestorian physician from the medical school. He was so impressed by the work of this man that he thereafter gave the strongest support to the institution at Jundi-Shapur.

The golden age of Baghdad occurred under the Khalifs Harun-al-Rashid (ruled 786–808) and al-Ma'mun (ruled 813–833). Both were strongly influenced by Persian culture, and both were eager collectors of Greek manuscripts. Under al-Ma'mun in 828–829 an institution called the House of Wisdom was established for the sole purpose of translating Greek medical and scientific manuscripts.[36] Under the direction of the most famous Nestorian translator, Hunain ibn Ishaq (809–877), an enormous number of first-class translations were made, both into Syriac and, in increasing numbers, into Arabic.[37] The alchemical manuscripts of Alexandria once again became available in a new language. For the first time since the early days of alchemy they were read by men who were interested in making new contributions, instead of merely commenting on the older work. Arabic alchemy was based largely on a Greek foundation, but it drew on another source not less rich, Chinese alchemy, which must also be considered.

REFERENCES

1. The history of this period is fully discussed in G. W. Botsford, *Hellenic History*, revised by C. A. Robinson, Jr., The Macmillan Co., New York, 1939.

2. *Ibid.*, p. 352.

3. S. Gandz, *Isis*, **32**, 263–266 (1940), published 1949.

4. *Hero of Alexandria, A Treatise on Pneumatics*, translated for and edited by Bennet Woodcroft, Taylor, Walton and Maberly, London, 1851, pp. 6–7.

5. *Ibid.*, p. 5.

6. C. A. Browne, *A Source Book of Agricultural Chemistry*, Chronica Botanica, Waltham, Mass., 1944, p. 10.

7. F. S. Taylor, *The Alchemists*, Henry Schuman, New York, 1949, pp. 6–17.

8. A. J. Hopkins, *Alchemy, Child of Greek Philosophy*, Columbia University Press, New York, 1934, pp. 31–37.

9. E. R. Caley, *J. Chem. Educ.*, **3**, 1149–1166 (1926).

10. *Ibid.*, **4**, 979–1002 (1927).

11. Taylor, *op. cit.*, pp. 25–29.

12. *Ibid.*, pp. 6–11.

13. Hopkins, *op. cit.*, pp. 92–103.

14. *Ibid.,* pp. 97–99.

15. Taylor, *op. cit.,* p. 49.

16. Hopkins, *op. cit.,* pp. 75–76.

17. Taylor, *op. cit.,* p. 44.

18. E. O. v. Lippmann, *Entstehung und Ausbreitung der Alchemie,* Vol. I, J. Springer, Berlin, 1919, pp. 600–607; J. M. Stillman, *The Story of Early Chemistry,* D. Appleton and Co., New York, 1924, p. 7.

19. Taylor, *op. cit.,* p. 53.

20. *Ibid.,* pp. 37–50.

21. M. Berthelot, *Collection des anciens alchimistes grecs,* G. Steinheil, Paris, 1888, Vol. 1–2, Translations, pp. 46–47.

22. Stillman, *op. cit.,* p. 157.

23. Hopkins, *op. cit.,* p. 94.

24. S. Mahdihassan, *J. Univ. Bombay,* **20,** part 2, 107–131 (1951).

25. L. Thorndike, *History of Magic and Experimental Science,* Vol. I, The Macmillan Co., New York, 1923, p. 766.

26. Taylor, *op. cit.,* pp. 51–66; John Read, *Prelude to Chemistry,* G. Bell and Sons, Ltd., London, 1936, pp. 85–94.

27. C. G. Jung, *Psychologie und Alchemie,* Rascher Verlag, Zurich, 1944; 2nd ed., Zurich, 1952; English translation, *Psychology and Alchemy,* Pantheon Books, New York, 1953; see also W. Pagel, *Isis,* **39,** 44–48 (1948).

28. Read, *op. cit.,* pp. 2, 23.

29. Hopkins, *op. cit.,* p. 246.

30. De Lacy O'Leary, *How Greek Science Passed to the Arabs,* Rutledge and Kegan Paul, Ltd., London, 1949, p. 36.

31. *Ibid.,* pp. 47–95.

32. *Ibid.,* p. 68.

33. *Ibid.,* p. 71.

34. *Ibid.,* pp. 131–145.

35. *Ibid.,* pp. 119, 147–148.

36. *Ibid.,* pp. 148–154, 161–162, 166.

37. M. Meyerhof, *Isis,* **8,** 685–724 (1926).

CHAPTER VI

CHINESE ALCHEMY

The combination of philosophy and technical ability that led to the earliest alchemy in Alexandria found a counterpart in China that resulted in a similar development at a slightly earlier period. Although alchemy took a somewhat different form in the Far East, there were enough resemblances to the western variety to have caused much dispute among historians concerning possible borrowings in one or the other direction. This cannot be definitely settled with the information now available, but it seems most probable that, although some ideas from each culture may have reached the other, actual development of alchemy in Egypt and China proceeded independently.[1]

Chinese technical arts involved chemistry from the earliest periods of Chinese civilization. Copper, gold, and silver were the first metals known. Gold was not as common as in the early civilizations of Egypt and Mesopotamia.[2] The other important metals had become familiar by the fourth century B.C. Various metallic compounds were prepared, especially from lead and mercury, which were metals particularly interesting to the alchemists. Fabrication of metal and porcelain objects was carried on with a high degree of skill. Li has discussed many of the chemical arts of China, and has shown the extensive knowledge of the Chinese artisans.[3]

The Chinese have long been noted for their philosophical speculations. Even in the earliest times they had a theory of the constitution

Fig. 5. Chinese still for preparing mercury. (From Li, *Chemical Arts of Old China.*)

of matter based on the five elements (*wu hsing*): metal, wood, earth, water, and fire. The combination of these gave rise to all material substances. So important was this concept that nearly everything, including planets, colors, virtues, was classified into five categories. Somewhat later, another very important idea appeared. This was the doctrine of *yin* and *yang*, the two contraries. The idea seems fully developed at the time it appeared. This has led to the belief that it was brought in from the West, where, as has been seen, it was of major significance in early cosmologies. In China this doctrine assumed an importance greater even than in the West. Instead of a number of contraries, as in the physics of Heraklitos, all opposite properties were summed up in the two great contraries: *yin,* the female principle, the moon, negative, heavy, earthy, dry, and symbolizing the less desirable properties of cold, darkness, death; and *yang,* the male principle, the sun, positive, active, fiery, and containing the more desirable characteristics.[4]

These concepts received their fullest development in the philosophy of Taoism in the centuries immediately before Christ. Taoism originated as a highly abstract philosophy during the sixth century B.C. Its founder was Lao Tzu ("the venerable viscount"), whose book, *Tao Te Ching,* The Classic concerning the Way and Values, is the basis of Taoism. The central concept of his philosophy was that everything is controlled by a passive force which he called *Tao,* a word meaning "way" or "path." Man should seek *Tao* by inaction, by solitude, and by various spiritual practices.[5]

Early Taoism was a very pessimistic and difficult philosophy, one that did not have a wide appeal, but it began to change its character soon after the death of its founder. The metaphysical idea of the *Tao* became more concrete with the passage of time. It came to stand for the Way of Nature, the physical means by which the cosmos operates. As such it incorporated the ideas of *yin* and *yang* and the five elements. Its devotees began to search for the Way not by mental and spiritual methods, as had Lao Tzu, but by physical operations. Magical concepts were introduced, and the adepts sought to control nature for their own advantage. Several centuries before the rise of Alexandrian alchemy, the Taoists introduced a characteristically Chinese alchemical system.

The cosmology of the Taoists was well summed up in the *Huai-nan-tzu,* written for Liu An (died 122 B.C.), King of Huai-nan, and an ardent Taoist:

> Before the universe took any definite form, it was absolutely shapeless and transparent, and was therefore called Great Brightness. *Tao* originated from emptiness and tranquility. Emptiness and tranquility created space and time, and space and time created ethereal essence (*ch'i*). The essence had boundaries. The portion which was thin and volatile floated up to form the sky, and the heavy and dense portion condensed and coagulated to become the earth. Since it is easier for volatile things to come together than for heavy and dense materials to condense and coagulate, the sky formed before the earth took definite shape. *Yin-yang* resulted from the concentration of the essence of heaven and earth. The essence of *Yin-yang* by its concentration formed the four seasons, and the essence of the four seasons by its distribution formed the multitude of things. The accumulation of the hot elements in *Yang* originated fire, the essence of which became the sun. The accumulation of the cold elements in *Yin* created water, the essence of which became the moon. By the interaction of the sun and moon, the heavenly bodies were produced. While the heaven received the stars and planets, the earth received water and dust.[6]

By this time, alchemy had become sufficiently well established to incur the suspicion of the authorities, just as it did in the West. In 144 B.C. an edict was issued against the makers of "counterfeit gold." [7] In 56 B.C., a high court official, Liu Hsiang, attempted publicly to make gold for the emperor, and failed completely. This resulted in even greater disfavor for the alchemists, so that references to the art disappear from the literature for a time.[8]

The alchemists, however, evidently continued their work. In about 142 A.D. appeared the *Ts'an t'ung ch'i* of Wei Po-yang. Davis calls this the earliest known work devoted exclusively to alchemy. It contains much material of a mystical character, and conceals many of its methods and reagents under fanciful names, just as was done in the West. Nevertheless, it gives evidence that its author was a practical chemist. The following description relates to some process in which volatilization and crystallization take place, and appeals to every chemist who has watched a violent reaction occur:

> Above, cooking and distillation take place in the caldron; below blazes the roaring flame. Afore goes the White Tiger, leading the way; following comes the Gray Dragon. The fluttering Scarlet Bird flees the five colors. Encountering ensnaring nets, it is helpless and immovably pressed down, and cries with pathos, like a child after its mother. Willy-nilly it is put into the caldron of hot fluid to the detriment of its feathers. Before half the time has passed, Dragons appear with rapidity and in great number. The five dazzling colors change incessantly. Turbulently boils the fluid in the caldron. One after another, they appear to form an array as irregular as a dog's teeth. Stalagmites which are like mid-winter icicles are spit out horizontally and vertically. Rocky heights of no apparent regularity make their appearance, supporting one another. When *Yin* and *Yang* are properly matched, tranquility prevails.[9]

This book also contains a passage which explains the central purpose of Chinese alchemy, a purpose that clearly distinguishes it from the Alexandrian, with its aim of making imitations of precious metals:

> Longevity is of primary importance in the grand triumph. *Huantan* (returned medicine) is edible. Gold is non-corruptible, and therefore the most valuable of things. The men of the art, feeding on it, attain longevity. Earth, traveling in all seasons, delineates boundaries and formulates rules to be observed. The gold dust, having entered the five internal organs, spreads foggily, like wind-driven rain. Vaporizing and permeating, it reaches the four limbs. Thereupon the complexion becomes rejuvenated, hoary hair regains its blackness, and new teeth grow where fallen ones used to be. If an old man, he will once more become a youth; if an old woman, she will regain her maidenhood. Such transformations make one immune from worldly miseries, and one who is so transformed is called by the name of *chen-jen* (true man).[10]

The Chinese alchemist wished to make gold, it is true, but not merely for the sake of gold itself. He believed that by eating gold, or some similar preparation, he could attain eternal life, and become a *hsien,* an immortal with almost limitless powers. While natural gold would serve this purpose, it was difficult to obtain, and most alchemists were poor. It was therefore more convenient for them to make the gold themselves. Thus Chinese alchemical literature is divided into two parts: the preparation of gold from baser metals, and methods of consuming it to achieve immortality. The second purpose was completely absent from Alexandrian alchemy.

The greatest alchemical work of China is the *Pao-p'u-tzu* of Ko Hung (about 281–361).[11] The title has been translated both as "The Master Who Preserves Pristine Simplicity"[12] and as the "Solemn Seeming Philosopher."[11] It was a name adopted by Ko Hung himself. The book is long, but in part it gives a very complete description of Chinese alchemy. Ko Hung explains the value of the Gold Medicine (*Chin tan*):

> The more the Gold Medicine is heated, the more exquisite are the transformations it passes through. Yellow gold will not be changed even after long heating in the fire, nor will it rot after long burial in the earth. The eating of these two medicines [*Huan tan,* returned medicine, and *Chin i,* gold fluid, or gold-making fluid[13]] will therefore strengthen one's body that he will not grow old and die. This is a case of deriving strength from an external substance, comparable to the maintenance of fire by oil and the protection of the leg from rotting in water by a smear of copper blue, which merely acts on the surface.[14] *

The book contains elaborate descriptions of the preparation of a number of different forms of the medicine. For example,

> The fourth medicine is called *Huan tan* (returned medicine). Immortality will come to the eater in a hundred days after eating. Above him will hover pheasants, peacocks, and red birds, and at his side will be fairies. Yellow gold will be formed immediately by heating a knife-blade full of the medicine admixed with a catty of quicksilver [the philosopher's stone]. Whoever has his money painted with it will have it back on the same day that he spends it. Words painted with this medicine on the eyes of common people will keep spirits away from them.[16]

Besides this magical material, Ko Hung also describes practical chemical operations such as the preparation of stannic sulfide, "mosaic gold," which resembles gold in appearance and which he obviously believed to result from the transmutation of tin:

> Tin sheets, each measuring six inches square by one and two eighths inches thick, are covered with a one tenth inch layer of a mud-like mixture of red salt and *Hui Chih* (potash water, lime water), ten pounds

---

* Needham[15] says that the translations of Wu and Davis are in general full of misunderstandings. When volume 5 of his extensive work on Chinese science appears, it will treat chemistry and industrial chemistry, and a considerable amount of new material on Chinese alchemy will undoubtedly be available.

of tin to every four of red salt. They are then placed in a red-earthen pot and properly sealed. After heating for thirty days with horse manure, all the tin becomes ash-like and interspersed with bean-like pieces which are the yellow gold. The gold may also be obtained by ten refinings by the action of burning charcoal. Twenty ounces of gold are obtained from every twenty pounds of tin used.[17]

As a result of recent translations of the Taoist classics, the general principles of Chinese alchemy are now fairly clear. Alchemy was under the control of the Deity of the Stove, a beautiful woman dressed in red. She was in charge of cooking and of preparing medicines, and thus also of alchemy. Sacrifices were made to her before attempting

Fig. 6.   Chinese alchemical furnace.   (From Li, *Chemical Arts of Old China.*)

the work.[18] The alchemists were well acquainted with mercury, which they regarded as a distinctive substance. They knew of its preparation from the red ore, cinnabar, and this mineral too was regarded with special reverence. In fact, at times cinnabar was more highly regarded than gold as a medicine for prolonging life. Several emperors are reputed to have died after partaking of mercury compounds in the attempt to secure immortality. The Chinese alchemist also believed that a special medicine could be used to cause transmutation. Often it was the same substance as that which produced immortality:

> As an instance from recent times, we may consider the case of Hua Ling Ssu, a talented, learned, and well-informed scholar who had been sceptical about things not found in the Classics. However, he once came across a *Tao-shih* (seeker of the Way) who professed to have knowledge of the method of the Yellow and the White. He asked the *Tao-shih* to make good his words by deeds, which were as follows: lead was treated in an iron vessel with a certain powdered medicine and silver was obtained. The silver was further treated with some other medicine, and gold was made.[19]

As in the quotation concerning the *Huan tan* previously given, this obviously refers to what later European alchemists called the philosopher's stone.

Like the Alexandrians, the Chinese alchemists used a wide variety of apparatus. Probably their most important piece of equipment was the *ting*, a caldron that usually stood on three legs, and that served as a reaction vessel for the experiments. A number of types of furnaces and baths existed, as well as crucibles and stills.[20]

The clearest exposition of the alchemy of China is found in the *Pao-p'u-tzu*. After this period, as in Alexandria, the mystical and magical phases of alchemy began to predominate. The Taoist philosophy was steadily degenerating into a religion of magic and superstition, and alchemy followed the same path. By the sixth century it had

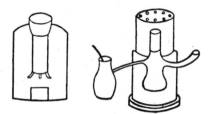

Fig. 7. Chinese furnaces containing water-cooled areas. (From Li, *Chemical Arts of Old China.*)

separated into two branches: exoteric alchemy (*wai tan*), which was still based on chemical methods, and the more predominant esoteric alchemy (*nei tan*), in which the terminology of chemicals and laboratory operations was used to express mystical and philosophic concepts. The *Wu Chên P'ien* (Essay on the Understanding of the Truth) of Chang Po-tuan (983–1082) is such a work.[21] Gradually even exoteric alchemy became lost in superstition, and so, in China, alchemy failed to contribute to any further advances. The conservative character of Chinese culture and the failure of the degenerate Taoism to appeal to the intellectuals were no doubt the chief causes of this failure.

If Chinese alchemy had little influence on the culture of China, its teachings were not lost. During the years in which it flourished, China was not an isolated nation. It is probable that some trade routes across Asia existed even in Babylonian times. This would explain the transmission of the doctrine of the contraries to China at an early period. In later times, contacts between China and the West were well established.

In 150–140 B.C., a tribe of nomads from northern China, the Yüeh-Chi, were driven from their homes. After many wanderings they finally settled in Bactria, the easternmost province of the Persian em-

pire, where Merv was located.   In 128 B.C. the Chinese general and
diplomat, Chang K'ien, visited this tribe and sent back a report to
the Emperor Han Wu-ti.   The way was opened for trade between these
territories.   This was of great importance, for Bactria also had a
flourishing trade with the Roman empire.   In 106 B.C. the first through
caravan along this "silk route" reached Persia, and subsequently regular traffic passed between the Roman West and the Chinese East.[22]
This traffic was intensified when Bactria became a great Buddhist
center under King Kanishka (120–153 A.D.).   Not only merchants but
also priests and pilgrims now made the journey from China to Persia.
Records of such journeys have been left by Fa Hsien (405–410), I Ching
(671–695), and others, showing that the way was kept open for centuries.[23]

Travel in the reverse direction was also common.   Marcus Aurelius
sent an embassy to China in 166 A.D.   The Nestorians carried their
missionary activity as far as China, and in 781 erected the famous
monument at Sian in Shensi which bears an inscription in both Chinese and Syriac.   Arabic travelers and traders continued the traffic
after the Arab conquests.   The accounts of Sulaiman the Merchant
and the geographer Abu Zaid tell of visits to China in the ninth century.   The story of Aladdin in the *Thousand and One Nights* shows
that China was known to the Arabs.[24]

India, which lay between Persia and China, could not avoid the
influence of both countries.   Buddhism, which originated in India,
spread to China which became its chief home.   Muslims invaded India
and introduced Mohammedanism as one of its chief religions soon
after the Arabic conquests began.   The Indians had developed profound philosophies from the earliest times, and they had undoubtedly
been in contact with Hellenistic thought from the time of Alexander
the Great, but India developed little chemistry and less alchemy until
the eleventh century.   Most of the science of India was connected with
her medical teaching.   When alchemy did arise, it was closely connected with the idea of healing.   This iatrochemical school, which
sought chemical remedies for disease, reached its peak from 1300 to
1550, at a time when a similar movement was beginning in the West.
It seems apparent from the studies of Ray that Indian alchemy was
chiefly an importation, both from the East and from the West.[25]

It is evident then that the ideas of Chinese alchemy could have
reached the West by a number of paths.   The study of Arabic alchemy clearly shows that they did.

REFERENCES

1. T. L. Davis, *Isis*, **28**, 73–86 (1938).

2. Dubs, *ibid.*, **38**, 84 (1947).

3. Li Ch'iao-p'ing, *The Chemical Arts of Old China*, Journal of Chemical Education, Easton, Pa., 1948.

4. Wu Lu-ch'iang and T. L. Davis, *Isis*, **18**, 210–289 (1932).

5. For further information on Taoism as a philosophy, see O. S. Johnson, *A Study of Chinese Alchemy*, Commercial Press, Ltd., Shanghai, 1928, and the article by H. H. Dubs, *Taoism*, in *China*, edited by H. F. McNair, University of California Press, Berkeley and Los Angeles, 1946, pp. 266–289.

6. T. L. Davis, *Isis*, **25**, 334–335 (1936).

7. Dubs, *ibid.*, **38**, 63–64 (1947).

8. *Ibid.*, pp. 74–78.

9. Wu and Davis, *op. cit.*, pp. 258–259.

10. *Ibid.*, pp. 240–241.

11. Wu Lu-ch'iang and T. L. Davis, *Proc. Am. Acad. Arts Sci.*, **70**, 221–284 (1935); T. L. Davis, *J. Chem. Educ.*, **11**, 517–520 (1934); T L. Davis and Wu Lu-ch'iang, *ibid.*, **13**, 103–105, 215–218 (1936).

12. Dubs, *op. cit.*, p. 79.

13. S. Mahdihassan, *J. Univ. Bombay*, **20**, part 2, 107–131 (1951).

14. Wu and Davis, *Proc. Am. Acad. Arts Sci.*, **70**, 236 (1935) .

15. J. Needham, *Science and Civilization in China*, Vol. I, Cambridge University Press, Cambridge, 1954, p. 7.

16. Wu and Davis, *op. cit.*, pp. 240–241.

17. *Ibid.*, pp. 264–265.

18. Dubs, *op. cit.*, p. 70.

19. Wu and Davis, *op. cit.*, p. 259.

20. W. H. Barnes, *J. Chem. Educ.* **11**, 655–658 (1934); **13**, 453–457 (1936); Li, *op. cit.*, pp. 18–24.

21. T. L. Davis and Chao Yün-ts'ung, *Proc. Am. Acad. Arts Sci.*, **73**, 97–117 (1939); *J. Chem. Educ.*, **16**, 53–57 (1939).

22. G. W. Botsford, *Hellenic History*, revised by C. A. Robinson, Jr., The Macmillan Co., New York, 1939, p. 340.

23. De Lacy O'Leary, *How Greek Science Passed to the Arabs*, Rutledge and Kegan Paul, Ltd., London, 1949, pp. 102–105, 128–129.

24. G. Sarton, *Introduction to the History of Science*, Vol. I, Williams and Wilkins Co., Baltimore, 1927, pp. 297, 381–382, 571–572, 636.

25. P. C. Ray, *A History of Hindu Chemistry*, 2 vols., 2nd ed., Williams and Norgate, Ltd., London, 1904–1909.

Arabic Alchemy

The beginnings of Arabic alchemy are traditionally associated with the names of men who were probably never alchemists. With the passage of time, the records of those who practiced the art become clearer, and by the tenth century, most of the alchemists are comparatively well-known figures. Their writings follow definite patterns, and some of the trends of their thought are surprisingly modern.

There is no doubt that the roots of Arabic alchemy lie in Greek science. Although the direct path of the translations of the Hellenistic alchemical manuscripts cannot be traced as accurately as those of astronomical and mathematical works, it is clear that alchemy reached the Arabs through Egypt and through Syria and Persia. There is also evidence that ideas from China helped to form the theories that were generally accepted in the tenth century.

Later Muslim alchemists ascribed the beginning of their science to Khalid ibn Yazid, historically an 'Umayyad prince who lived about 665–704. He was supposed to have learned the details of the art from a Christian monk, Stephanos, whose name recalls that of a famous Byzantine alchemist. Khalid was said to have been responsible for the translation of many alchemical manuscripts.

The next great alchemist, according to later accounts, was Ja'far al-Sadiq (699/700–765), the sixth Imam, or descendant of Mohammed's son-in-law Ali, who was the last member of the Prophet's family to hold the Khalifate. Ja'far, these accounts say, became a master of the art and in turn trained the most celebrated of the Arabian alchemists, Jabir ibn Hayyan, who was supposed to have flourished in the ninth century.

Practically all of these accounts have now been shown to be incorrect. There is no evidence that the actual Khalid [1] or the actual Ja'far [2] ever concerned themselves with alchemy. The writings of Jabir are the compilations of a religious sect.[3] "The first important authentic records of Arabic alchemy appear at the time of the great flowering of Arabic science in Baghdad in the tenth century."

This is not to say that there were no alchemists in the Muslim world before that time. These adepts of the earlier period seem to have written mystical works of which only fragments have come down to us. The so-called *Book of Krates* (Krates is an Arabic distortion of the name Demokritos) was probably composed in Egypt by a Copt, possibly earlier than the eighth century. It is a typical visionary and revelational book of Hermetic literature.[4] An Egyptian mystical alchemist, Dhu-l-Nun (died 859–860),[5] carried on this tradition, which was no doubt taken directly from the late Greek alchemists who had almost abandoned practical work.

The mystical school was represented during the golden age of Arabic alchemy by Muhammad ibn Umail (about 900–960), whose *Silvery Water and Starry Earth* [6] served as the source for many later mystical writings. This compilation of alchemical writings, ascribed to Greek philosophers and alchemists, Egyptian kings, Roman emperors, and Arabic Khalifs and princes, is typical of the allegorical alchemy that flourished on Egyptian soil.[7] At about the same time (900) appeared a work best known in its Latin translation as the *Turba Philosophorum,* in which an attempt was made to adapt Greek cosmological and alchemical theories to Arabic science. It took the form of a conversation among nine pre-Socratic philosophers who discussed their views and finally reached a compromise that fitted well into Arabic thought.[8] Although this work was more rational than the writings of the mystics, it stood with their works in almost complete opposition to the relatively clear ideas and actual experiments of the Jabir Corpus and of al-Razi, whose works must now be considered.

It was with the writings ascribed to Jabir ibn Hayyan that firmer ground was finally reached. These comprise a vast collection of works on all phases of alchemy, astrology, cosmology, mysticism, and related topics that were said to have been written by Jabir, the pupil of Ja'far al-Sadiq. The writings have been examined in great detail by Kraus [3] and have been shown to represent the compilations of a Muslim sect known as the Isma'iliya. According to the beliefs of this sect,[9] the descendants of the son-in-law of Mohammed, Ali, were the true leaders of Islam, and Muhammad ibn Isma'il, the seventh of these, and hence the seventh Imam, occupied an especially important place. Therefore his father, Ja'far al-Sadiq, the sixth Imam, was also an important leader. To him they ascribed knowledge of every kind. The sect tended strongly to mystical doctrines, neo-Pythagorean numerology, and a cosmology that stressed the relation between macrocosm and microcosm. They were particularly interested in alchemy, astrology, talismans, and numerological speculations. They gained great power in the Muslim world, governing Egypt from the tenth to the twelfth centuries. The famous Assassins, under the Old Man of the Mountain, were a branch of the Isma'iliya, and the sect exists today.

The interests of this sect, in spite of mystic tendencies, led them to study the sciences of their time and to compile encyclopedic works that included surveys of all the available alchemical literature. Alchemists among them apparently carried on original work. It is quite possible that there was actually an alchemist named Jabir whose father, Hayyan, was an active member of the Isma'iliya, and who was murdered while working for this sect.[10] This Jabir may even have written the *Book of Mercy,* one of the earliest works in the Jabir Corpus.[11] However, the internal evidence shows clearly that the vast number of books ascribed to Jabir (over two thousand in the Kraus bibliography) could not have been written in the ninth century, the time of their supposed composition, nor by one author. Rather, they were written over a period of years by a number of different authors belonging to the Isma'iliya. The earliest works are more technical, the later more speculative and mystical. Throughout all of them the doctrines of the Isma'iliya are clearly expressed. Reference is continually made to "my master, Ja'far al Sadiq." The works were evidently completed by 987 when al Nadim compiled his famous *Fihrist,* the "Book of the Catalogue," which lists all the learned works known to the author, and which includes in the section on alchemy a long list of books by Jabir. Al Nadim gives a biographical account of Jabir [12] in which he expresses doubt concerning the authenticity of the works. Later Arabic alchemists had no such doubts, however, and Jabir was recognized as the master alchemist of the Muslim world. His fame extended to the West where works attributed to him under the name of Geber subsequently exerted a great influence.

The basic ideas of the Jabir Corpus [13] can be traced to the Greek alchemists of Alexandria, and hence to the theories of Aristotle. The Jabir concept of matter is founded on the four Aristotelian principles, heat, cold, moisture, dryness. Actual metals consist of a combination of two of these, which give to the metal its properties. These are called the "exterior" qualities. In addition, the metal contains innately the other two qualities as "interior" qualities. Thus gold has the exterior qualities heat and moisture, but the interior qualities of cold and dryness. These are the exterior qualities of silver. In order to convert silver to gold, it is only necessary to bring out the interior qualities of the gold. This is done by the use of an "elixir," a substance that is not mentioned explicitly in Greek alchemy. It is mentioned frequently by the Chinese alchemists with whom the gold medicine is an essential part of the system. It is thus probable that the two streams of alchemy, East and West, have met and fused in the central Arab world. The doctrine of the two contraries, derived from both systems of alchemy, is encountered in Jabir where the two immediate constituents of the metals, as opposed to their more fundamental qualities, are taken to be sulfur and mercury. This doctrine has a long subsequent history.

A peculiarity of the Jabir system is its emphasis on the use of vegetable and preferably animal substances in the preparation of the elixir. Like most other Arabian alchemists, the Jabir works lay great stress on sal ammoniac, a substance not known to the Greeks. This was first introduced to the Arabs under the Persian name *nushadur,* and the name sal ammoniac, which had been applied to a special kind of rock salt from the neighborhood of the oracle of Ammon in Egypt, was later transferred to it. The Persian name suggests that ammonium salts originally came from Persia or even farther east, but it has not yet been possible to determine when or where they were introduced to the Arabic alchemists.[14] At any rate, two varieties were known, one obtained from mineral sources, the other from distillation of animal products such as hair. The latter would actually be a crude ammonium carbonate rather than ammonium chloride. The volatility of these salts apparently impressed the Arabs greatly, and much importance was attached to them. It may have been because of the animal origin of some of this *nushadur* that animal substances were considered so significant in the Jabir system.

The Jabir system departs most sharply from Aristotelian ideas in the concept of the four principles. To Aristotle, the principles were simply accidents that differentiated the prime material. The Jabir

Corpus, influenced by the theories of the Stoics,[15] gave them a far more material nature. Heat, cold, dryness, and moisture were actual natures that could be separated from material substances, and that combined in definite proportions to form material substances once more. They had an independent and concrete existence. The task of the alchemist was therefore to determine the proportion in which they entered into substances, to prepare the pure natures, and to combine them in the proper amounts to give the desired products. This idea may seem very modern, but it was not applied in a modern way.

The determination of the amount of each nature in a substance was based on the principles of numerology. The "Principle of the Balance," as worked out in the later books of the Corpus, involved elaborate arithmetical computations, but its basis was mystical, neo-Pythagorean numerology. It makes no appeal to the modern reader.

The second part of the problem led more directly to chemical operations. The Greek alchemists had used distillations in many of their processes, but they did not apply them as extensively to animal products as did Jabir. The Jabir works describe the destructive distillation of a very large number of such substances. This almost always resulted in the formation of gases, inflammable materials, liquids, and ash. These results fitted perfectly into the concept of the four elements, corresponding to air, fire, water, and earth. These "elements" were considered to be themselves composed of two natures, one predominating, and both linked to substance, the prime matter of Aristotle. Therefore a continuation of the distilling process was expected to separate the individual natures. Addition of substances that would absorb one nature during the distillation was also of value.

> Water is put into a cucurbit, and a substance is added which has a strong dryness, such as sulfur or a similar thing. Thus the moisture of the water will be dried by the dryness (of the sulfur) and by the heat (of the fire of distillation); the moisture will be entirely burned off, and there will remain (of the water) only the isolated cold.[16]

Repetition was the secret of success. The water should first be distilled alone seventy times. "This number of distillations is indispensable."[17] Then a sponge impregnated with the drying material was added, the liquid was distilled, a fresh impregnated sponge was added to the distillate, and the distillation repeated. Seven hundred such distillations were required to give pure Cold, "a white and pure substance which, when it is touched by the air, congeals into a white body, and, when it is touched by the smallest degree of moisture, dissolves and is again transformed into water."

When these pure qualities were thus obtained, they were combined in the proper amounts to produce a desired substance. It is unlikely that seven hundred and seventy such distillations were actually carried out with the apparatus available at the time, but the theory on which the alchemists worked convinced them that, if they did succeed in this number of operations, they would certainly obtain the predicted result.[18]

This led to the use of apparatus of all kinds, and the Jabir Corpus contains many descriptions of the practical laboratory apparatus used by the alchemists of that day.

The natures produced in the manner described were true elixirs in the Chinese sense, and were used to "cure" the "sick" metals, that is, the imperfect ones, converting them to the perfection of gold by bringing about the proper proportion of natures. This is a Chinese concept, though modified by the numerological ideas on which so much of the Jabir theory is based.

It can be seen that the Jabir theory of alchemy is much more precise and logical than any of the Greek alchemical ideas that have come down to us. The classification of substances shows a similar logic and clarity of thought that seems to have been characteristic of the practical Arabic alchemists, as distinguished from the mystical type represented by ibn Umail. Minerals were classified [19] as "spirits," substances that volatilize entirely in fire; "metallic bodies," fusible substances that can be hammered out giving off a noise; and "bodies" or minerals, fusible or non-fusible, but which shatter and are pulverized when hammered. The spirits include sulfur, arsenic (the sulfides), mercury, sal ammoniac, and camphor. Metals include lead, tin, gold, silver, copper, iron, and *khar sini,* the "Chinese barb," an alloy whose exact composition is not known. This name strongly implies a relation with China. In some of the Jabir books, mercury is classed as a metal, and, in this case, *khar sini* is not mentioned. It evidently was used to complete the seven traditional metals when mercury was classed with the spirits. Minerals were divided into three groups: those that contain some spirit, but have the form of a body, such as malachite, lapis lazuli, turquoise, or mica; those with a small amount of spirit: shells, pearls, vitriols; and those with almost no spirit: onyx, dust, and aged vitriols. There are many subclassifications of the major groups. This tendency to classify substances in terms of what are essentially physical properties is very characteristic of the better Arabian alchemists.

The group of works that make up the Jabir Corpus is similar to the encyclopedic productions of another Isma'iliya society, the *Ikhwan al-Safa,* the Brethren of Purity (sometimes called the Faithful Brethren) which flourished at Basra, the seaport of Baghdad, in the second half of the tenth century. Their writings also include compilations of alchemical, astrological, numerological, and related material. Their chemical ideas closely resemble those issued under the name of Jabir ibn Hayyan.[20]

The second great name in Muslim alchemy also belongs to the tenth century. Abu Bakr Muhammad ibn Zakariya al-Razi (860–925), called Rhazes in Latin, was one of the greatest Muslim physicians. Most of his works deal with medical matters, but he was also greatly interested in chemical topics. He brought to his chemical studies a practical, scientific approach that had scarcely been seen before him. He is the first of the distinguished physicians who, for the next five hundred years, were the chief contributors to the advance of chemistry as a science. He wrote a number of alchemical books, of which the *Kitab Sirr al Asrar,* the "Book of Secret of Secrets," is the best known.[21] In spite of the name, this is actually a book of technical recipes. It reflects the fact that al-Razi was not at all interested in the mystical and allegorical aspects of alchemy. Although he believed in the possibility of transmutation, he was first and foremost a practical chemist.

In three sections of this book he discusses substances, apparatus, and methods. The classification of substances is very elaborate. In the main, it is similar to that of Jabir: the volatile spirits, the metallic bodies, and the stones, vitriols, borax, and salts. Numerous recipes are given for preparing these substances. For comparison with the Leiden Papyrus (p. 39), the recipe of al-Razi for preparing calcium polysulfide follows:

> Take 2 parts of lime that has not been slaked, and 1 part of yellow sulfur, and digest this with 4 times (the weight) of pure water until it becomes red. Filter it, and repeat the process until it becomes red. Then collect all the water, and cook it until it is decreased to half, and use it. And Allah knows (what is best).[22]

This is much clearer than the Greek recipe, but, from the chemical point of view, it is essentially the same. Much more original is the following:

> Take equal parts of calcined *al-Qili* (sodium carbonate) and unslaked lime and pour over them 4 times their amount of water and leave it for 3 days. Filter the mixture, and again add *al-Qili* and lime to the extent of one-fourth of the filtered solution. Do this 7 times. Pour it into half

(the volume) of dissolved sal ammoniac. Then keep it; for verily it is the strongest sharp water. It will dissolve *Talq* (mica) immediately.[23]

These sharp waters were an important discovery of the Arabic alchemists, including, as the example shows, caustic alkalies. The origin of the word alkali is also apparent from the recipe. *Al-Qili* was crude sodium carbonate obtained by leaching ashes. The term sharp waters also included such acids as were used: vinegar, sour milk, and lemon juice. These sharp waters were used as solvents for metals and other substances. The addition of ammonium salts to the alkalies increased their effectiveness for such purposes.

One of the books of the Jabir Corpus, the *Kitab al-Rijad al-akbar*, the "Great Book of the Garden," contains recipes for sharp waters that closely resemble those of al-Razi, though Jabir's descriptions are usually more detailed. Both authors may have used the same sources, but it is more probable that one drew from the other. It is not clear which book was written first.[24]

The writings of Jabir and al-Razi were particularly notable for their clarity and freedom from mysticism and allegory. They naturally appealed to the more practically minded alchemists and they exerted a great influence on later Arabic alchemists, as well as on alchemists of the West.[25] Their classification of substances and their descriptions of apparatus and methods were widely copied. Both these authors tacitly assumed the reality of transmutation, although they did not give it the central place in their systems that was assigned to it by the mystics.

Nevertheless, there was one famous Arab physician who doubted even the reality of transmutation. This was Abu 'Ali al-Husain ibn Abdallah ibn Sina (980–1037), called Avicenna in the West, the greatest physician of Islam. His *Canon* of medicine became the standard work on the subject and was studied both in the East and the West for six centuries. His works cover nearly every branch of natural science. Many of his observations on chemistry are included in the *Kitab al-Shifa*, the "Book of the Remedy."[26] In the physical section of this work he discusses the formation of minerals, which he classifies into stones, fusible substances, sulfurs, and salts. Mercury is classified with the fusible substances, metals, because "it is the essential constituent of malleable bodies, or at least is similar to it." This idea is due to the fusibility of metals, for he later says, "It seems that mercury or something resembling it is the essential constituent element of all fusible bodies, for all of them are converted into mercury on fusion." The

ideas of ibn Sina are basically Aristotelian, but he identifies the vaporous and smoky exhalations that Aristotle thought formed metals and
earths with mercury and sulfur, an idea already expressed by Jabir.

The true originality of ibn Sina is best seen in his views of the
possibility of alchemical transmutation. He says,

> As to the claims of the alchemists, it must be clearly understood that
> it is not in their power to bring about any true change of species. They
> can, however, produce excellent imitations, dyeing the red (metal) white
> so that it closely resembles silver, or dyeing it yellow so that it closely
> resembles gold. They can, too, dye the white (metal) with any color they
> desire, until it bears a close resemblance to gold or copper; and they can
> free the leads from most of their defects and impurities. Yet in these
> (dyed metals) the essential nature remains unchanged; they are merely
> so dominated by induced qualities that errors may be made concerning
> them, just as it happens that men are deceived by salt, qalqand (green
> vitriol), sal ammoniac, etc.
>
> I do not deny that such a degree of accuracy may be reached as to
> deceive even the shrewdest, but the possibility of eliminating or impart-
> ing the specific difference has never been clear to me. On the contrary,
> I regard it as impossible, since there is no way of splitting up one com-
> bination into another. Those properties which are perceived by the
> senses are probably not the differences which separate the metals into
> species, but rather accidents or consequences, the specific differences be-
> ing unknown. And, if a thing is unknown, how is it possible for anyone
> to endeavor to produce it or to destroy it? . . .
>
> It is likely that the proportion of the elements which enter into the
> composition of the essential substance of each of the metals enumerated
> is different from that of any other. If this is so, one metal cannot be
> converted into another unless the compound is broken up and converted
> into the composition of that into which its composition is desired. This,
> however, cannot be effected by fusion, which maintains the union, and
> merely causes the introduction of some foreign substance or virtue.
>
> There is much I could have said upon this subject if I had so desired,
> but there is little profit in it nor is there any necessity for it here.[27]

The skepticism of a rational physician like ibn Sina was not found
even in the writings of the other great Arabic physician, al-Razi, who
accepted the truth of alchemy. Nevertheless, this opinion of ibn
Sina reached the West and had considerable influence on the later
course of alchemy there.

The Arabic alchemists thus far discussed were residents of the eastern half of the Muslim world. Many were Persians, like al-Razi, and
there seems little doubt that Hellenistic learning, including practical
alchemy, came largely through Persia. The more mystical branch of
alchemy, as has been seen, developed largely in Egypt. After the great
advances in alchemy during the tenth century, little time was required

for this subject to spread to the Khalifate of Cordova, and **Moorish** alchemists soon appeared.

Greek physical and mathematical works reached Spain at the end of the tenth century, and the works of Jabir and al-Razi probably arrived at about the same time.[28] It is significant that the name of the noted Moorish astronomer, Maslama al-Majriti (died about 1007), is attached to one of the first alchemical books known to have been written in Spain, for Maslama, or one of his pupils, introduced the writings of the Brethren of Purity to the West, and thus helped to introduce the ideas of alchemy there. The book, *Rutbat al-Hakim,* "The Sage's Step," an alchemical treatise which Maslama is supposed to have written, was actually composed after his death.[29] The alchemical theories that it contains are typical, but one of its recipes is interesting for its description of the calcination of mercury:

> I took natural, quivering mercury, free from impurity, and placed it in a glass vessel shaped like an egg. This I put inside another vessel like a cooking pot and set the whole apparatus over an extremely gentle fire. The outer pot was then in such a degree of heat that I could bear my hand on it. I heated the apparatus day and night for 4 days, after which I opened it. I found that the mercury (the original weight of which was ¼ of a pound) had been completely converted into a red powder, soft to the touch, the weight remaining as it was originally.[30]

This is very clearly the work of an experienced chemist. The Arabs had no balances sensitive enough to record the actual change in weight in this reaction, but the quantitative spirit shown in the description as well as the theories of Jabir on the amounts of the natures in substances show that many Islamic alchemists were groping toward a quantitative approach.

During the eleventh, twelfth, and thirteenth centuries, a number of alchemists wrote original books and commentaries on the older writings, but they added almost nothing to the work of the great chemists of the tenth century. During these years, the orthodox party in Islam gained the mastery, and more mystical ideas prevailed, so that the promise of a true scientific approach to chemistry was not fulfilled. Muslim science lost its drive, and scientific leadership passed into other hands. Fortunately, at this time, the West, which would have been quite unready to receive Greek scientific ideas at an earlier period, was able to accept the theories that were passed on by the Arabs. Thus the tradition of science was not lost, as it had been in China where no new group was able to carry on when Taoism degenerated into mysticism and charlatanism.

The Arabs performed their greatest service in passing on the ideas of Hellenistic civilization and the Hellenistic adepts who were the true founders of alchemy, but this was by no means their only contribution. Combining ideas from both Alexandria and China, they gave to alchemy the explicit formulation of the sulfur-mercury theory of the composition of substances, they added a clear statement of the doctrine of the elixir, the philosopher's stone, and, probably again under Chinese influence, they clarified the concept of the therapeutic virtues of the stone in curing "sick" metals, and perhaps human illnesses as well. On the practical side, they discovered sal ammoniac, they prepared caustic alkalies, they recognized the properties of animal substances and their importance to chemistry, and they introduced on a broad scale the method of destructive distillation of these substances as a means of analyzing them into their "ultimate components." Their classification of minerals became the basis for most of the systems used later in the West. Chemistry owes the Arabic alchemists far more than has usually been recognized, and their contribution to the development of the science was a major one.

REFERENCES

1. J. Ruska, *Arabische Alchemisten*, Vol. I, *Chalid ibn Jazid Mu'awija*, C. Winter, Heidelberg, 1924.

2. J. Ruska, *Arabische Alchemisten*, Vol. II, *Ga'far Alsadiq, der sechste Imam*, C. Winter, Heidelberg, 1924.

3. P. Kraus, *Jabir ibn Hayyan. Contribution à l'histoire des idées scientifiques dans l'Islam*, Vol. I, *Le Corpus des écrits jabiriens;* Vol. II, *Jabir et la science grecque;* Impr. de l'Institut français d'archéologie orientale, Cairo, 1942–1943.

4. J. Ruska, *Tabula Smaragdina*, C. F. Winther, Heidelberg, 1926, pp. 51–52.

5. G. Sarton, *Introduction to the History of Science*, Vol. I, Williams and Wilkins Co., Baltimore, 1927, p. 592.

6. H. E. Stapleton and M. Hidayat Husain, *Mem. Asiatic Soc. Bengal*, **12**, 1–213 (1933).

7. J. Ruska, *Isis*, **24**, 310–342 (1936).

8. M. Plessner, *ibid.*, **45**, 331–338 (1954).

9. P. Kraus, *Dritter Jahresber. Forsch.-Institut Geschichte Naturwiss. Berlin*, 23–42 (1930).

10. E. J. Holmyard, *An Essay on Jabir ibn Hayyan*, in *Studien zur Geschichte der Chemie. Festgabe für E. O. von Lippmann*, Berlin, 1927, p. 28.

11. P. Kraus, *Jabir ibn Hayyan*, Vol. I, *op. cit.*, p. lxiv.

12. J. W. Flück, *Ambix*, **4**, 81–144 (1951).

13. P. Kraus, *Jabir ibn Hayyan*, Vol. II, *op. cit.*

14. J. Ruska, *Sitzber. heidelberg. Akad. Wiss., Phil.-hist. Kl.* (1923); *Abhandl.* **5**, 23 pp.; *Z. angew. Chem.*, **41**, 1321–1324 (1928).

15. P. Kraus, *Jabir ibn Hayyan*, Vol. II, *op. cit.*, p. 164.

16. *Ibid.*, p. 10.

17. *Ibid.*, p. 12.

18. F. S. Taylor, *The Alchemists,* Henry Schuman, New York, 1949, p. 84.

19. P. Kraus, *Jabir ibn Hayyan,* Vol. II, *op. cit.*, pp. 18–23.

20. J. M. Stillman, *The Story of Early Chemistry,* D. Appleton and Co., New York, 1924, pp. 210–217.

21. H. E. Stapleton, R. F. Azo, and M. Hidayat Husain, *Mem. Roy. Asiatic Soc. Bengal,* **8,** 317–418 (1927) ; J. Ruska, *Der Islam,* **22,** 281–319 (1935); *Quell. und Stud. Geschichte Naturwiss. und Medizin,* **4,** 153–239 (1935); J. R. Partington, *Ambix,* **1,** 192–196 (1938).

22. Stapleton, Azo, and Husain, *op. cit.*, p. 391.

23. *Ibid.*, p. 392.

24. J. Ruska and K. Garbers, *Der Islam,* **25,** 1–34 (1938).

25. J. Ruska, *Der Islam,* **22,** 305–310 (1935).

26. E. J. Holmyard and D. C. Mandeville, *Avicennae De Congelatione et Conglutinatione Lapidum,* being Sections of the Kitab al-Shifa, Paris, 1927, 86 pp.

27. *Ibid.*, pp. 41–42.

28. J. Ruska, *Z. angew. Chem.*, **46,** 337–340 (1933).

29. E. J. Holmyard, *Isis,* **6,** 293–305 (1924) .

30. *Ibid.*, p. 302.

THE TRANSMISSION OF CHEMISTRY

TO THE WEST

During the long period when alchemy was passing to the Arabs and undergoing an important systematization at their hands, the art was lost to western Europe. The Romans had never taken the interest in the theories of nature that had been so characteristic of the Greeks, and, with the decline of the Western Roman Empire, almost all traces of scientific speculation disappeared in the regions that had been under its control. Technical arts must have continued to exist, but the requirements of feudal society were relatively limited, and no written records remain of the methods employed by the artisans of this time.

Conditions in the eastern half of the Empire were somewhat more favorable to the preservation of scientific ideas, for the Byzantine Empire was essentially Greek in culture, and it preserved the Greek classics and much of Greek science. The efforts were confined almost entirely to preservation, however, with little or no addition of new knowledge. Thus it was that, while the Muslim alchemists were enlarging and organizing alchemy in a very significant way, the Byzantine alchemists were merely copying or commenting on the alchemical manuscripts of earlier days.

The technical arts of Constantinople seem, in general, to have followed the same path. Methods already familiar to us from the papyri of Leiden and Stockholm were transmitted orally from one generation to the next. There was, however, one notable exception to this statement. In the middle of the seventh century the architect Kallinikos of Heliopolis discovered the inflammable mixture known as Greek fire, or marine fire. This was a burning liquid which was projected from tubes called "siphons" onto enemy ships. It caused fires that could not be extinguished by water. Mixtures of materials such as bitumen, resin, and naphtha had been in use long before to set fire to enemy ships or fortresses, but this Greek fire evidently contained a new principle that increased its inflammability and permitted its forced ejection from the siphon. The composition was kept a state secret, known only to the Emperor and to the family of Kallinikos, who prepared the material. Even today we are not sure what was the essential ingredient. It seems possible that it was saltpeter, a substance that had not been known before, and that is not specifically mentioned in manuscripts until the twelfth century.[1]

The Byzantines obtained Greek fire at a time when their military position was extremely weak, and when the Arabs were making their greatest conquests. By the use of the fire the Greeks were able to destroy the attacking Arab fleets shortly after 672 and again in 717. They thus prevented the capture of Constantinople, which would otherwise almost certainly have occurred. If this had happened in the seventh or eighth centuries, much of the learning of Greece would have been lost, for western Europe was not then prepared to accept scholarship as it was in the fifteenth century when Constantinople finally fell and Greek scholars fled to find a ready welcome in renaissance Europe. Here then is an instance in which chemical discovery played an important part in the cultural history of the West.

Apart from the invention of Greek fire, which was kept so secret that it had almost no effect on the development of chemistry, the artisans of Constantinople did occasionally compile books of miscellaneous recipes, and some of these found their way west. By the tenth century, there were signs that a new interest in science and technology was beginning to arise in this area. The first evidences were found in the circulation of manuscripts containing such collections of recipes. At first these recipes were very similar to, or even identical with, those of the Leiden and Stockholm Papyri, but with the passage of time, new methods and discoveries were incorporated, and the compilations grew in size and originality.

The earliest of these compilations was the *Compositiones ad tingenda* or *Compositions for coloring mosaics, skins, and other things, for gilding iron, concerning minerals, for writing in letters of gold, for making certain cements, and other documents relating to the arts,* to give it its full and descriptive title.[2] It was probably composed in Alexandria about 600 and translated into Latin by a Lombard about 750.[3] Similar to it are the *Mappae Clavicula,* or "Little Key to Painting," known in manuscripts of the tenth and twelfth centuries, but probably first composed about 800; the book of Heraclius *On the Colors and Arts of the Romans* of about 1000; and the *List of Various Arts* of the monk Theophilis, also of about 1000. All these works are technical compendia which contain recipes for gilding, dyeing, and working glass and metals.[2, 3] The *Compositiones ad tingenda* first uses the term "vitriol" to refer to impure iron sulfate, which had previously been called chalcanthum.[4] The work of Theophilis, which first describes the art of painting in oils, is noteworthy for the clarity and detail of its recipes.[5]

None of these works contains any theoretical discussion; none has an alchemical character. They represent the development of the technological side of chemistry, which for so long had shown no evidence of originality. Now, from the eleventh century on there was an awakening that was reflected in these and similar manuscripts.

One of the important technical advances of the period was a great improvement in the art of distillation. The Hellenistic alchemists had invented apparatus and methods; the Arabs, with their interest in resolving substances into spirits and bodies, had utilized the Hellenistic operations, but all these efforts had been limited by the quality of glass for the apparatus and the crude methods for condensing and receiving the distillate. Now the artisans in Italy began to improve glassware. This better glass was used at the famous medical school of Salerno in southern Italy, and about 1100 a further important step was taken.

Perhaps influenced by the suggestions of the Arabs that something to absorb one nature should be added in attempting to purify another nature (see p. 66), various salts such as common salt or tartar (potassium carbonate) were added to wines in a distilling vessel. These absorbed part of the water and permitted recovery in the distillate of a "water" which burned.[6] A recipe of Master Salernus of Salerno (died 1167) gives an early description of such a water, and the twelfth century manuscript of the *Mappae Clavicula* (though not the tenth century version) contains a recipe, partly given as a cryptogram, which read as follows: "By mixing pure and strongest wine with three parts of salt and heating in a vessel customary for that purpose, a water is produced which, when kindled, inflames, yet leaves the material unburned." [7] This was obviously a dilute alcohol solution that burned at a temperature so low as not to inflame the material on which it was placed. Such a solution became known as *aqua ardens,* burning water. Interest in this substance developed rapidly. The Florentine physician, Thaddeus Alderotti, devised methods of cooling the coil and receiver of his distilling apparatus instead of merely the stillhead, as had been the previous practice.[8] It soon became possible to prepare strong solutions of alcohol, which were known as *aqua vitae,* water of life. These were widely used by physicians of this and later periods, such as Arnold of Villanova [9] and John of Rupescissa. The latter ascribed to alcohol the quality of the supreme remedy against corruption, the fifth element, or quintessence,[10] and this view became common among physicians. It was probably ultimately derived from the old Greek concept of the *pneuma,* which could act on everything and become potentially everything.[11] After the thirteenth century, recipes for preparing alcohol are frequent, though the present name was not applied until its use by Paracelsus in the sixteenth century. He derived the name from the Arabic term *al kohl,* which had first been applied to powdered antimony sulfide used in darkening the eyebrows. In time the word came to mean any fine powder, and so to signify the essence of things. Alcohol was the essence of wine, and so Paracelsus referred to *alcool vini* or *alcohol vini.* Later the word vini was dropped and the name alcohol assumed its modern significance.[9, 12]

An even more important result of the improvement of distillation methods was the discovery of the mineral acids. This apparently occurred in the early thirteenth century. Hellenistic alchemists had frequently calcined vitriols, but they had never condensed the volatile products. This was now done. A Byzantine manuscript of the end of the thirteenth century describes the preparation of nitric and sulfuric acids. The important works issued under the name of Geber, to be discussed later, which were composed in the early fourteenth century, also describe methods of distilling mixtures of vitriol and saltpeter or sal ammoniac. Nitric acid and aqua regia soon became common reagents and were produced on a large scale. Sulfuric acid was less frequently prepared, and free hydrochloric acid was not described until the time of Libavius in the sixteenth century.[13]

The discovery of the mineral acids greatly increased the power of the chemist to dissolve substances and to carry out reactions in solution. The advance over the use of weak organic acids was tremendous. In addition, the demand for such substances as alcohol and mineral acids gradually tended to bring about the development of a primitive chemical industry. Chemical progress began to be made, not in the monasteries and homes of the workmen, but in apothecary shops and actual chemical centers.[14] This trend was important, for it helped the decline of feudalism by stimulating the growth of towns and a middle class at the end of the middle ages.

In the preparation of nitric acid, saltpeter was required. As was shown earlier, this substance may have been known in Constantinople in the seventh century, but it was not described in any manuscript of that time. Its first public use seems to have been in Italy about 1150. Aside from its utilization in the manufacture of nitric acid, it found its chief application in making black powder, a mixture of sulfur, charcoal, and saltpeter. The history of this substance is far from clear. Popular tradition ascribes the discovery either to the English friar, Roger Bacon, or to the German monk, Berthold Schwarz. It is practically certain that Bacon was not the discoverer,[15] for he himself wrote in his *Opus Majus* (1267–1268):

> Certain things inspire such terror at sight that the flashes from storm clouds disturb far less—beyond comparison; by works such as these Gideon is believed to have operated in the case of the Midianites. And an experiment of that character we take from that boyish trick which is performed in many parts of the world, namely that by a device made of a size as small as a human thumb, by the force of that salt called sal petrae, such a horrible noise is produced in the rupture of such a small thing as a little parchment that it is felt to surpass the noise of violent thunder, and its light surpasses the greatest flashes of lightning.[16]

Thus the properties of gunpowder and its use in firecrackers were well known by the mid-thirteenth century.

The monk, Berthold Schwarz, is probably a mythical figure, but he was supposed to have lived in Freiberg, which became a center for the manufacture of cannons, first used about 1360.[17] This may account for his supposed association with gunpowder.

The actual invention of gunpowder took place in China, and the first mention of it appeared about 919. By 1000, explosive bombs were used in catapults and this *huo yao* (fire chemical) began to be used in a number of devices for naval and land warfare. It is likely that the Mongols carried the knowledge of this substance to the West.[18]

The first western description is found in the *Book of Fires for Burning Enemies*, ascribed to Marcus Graecus. The first compilation of this work probably took place in the eighth century,[19] but the earliest manuscript in western Europe dates from the late thirteenth century and no doubt represents a compilation of recipes from all preceding periods.[20] It describes the preparation of substances resembling Greek fire, discusses saltpeter, and gives methods for preparing black powder. The development of gunpowder as an instrument of warfare took place chiefly in the fourteenth century, and this chemical product, perhaps more than anything else, was responsible for the overthrow of the feudal system. Again a chemical product produced a major revolution in society.

The advances discussed so far, revealed for the most part in the technical manuscripts of the eleventh to thirteenth centuries, are essentially those of practical chemists. Cosmological theories of the origin of metals and the causes for the changes observed throughout the world are not found. It is quite likely that some of the observations recorded may have been under the influence of the stimulation of knowledge that resulted from the close contact between Arabic and European scholars in the period under discussion, but the effects of this contact have been recorded in quite a different class of manuscripts.

Beginning with the work of Constantinus Africanus (c. 1020–1087) in the eleventh century, a large number of western scholars became aware of the scientific treasures available in the Arabic language. By the twelfth century this was recognized especially in Spain where the contact between Moors and Spaniards was very close. It was soon realized that a vast store of material lay at hand in the fields of philosophy, science, and medicine, not only of Arabic origin, but also going back to the Greek period. A similar realization occurred in Sicily and southern Italy, where the Italians were in contact not only with Arabs from Africa, but also with Greeks from Constantinople. As a result there arose in these regions schools of translation and individual translators who made it their life work to hand over to Latin workers the treasures of the Arabic world.

Just as the Syrian schools of translation had made the Greek manuscripts available to the Arabs, now the Spanish and Italian scholars furnished Latin versions of the works of Aristotle and Ptolemy, of al-Razi and ibn Sina. Such men as Hugh of Santalla (1119–1151), Robert of Chester (fl. 1145), and Gerard of Cremona (1114–1184) made their versions of the philosophical, astronomical, mathematical, and medical treatises available to western scholars.[21] We are well acquainted with the specific translations that these men made in these fields, but, just as with the Syrian translations of alchemical manuscripts, which were mostly anonymous, so we find that the names of

the men who produced the Latin versions of the alchemical manuscripts were seldom attached to their work. Robert of Chester, in
1144, is supposed to have translated the alchemy of Khalid ibn Yazid
and his Christian teacher (here called Morienus instead of Stephanos
as in the Arabic version),[22] but even this translation may have been
falsely attributed to Robert.[23]

In any case, whoever the translators may have been, there appeared
throughout Europe in the twelfth and thirteenth centuries a flood
of Latin alchemical manuscripts which were almost entirely translations from the Arabic, though in the latest period some additions may
have been made by the western alchemists themselves. All schools of
Arabic alchemy were represented. The mystical alchemy of Egypt is
found in the *Tabula Chemica* of "Senior Zadith Filius Hamuel" [24]
(that is, ibn Umail); in the *Turba Philosophorum* with its discussion
of the cosmological theories of the alchemists; and in the famous
Emerald Tablet of Hermes [25] in which these ideas are expressed in a
condensed and allegorical style. The Emerald Tablet was one of the
most quoted documents of later alchemists. The elaborate classification of material substances of the more practical alchemists, such as
the Jabir Corpus or the works of al-Razi, are represented by a number
of translations. The *Book of Secret of Secrets* of al-Razi was translated in Sicily, and a number of works by followers of al-Razi were
translated and ascribed to the master himself.[26]

The most famous of these was the book *On Alums and Salts,* which
was actually written by a Moorish alchemist of the eleventh or twelfth
century, and was translated into Latin at the beginning of the thirteenth century. The work draws from many sources, including al-Razi
and Jabir, as well as from some of the more mystical alchemists, and
it includes observations made by the author himself. It uses the classification of substances into spirits, metals, stones, and salts, and gives
descriptions of the properties of many materials.[27] Such classifications
were carried still further in the various *Lapidaries,* such as that ascribed to Aristotle.[28] In these the Aristotelian theories were used to
explain the nature of gems and minerals, including their medicinal
uses.

By the beginning of the thirteenth century, the theories, classifications, and methods of the Arabic alchemists were easily available to
western scholars. The number of alchemical manuscripts from this
time proves the great appeal that this subject held. The scattered
location of the various manuscripts, however, sometimes made it difficult for any one reader to obtain more than a limited idea of the

subject. In the thirteenth century this difficulty was overcome. The century was pre-eminently one of great encyclopedists, men who systematically compiled, organized, and digested the great amount of scientific knowledge that had become available. The chief names among them are Batholomaeus Anglicus (fl. 1230),[29] Vincent of Beauvais (c. 1190–c. 1264),[30] and Albertus Magnus (1193–1280).[31] These men took all knowledge for their field. They consulted all the learned manuscripts they could find, and sometimes they added to these their own observations. Most of their descriptions were necessarily second hand, however, and errors are found in their works. Nevertheless it is surprising how thorough and accurate a picture of the world they were able to give.

Their theories of the nature of matter were basically Aristotelian, usually expressed in terms of the sulfur-mercury theory of metallic composition. As believers in Aristotle, they did not deny the truth of the possibility of transmutation, although both Vincent and Albert expressed reservations concerning the conditions under which it could be carried out. They knew that many charlatans claimed to be alchemists. On the whole, these encyclopedists were rational and clearsighted men. They did not indulge in mystical speculation and allegorical imagery. They performed the task that they set for themselves: collecting and systematizing the various facts and the theories of the nature of the world and the properties of substances. It is true that they seldom consulted the recipe books of the practical chemists, and so knew little of the new discoveries that were being made. Albertus mentions alcohol, but otherwise none of this work was mentioned in their encyclopedias. They themselves made no new discoveries, but their labors paved the way for the workers who followed, and their books were everywhere consulted by the alchemists and chemists who lived after them.

Practically contemporary with these great scholars were three other men who themselves contributed little to chemical advance, but who, because of their authority in other fields, later came to be considered authorities in alchemy as well. These were the Catalan scholar and missionary, Raymond Lull (c. 1235–1315),[32] the Catalan physician, Arnold of Villanova (died 1311),[33] and the English friar, Roger Bacon (died c. 1292).[34]

The period of the twelfth and thirteenth centuries was one of great importance in the history of chemistry. It marks the beginning of the great advance of chemistry in western Europe, an advance that at first had a somewhat tentative character. Greek and Arabic alchemical theories became known to the scholars, while fundamental discoveries were being made in practical chemistry. As yet, there seemed to be little connection between the two movements. The practical discoverers did not theorize; the scholars did not keep abreast of the practical advances. Yet, there must have been many men with chemical interests who were aware of both movements. It was only a matter of time, therefore, before the two branches of chemistry would once more join hands.

Meanwhile, there was a rather notable absence of the mystical element in chemical theory. The scholars thought of transmutation, if it occurred, as a physical phenomenon, obeying natural laws. Wilson [35] has drawn a parallel with the early days of Greek alchemy, where the period of contemplative mysticism came later than the period of actual discovery. This parallel can be extended to China and Arabia, in both of which alchemy degenerated after an initial period of a more scientific viewpoint. It was because this tendency toward degeneration, which was later seen also in the West, did not assume overwhelming force that it was possible for a science of chemistry to develop in western culture, though it had failed to appear in every other culture mentioned.

REFERENCES

1. N. D. Cheronis, *J. Chem. Educ.*, **14**, 360–365 (1937).

2. J. M. Stillman, *The Story of Early Chemistry*, D. Appleton and Co., New York, 1924, pp. 185–187.

3. C. Singer, *The Earliest Chemical Industry*, Folio Society, London, 1948, pp. 43–47.

4. Stillman, *op. cit.*, p. 186.

5. *Ibid.*, pp. 221–229.

6. R. J. Forbes, *Short History of the Art of Distillation*, Brill, Leiden, 1948, pp. 88–89.

7. Stillman, *op. cit.*, p. 189.

8. Forbes, *op. cit.*, pp. 60–61.

9. E. O. v. Lippmann, *Abhandl. Vorträge Geschichte Naturwiss.*, **2**, pp. 203–215 (1913).

10. Forbes, *op. cit.*, pp. 64–65.

11. F. S. Taylor, in *Science, Medicine, and History. Essays in the Evolution of Scientific Thought and Medical Practice, Written in Honour of Charles Singer*, Vol. I, edited by E. Ashwood, Oxford University Press, London, 1953, pp. 247–265.

12. Forbes, *op. cit.*, pp. 89–90; Stillman, *op. cit.*, p. 192.

13. Forbes, *op. cit.*, pp. 86–87.

14. *Ibid.*, p. 57.

15. L. Thorndike, *A History of Magic and Experimental Science*, Vol. II, The Macmillan Co., New York, 1923, pp. 688–691.

16. Roger Bacon, *Opus Majus*, Bridges ed., Vol. II, pp. 217–218.

17. R. E. Oesper, *J. Chem. Educ.*, **16**, 303–306 (1939).

18. Joseph Needham, *Science and Civilization in China,* Vol. I, Cambridge University Press, Cambridge, 1954, pp. 131, 134–135, 222.

19. T. L. Davis, *The Chemistry of Powder and Explosives,* Vol. I, John Wiley & Sons, New York, 1941, p. 34.

20. Forbes, *op. cit.*, p. 89.

21. C. H. Haskins, *Studies in the History of Medieval Science,* 2nd ed., Harvard University Press, Cambridge, Mass., 1927.

22. Thorndike, *op. cit.*, pp. 215–217.

23. J. Ruska, *Arabische Alchemisten,* Vol. I, C. Winter, Heidelberg, 1924, pp. 35–37.

24. J. Ruska, *Archeion,* **16**, 273–283 (1934).

25. J. Ruska, *Tabula Smaragdina,* C. F. Winther, Heidelberg, 1926; T. L. Davis, *J. Chem. Educ.*, **3**, 863–875 (1926).

26. J. Ruska, *Osiris,* **7**, 31–93 (1939).

27. J. Ruska, *Das Buch der Alaune und Salze,* Verlag Chemie, Berlin, 1935.

28. J. Ruska, *Das Steinbuch des Aristoteles,* C. Winter, Heidelberg, 1912.

29. Thorndike, *op. cit.*, pp. 401–435; Stillman, *op. cit.*, pp. 233–237.

30. Thorndike, *op. cit.*, pp. 457–476; Stillman, *op. cit.*, pp. 237–248.

31. Thorndike, *op. cit.*, pp. 517–592; Stillman, *op. cit.*, pp. 248–256.

32. Thorndike, *op. cit.*, pp. 862–873.

33. *Ibid.*, pp. 841–861.

34. *Ibid.*, pp. 616–691.

35. W. J. Wilson, *Osiris,* **6**, 10 (1939) .

THE FOURTEENTH AND

FIFTEENTH CENTURIES

By the end of the thirteenth century, most of the translations from the Arabic had been completed. European scholars could now carry on their work independently. This new independence, however, did not at once lead to a rapid development of science. Rather, it seemed that the scholars had to work over their material and ponder it for a prolonged period before they could use it creatively. The writers of the fourteenth and fifteenth centuries were, therefore, less original than might have been expected in view of the striking advances of the twelfth and thirteenth centuries. Actually, the great achievements of this later period lay in the founding of new universities and the organization of those already in existence, the discovery of printing, and the tremendous expansion of knowledge of the world brought about by the activities of the explorers. The results of these achievements for science become more apparent among the scholars of the sixteenth century.

This period of relatively slow progress was found in chemistry as well as in other sciences. There was no lack of activity, but it did not lead toward scientific chemistry as we know it today. Rather, activity centered in the production of more and more alchemical manuscripts. Since alchemical theories were well established and practical procedures did not vary greatly, most of the manuscripts merely repeated what had been said earlier. An increasing tendency toward allegory and mysticism characterized the period, and charlatans were frequent. Once again alchemy fell into disrepute in official circles. Pope John XXII issued a decretal against it, and various civil and ecclesiastical authorities denounced it.[1] There was considerable popular distrust of alchemists, reflected in the satirical Cannon Yeoman's Tale of Chaucer and the fact that Dante placed the alchemists deep in the Inferno. None of this disapproval seems to have hindered the popularity or spread of alchemy itself, or the production of new manuscripts on the subject.

One of the most influential books of this period, and one that was quoted and copied very frequently, was written about 1310, apparently by a practicing Spanish alchemist who ascribed his work to the great Arabic alchemist, Geber. This is a Latin form of the name Jabir, but there is otherwise almost no connection with the actual works of the Jabir Corpus.[2] Four books are usually ascribed to Geber: *The Investigation of Perfection, The Sum of Perfection or the Perfect Magistery,* *The Invention of Verity,* and the *Book of Furnaces.* These discuss at some length the reasons for the truth of alchemy. They then give the accepted theories of the compositions of metals, in which the smoky and humid exhalations of Aristotle are identified with sulfur (and arsenic sulfide too, in this case) and mercury. The metals other than gold are considered imperfect, or sick, and are to be cured by the philosopher's stone, which converts them to gold.

The most significant part of the Geber books lies in the practical directions. These show clearly that the author was familiar with laboratory apparatus and operations. He describes furnaces and other equipment in detail, and gives clearer directions for purifying or preparing substances than the instructions of his forerunners, and even those of many who followed him.

His description of the purification of salt, for instance, could be followed by anyone: "Common salt is cleansed thus: First burn it, and cast it combust into hot Water to be dissolved; filter the Solution, which congeal by gentle Fire. Calcine the Congelate for a Day and a Night in Moderate Fire, and keep it for use." [4]

Of more importance is his recipe for a "dissolutive water."

First ℞ of Vitriol of Cyprus, lib. I of Saltpeter, lib. II and of Jamenous Allom one fourth part; extract the Water with the Redness of the Alembeck (for it is very Solutive) and use it in the before alleadged

---

* The term "magistery," which is widely used in alchemical literature, originally signified a method. It retained this meaning, but gradually came also to mean the agent used in the process in which this method was utilized.[3]

Chapters. This is also made much more acute, if in it you shall dissolve a fourth part of Sal ammoniac; because that dissolves Gold, Sulphur, and Silver.[5]

This is one of the best descriptions of the preparation of mixtures of sulfuric, nitric, and hydrochloric acids yet to be given.

The books make it clear that Geber was also a practical metallurgist, for the properties of the metals are well described, and the cupellation method of separating gold and silver is given in detail. This is a process in which samples of gold or silver are heated with lead in a vessel made of bone ash. The lead forms litharge which separates with the impurities, while the heavier gold or silver sinks to the bottom as a metallic globule. The process is a very old one, and presupposes some acquaintance with the use of a balance,[6] but it had not been so clearly described before. The works of Geber show that behind the speculations of the alchemists there had developed a large amount of practical chemical knowledge, especially relating to the metals. This knowledge was not openly published again for another two hundred years.

As Geber explained the practical details of chemistry more clearly than had been done previously, so the physician Petrus Bonus of Ferrara gave an especially clear exposition of alchemical theory in his *Pretiosa Margerita Novella,* the "Precious New Pearl," published in 1330:

Thus, in the generation of metals, we distinguish two kinds of moisture, one of which is viscous and external, and not totally joined to the earthy parts of the substance; and the same is inflammable and sulphureous; while the other is a viscous internal humidity, and is identical in its composition with the earthy portions; it is neither combustible nor inflammable, because all its smallest parts are so intimately joined together as to make up one inseparable quicksilver: the dry and the moist particles are too closely united to be severed by the heat of fire, and there is perfect balance between them.

The first matter of all metals, then, is humid, viscous, incombustible, subtle, incorporated in the mineral caverns with subtle earth, with which it is equally and indissolubly mixed in its smallest particles. The proximate matter of metals is quicksilver, generated out of their indissoluble commixtion. To this Nature, in her wisdom, has joined a proper agent, viz., sulphur, which digests and moulds it into the metallic form. Sulphur is a certain earthy fatness, thickened and hardened by well-tempered decoction, and it is related to quicksilver as the male to the female, and as the proper agent to the proper matter. Some sulphur is fusible, and some is not, according as the metals to which it belongs are also fusible or not. Quicksilver is coagulated in the bowels of the earth by its own proper sulphur. Hence we ought to say that these two, quicksilver and sulphur, in their joint mutual operation, are the first principles of metals. The possibility of changing common metals into gold lies in the fact that in ordinary metals the sulphur has not yet fully done its work; for if they were perfect as they are, it would be necessary to change them back into the first metallic substance before transmuting them into gold; and this has been admitted to be impossible.[7]

The definition of sulfur as an "earthy fatness" should be particularly noted, for this idea became the basis for later theories of combustion.

Upon these techniques and ideas, the alchemists of the fourteenth and fifteenth centuries based their writings. In general, they merely repeated them endlessly, without introducing any new ideas. Most of the manuscripts were attributed to some famous writer of the past, probably in the hope that the well-known name would attract more readers. Thus a considerable body of manuscripts was attributed to Arnold of Villanova. These writings were similar to each other and tended to stress mercury as the main source of the philosopher's stone at the expense of sulfur, whose importance was minimized. Animal substances were considered to be of little value.[8] Although this school of alchemical thought was prominent in the fourteenth century, it was vigorously opposed by many writers, and eventually, as will be seen, sulfur came to hold the main place in chemical theory.

Support for the importance of sulfur came from the large body of writings attributed to Raymond Lull. These works were written after the death of Lull, who, in his genuine writings, declared his disbelief in alchemy. In the Lullian Corpus, sulfur, artificially made, is the natural heat, and mercury is the material substance and radical humidity of all liquefiable substances.[9]

In similar fashion, works of later alchemists were attributed to Vincent of Beauvais, Roger Bacon, and Albertus Magnus, although some authors did publish under their own names. None does much more than repeat the general theories and typical recipes that have been described. It is therefore obvious that, in the alchemical manuscripts themselves, chemistry had reached something of a dead end. This type of literature continued well into the eighteenth century, and has not entirely vanished even today.[10] It became increasingly mystical and allegorical. Eventually, its devotees came to regard practical laboratory chemistry as an inferior species, whereas the true adepts were concerned only with the perfection of the human soul.

It is therefore necessary to look elsewhere if we wish to trace the development of chemistry as a science. During the fourteenth and fifteenth centuries, such a development can be followed chiefly through incidental references in medical and scientific works. Physicians and natural scientists were concerned with chemical substances, and though they might accept the theories of the alchemists (which were, of course, essentially the Aristotelian ideas of all educated men of this time), they did not use these theories solely to justify or explain alchemical transmutations. Such men were far more practical, and they were using chemical compounds for practical purposes. In addition, physicists were studying principles that later became of great importance in chemistry.

For example, the theory and construction of balances was under active study. Jordanus Nemorarius in the thirteenth century had written on this subject, and his work was commented upon and enlarged by Blasius of Parma (died 1416).[11] Nicholas of Cusa (1401–1464), a leading humanist, advocated continual use of the balance, and even suggested an experiment of weighing earth and seeds, and then the plants that resulted, and the ashes from burning the plants. This would show how much earth entered into the composition of plants.[12] He did not carry out the experiment, but his idea shows that a quantitative approach was developing. The experiment obviously contains the germ of the idea tested by Van Helmont in 1648 (p. 105), although the latter was more interested in water than in earth as a component of plants.

Giovanni da Fontana (fl. 1440), a military engineer and physician, used rockets and gunpowder to construct diabolical figures that flew in the air or were propelled under water, greatly alarming the spectators. That he could safely use his knowledge of chemicals to perform these tricks without suffering as a magician, indicates the more sceptical attitude toward supernatural matters that was beginning to appear.[13]

It was natural that physicians should be well acquainted with chemical compounds. Even though many of their medicines were composed of elaborate mixtures of animal products, sometimes of an exceedingly disgusting nature, they utilized many substances that had first been prepared by the alchemists, and that were prepared by the apothecaries as soon as a demand arose. Further, the notion that the elixir not only cured metals, but also could prolong life and cure human diseases, made it imperative for progressive physicians to keep abreast of alchemical theory. Many physicians were also alchemists. Hence the use of chemical substances as medicines was widespread.[14] Iatrochemistry, the use of chemicals for healing human illnesses, was established before the days of Paracelsus, although it was he who first popularized the subject.

The views of John of Rupescissa on alcohol as the quintessence of wine have already been mentioned. He went on to develop the theory that quintessences could be extracted from nearly everything. Thus he is enthusiastic over the quintessence of antimony, prepared as a sweet, red liquid by extracting "mineral antimony" (the sulfide) with vinegar.[15] Rupescissa had already shown in an alchemical work, the *Liber lucis,* that he was acquainted with alchemy and could describe its methods with unusual clarity. In his espousal of alcohol as the quintessence, he applied his alchemical ideas to medicine, and so may be considered the founder of medical chemistry.[16]

Michel Savonarola, grandfather of the reforming monk of Florence, was familiar with chemical remedies. He used chemical methods in his studies on the evaporation of mineral waters, which he described in a book on baths published about 1450. He gave qualitative tests for distinguishing salt from soda.[17]

It can be seen from these incidental references that chemical methods were gradually being applied in a number of fields, and that an appreciation of the possibility of using these methods was developing among scholars in fields other than alchemy. Nevertheless, it is not possible to judge from these references how far chemical technology and the chemical approach had actually progressed. With the coming of the sixteenth century, this situation changed completely. For the first time, chemical methods were described in full detail. Chemistry still did not stand on its own feet; it was still a servant of medicine, mining, and other specialties, but the writings of the sixteenth century scientists at last show how far chemistry had progressed, and how it could be used to further scientific advance. The way was opened for the men who, in the seventeenth century, could be called chemists.

REFERENCES

1. L. Thorndike, *History of Magic and Experimental Science,* Vol. III, Columbia University Press, New York, 1934, pp. 31–33.

2. J. Ruska, *Ann. Guebhard-Severine,* **10,** 410–417 (1934); J. M. Stillman, *The Story of Early Chemistry,* D. Appleton and Co., New York, 1924, pp. 278–285.

3. W. J. Wilson, *Osiris,* **2,** 303–304 (1936).

4. E. J. Holmyard, editor, *The Works of Geber, Englished by Richard Russell, 1678,* J. M. Dent & Sons, London, 1928, p. 7.

5. *Ibid.,* pp. 223–224.

6. Wilson, *op. cit.,* pp. 286–289.

7. Petrus Bonus, *The New Pearl of Great Price*, translated by A. E. Waite, J. Elliott and Co., London, 1894, pp. 191–193.

8. Thorndike, *op. cit.*, pp. 52–84.

9. Thorndike, *op. cit.*, Vol. IV, p. 35.

10. D. I. Duveen and Emil Offenbacher, *An Alchemical Correspondence in Germany under the Nazi Regime*, Reinitz Soap Corp., Long Island City, N. Y., 1951.

11. Thorndike, *op. cit.*, Vol. IV, pp. 73–75.

12. *Ibid.*, p. 389.

13. *Ibid.*, pp. 174–175.

14. *Ibid.*, p. 231.

15. Thorndike, *op. cit.*, Vol. III, pp. 359–360.

16. R. P. Multhauf, *Isis*, **45**, 359–367 (1954).

17. Thorndike, *op. cit.*, Vol. IV, pp. 211–212.

CHAPTER X

THE SIXTEENTH CENTURY,
A PERIOD
OF TECHNICAL CHEMISTRY

The sixteenth century was a period of great scientific advance. Many of the new social and cultural developments favored a different approach to old problems. Among these were a widened geographical outlook due to the discovery of the New World, the spread of knowledge through the printing press, and the increased availability of the classic Greek authors due to the dispersal of the Byzantine scholars after the fall of Constantinople in 1454. As a result, all sciences showed a period of active development. This was most spectacular in the older, better-established sciences, and the names of Vesalius (1514–1564) in anatomy and Copernicus (1473–1543) in astronomy testify to the vigorous new spirit that was abroad.

Chemistry was not yet a science pursued independently for its own sake, and did not make the rapid progress that occurred in other fields. Nevertheless, in less obvious ways, it made significant advances. For the first time, chemical methods were described by most of the chemical authors in a full and clear manner. The technologists who employed chemical processes were not alchemists and often did not believe in the possibility of transmutation. Their interest lay in the actual accomplishment of some practical purpose. Such men had always existed, and the hints of their activities discussed in the previous chapter indicate that they had been making rapid progress. With the opening of the sixteenth century, the extent of this progress became apparent.

Books on practical technology appeared with increasing frequency. Such works seldom discussed chemical theory in detail. The old ideas of Aristotle and the sulfur-mercury modification of these were taken for granted, and, when any theoretical explanation was offered, it was in these terms. Theory, however, was seldom stressed. The chief chemical works of the period discussed methods, apparatus, and reagents.

This is not to say that the alchemists were inactive. Printing of alchemical books had begun slowly, and few appeared before 1500. After that time, however, a great flood of such works came from the presses. The older classics were printed in collected editions, and many new authors appeared in print.[1] Since nearly all of these merely repeated what had been said earlier, this type of literature made almost no contribution to chemical progress. In addition, the increasing tendency toward allegory and mysticism in alchemical writings showed that the subject was following the same course in Europe as it had in Alexandria, China, and the Muslim world. It was only because of the new scientific outlook of the western world that chemistry did not again sink into the morass of sterile commentary and superstition that had characterized the later period of the other cultures. The practical technologists gave a new impetus to chemical thought which permitted chemistry to continue to advance in new directions.

The period under discussion is thus one in which the technological branch of the science progressed while the theoretical side remained relatively inactive. As has been said, this was not a condition favorable for the most rapid advance of chemistry as a whole. Nevertheless, the new discoveries and the new outlook of the technologists uncovered so many new facts that new theories had to be evolved to explain them. The technological advances carried with them the seeds of new theories, and, in the seventeenth century, theoretical progress once more became rapid.

The opening of the sixteenth century was marked by the publication of an important book, the *Liber de arte distillandi de simplicibus,* usually called the *Little Book of Distillation* by Hieronymus Brunschwygk (c. 1450–1513), which appeared in 1500. Brunschwygk was interested in obtaining the essential medicinal agents of plants by distilling "waters" from them. The plants were macerated and mixed with water or alcohol before treatment, thus giving, in effect, steam distillation. He frequently used a water bath in his distillations, and con-

Ff follicßer maffen magfftu ouch eyn   fens fy vff einer firen in ß wyte ein ßalß ellé

Fig. 8. Water bath and stills with *Rosenhut.* (From H. Brunschwygk, *Liber de arte distillandi de simplicibus.*)

densed the plant essences in a conical alembic cooled by air, which was called a *Rosenhut.*[2] All his apparatus and methods were described in detail. In 1512 he published an enlarged edition of his work, the *Great Book of Distillation.* The impetus thus given to the study of distillation and the preparation of medicines from plants was influential throughout the century, as shown by the number of distillation books that were published at this time.[3]

Of even greater significance was the progress in metallurgical and mineralogical chemistry. It is clear that miners and assayers had been active for a long time and had developed their methods to a high degree without recording them in permanent form, for early in the sixteenth century there appeared two anonymous books that described an advanced state of the art. They were published in German rather than in Latin, and so show that they were the work of practical miners and not scholars. Such men were now willing to explain their methods for the benefit of younger workers.

The two books were the *Nützliches Bergbüchlein* and the *Probier-*

büchlein.[4] They first appeared about 1510 and were reprinted frequently in the following years, often with the addition of new material. The first is chiefly of geological and mineralogical interest; the second is mainly concerned with assaying. The early hints of assaying methods given by Geber are shown to be part of a well-developed system for testing the values of ores, chiefly those of gold and silver. The methods of dry assaying given in the *Probierbüchlein* are still valid today. Most important is the fact that the methods are quantitative. Balances are used routinely, and it is assumed that they can be easily bought. Careful directions are given for the manufacture and calibration of weights.[5] Obviously, in the mineralogical field, quantitative determinations are taken for granted. In most cases the alchemists had employed very crude methods of weighing, but the care and accuracy of the assayers is now revealed. This could not fail to influence workers in other fields of chemistry. The spread of quantitative ideas is shown in the work of Giovanbattista della Porta (1545–1615) who described the distillation of essential oils for perfumes, and for the first time gave yields.[6]

The publication of these small practical handbooks of mining and metallurgy shows that these subjects were of widespread interest. The fact that they appeared in Germany indicates that the northern European countries were becoming active scientifically. The chief scientific center in earlier centuries had been Italy, but now the rest of Europe was taking up the work.

The interest in metallurgy was greatly stimulated by the appearance of three outstanding works on this subject in the sixteenth century. These were the *De la pirotechnia* of Vannuccio Biringuccio (1480–c. 1539), published in 1540,[7] the *De re metallica* of Georg Bauer, usually called by the Latin form of his name, Agricola (1494–1555), published in 1556,[8] and the *Treatise on Ores and Assaying* of Lazarus Ercker (died 1593), published in 1574.[9] All these works gave detailed descriptions of the practice of mining, the treatment of ores, and the preparation of reagents such as mineral acids and salts needed in the chemical processes employed.

Biringuccio was a practical metallurgist who wrote, in Italian, the earliest work to cover the whole field of metallurgy. It was largely based on his own observations and experience. As in the *Probierbüchlein,* the quantitative spirit was evident. The accuracy of his assaying methods was clear, since he stated that whatever was promised by the assay should be obtained in the full-scale operation.[10] This was obviously a matter of great importance to the mine owners, and it shows that the development of quantitative methods was due to very practical considerations which did not interest the alchemists.

Lazarus Ercker was superintendent of mines for the Emperor Rudolf II. His book also records the results of his own experiences and was written, as he stated, for the instruction of young miners. He devoted much attention to the construction of balances and the calibration of weights, and dismissed all theoretical ideas in a few brief sentences.

Georgius Agricola was a physician in the mining regions of Germany. He was the most learned of these metallurgical authors. He wrote a number of books in Latin on various aspects of mining. In his *De natura fossilium,* published in 1546, he classified minerals into earths, stones properly so-called (including gems as distinct from rocks), solidified juices (salts), metals, and compounds (such as galena or pyrites).[11] This was clearly derived from the Arabic classifications, and was based on physical properties, the only possible basis at that time. Because of its style, completeness, and excellent illustrations, his *De re metallica* became a very popular work. Although Agricola was not a practical metallurgist as were Biringuccio and Ercker, he had observed the mining industry for most of his life, and he described the processes of metallurgy with a clarity that was new. The full description of the preparation of chemical substances found in the last part of the volume set an example that influenced writers of more purely chemical books in later times.

The works of these metallurgical writers were of importance also in that they set down, for the first time, some of the observations of the practical miners who were more influenced by what they saw than by any theory of the alchemists. The latter, for example, held firmly to the belief that there could be only seven metals, corresponding to the seven heavenly bodies. The miners noticed other metals, and some of these were mentioned in the metallurgical books. Zinc, cobalt, and bismuth were first discussed in these publications. Even more important for the future of chemistry was the stress laid on the need for accuracy and quantitative methods, and the fact that an example was set for describing chemical methods, apparatus, and preparations with full detail and clearness, so that anyone could repeat the work.

Of still greater significance for chemical progress was the work of an entirely different type of man. Philippus Theophrastus Bombastus von Hohenheim (1493–1541), who called himself Paracelsus, was one of the most controversial figures in the history of both medicine and chemistry. A physician of great originality of mind and extreme violence of temper, he spent most of his life wandering from place to place engaging in stormy controversies with the regular physicians who still followed the theories of Galen. So violent was the opposition he aroused, that most of his writings could not be published during his lifetime. About twenty years after his death they began to be printed. They soon attracted a large number of readers. The ideas of Paracelsus changed the course of medicine and chemistry decisively.

Paracelsus drew his ideas from the writings of men like John of Rupescissa and Arnold of Villanova, who had stressed the use of chemical remedies to cure disease, from the distillation books of Brunschwygk and his successors, and from the metallurgical writers of the period. He grew up in a mining district and so had first-hand knowledge of metallurgy. He was also influenced by the astrological theories of his day, and many of his works are marred by a mystical approach, by a strange terminology, and by a very confused style of writing. In many instances, it is by no means clear exactly what his ideas were. The main outlines of his chemical theories of medicine are well established, however.

To Paracelsus, the term alchemy had a much wider meaning than had previously been given to it. It signified any process in which natural products were made fit for a new end. This included even such processes as working iron or baking bread. Since he believed strongly in the theory of the similarity between the macrocosm, the great world, and the microcosm, man, he held that human digestion was also an alchemical process, directed by an alchemist whom he called the Archaeus. This alchemist separated poisonous substances from nutritious ones in the body. The most important aim of alchemy was to prepare medicines, or *arcana,* which could restore bodily balance disturbed by disease. Therefore, though Paracelsus believed in the possibility of transmutation, he held that this was not the chief purpose of the alchemist. His views brought him much nearer to the modern concept of chemistry than anyone before him.

To prepare his medicines, he subjected a large number of metals to a standardized set of reactions, thus obtaining a series of salts of the various metals in solution. Such salt solutions he called "oils." In this way, for the first time he generalized chemical reactions instead of considering every process as an individual treatment of a separate substance.[12] At the same time, the use of mineral substances in medicine greatly increased the number of remedies available, although there is little doubt that in some cases the remedies were distinctly dangerous to the patient.

The stress laid by Paracelsus on iatrochemistry, the use of alchemy (or chemistry) for preparing remedies, strongly modified the older theories of medicine. Although his ideas encountered strenuous opposition among conservative physicians, a large group of Paracelsists arose in the second half of the sixteenth century and spread his iatrochemical doctrines widely.[13] The new outlook of the iatrochemists laid the foundations for the modern idea of chemotherapy. At the same time it stimulated the search for new remedies, and so hastened the discovery of new chemical substances.

In addition to this effect of the work of Paracelsus in practical chemistry, he made one contribution to theoretical chemistry that was quickly adopted by almost all chemists. Besides the traditional mercury and sulfur as components of the metals, Paracelsus added a third component, salt. This was actually only a concrete expression of the older idea of spirit, soul, and body, or, more accurately, gas, liquid, and solid, which had always been in the minds of the alchemists. The mercury-sulphur theory left no satisfactory place for the body. By the time of Paracelsus, air (which Paracelsus often called by the general name "chaos") had lost its previous importance among the elements, and fire had taken its place. Fire was most often considered a combustible principle. Sulfur represented this inflammable principle, the soul; mercury was the "water" or spirit; and now salt became the earthy body. Thus, when wood burns, "that which burns then is sulfur, that which vaporizes is mercury, that which turns to ashes is salt."[14] This concept fitted in so well with the observations made when substances were dry-distilled, as was commonly done when they were "analyzed," that it was accepted easily, and this doctrine of the *tria prima* almost completely replaced the older mercury-sulfur theory. It should be noted that Paracelsus still assumed the four Aristotelian elements as basic, though he laid little stress on them, and that his sulfur, mercury, and salt were not the common substances familiar under those names, but their more abstract essences.

The contributions of Paracelsus tended to change the course of chemical development, but there was so much fantasy and mystical speculation in his writings that his ideas did not begin to spread immediately. Active publication of his manuscripts began about 1560, after the appearance of a number of alchemical books had somewhat prepared the reading public for his type of reasoning.[15] The violent polemics between his adherents and opponents helped to publicize his doctrines. The first Paracelsans accepted his theories with most of their attendant fantasies. Gradually, however, the more chemically minded began to sift out his chemical contributions, and later iatro-chemists by no means accepted all his ideas.

About the end of the sixteenth century, several publications ap-peared that were supposed to have been written in the fifteenth cen-tury, before the time of Paracelsus. Of these, the writings of Johann Isaac Hollandus and Isaac Hollandus, father and son, show little originality, but include many ideas that are typically Paracelsan.[16] Since these works claimed to precede those of Paracelsus, many of the anti-Paracelsus faction were happy to accuse Paracelsus himself of plagiarism. It has now been positively established that these works date from the last part of the sixteenth century, and drew their ideas from Paracelsus, rather than the opposite.

A similar claim to a fifteenth century dating is found in the works, more important in the history of chemistry, that are attributed to Basil Valentine, a supposed Benedictine monk. His works were pub-lished by Johann Thölde of Hesse, who had himself written a book on salts. The works of Basil Valentine resemble those of Paracelsus in many respects, using the terms Archaeus, arcanum, and chaos, and the concept of the *tria prima*. They were also used by the anti-Para-celsans to belittle the originality of their chief foe.[17] No evidence for the existence of a Basil Valentine has been discovered, and it is now known that the writings issued under his name are post-Para-celsan. It is usually thought that the publisher Thölde was the actual author of the Valentine literature,[18] though this conclusion is not accepted by everyone.[17] There is no doubt, however, that the works were written at the end of the sixteenth century.

The most famous of the books of Basil Valentine is the *Triumphal Chariot of Antimony*, published in 1604, which extols the medicinal use of this metal and its salts. From a chemical point of view it gives very clear descriptions of the preparation of antimony compounds. It has been called the first monograph devoted to the chemistry of a single metal. The book is an excellent example of the clear descrip-tion of chemical methods and results typical of the late sixteenth century.

This clarity of presentation reached a new height in the works of Andreas Libau, or Libavius in the Latin form (c. 1540–1616), a school teacher and physician whose interest in chemistry increased as he grew older, so that at length he was able to write the first true text-book of chemistry. Libavius was an iatrochemist, but not a blind follower of Paracelsus. In spite of his belief in a number of medieval superstitions,[19] his mind was far more logical and rational. He was strongly influenced by the work of Agricola, whom he resembled in many respects.

His chief work, the *Alchemia,* published in 1597, attempts to include in a single book all the subjects that are today regarded as chemical, but that, until his time, had been scattered through the literatures of alchemy, pharmacy, metallurgy, and similar subjects.[20] He used the term alchemy, as did Paracelsus, to include what we now term chemistry, and in his opening sentence defines it as follows: "Alchemy is the art of producing magisteries and of extracting pure essences by separating bodies from mixtures."[21] He divided alchemy into two parts, *encheria,* the methods of operation, and *chymia,* the combining of chemical substances. His classification of the divisions of chemistry was logical, and his descriptions were clear. The book long served as a textbook of chemistry. It is interesting to note that Libavius still admitted the truth of alchemical transmutation, in spite of his logical treatment of chemistry. He was not clear in his explanation of the theory of a number of chemical reactions, such as the precipitation of copper by iron, or the conversion of metals to oxides, which he regarded as a kind of transmutation.[22]

He was more accurate in his practical directions, especially in his book on technical chemistry, the *Syntagma,* which he published in 1611–1613. Here he gave clear directions for the preparation of aqua regia and sulfuric acid. He recognized the identity of this acid prepared by burning sulfur in moist air with the acid prepared from vitriol. He gave the first directions for the preparation of hydrochloric acid (*spiritus salis*) by heating salt with water in the presence of clay, that is, in clay crucibles. His name was long associated with tin tetrachloride (*spiritus fumans Libavii*), whose preparation he described briefly. He drew up detailed plans for the construction of a chemical laboratory, although such a laboratory was not constructed until 1683 at Altdorf.[23]

His books thus sum up the spirit of the sixteenth century, with its emphasis upon the practical at the expense of the theory, and with its great success in establishing chemistry as a science in its own right, one worthy of independent study. The emphasis on chemistry by the metallurgists and the Paracelsans had finally resulted in a true textbook of chemistry.

REFERENCES

1. L. Thorndike, *A History of Magic and Experimental Science,* Vol. IV, Columbia University Press, New York, 1934, p. 332; Vol. V, New York, 1941, pp. 533–549.

2. R. J. Forbes, *Short History of the Art of Distillation*, Brill, Leiden, 1948, pp. 83–84, 116.

3. *Ibid.*, pp. 109–111.

4. *Bergwerk- und Probierbüchlein*, translated by Anneliese Grünhaldt Sisco and Cyril Stanley Smith, American Institute of Mining and Metallurgical Engineers, New York, 1949.

5. J. M. Stillman, *The Story of Early Chemistry*, D. Appleton and Sons, New York, 1924, pp. 303–304.

6. Forbes, *op. cit.*, p. 120.

7. V. Biringuccio, *De la pirotechnia*, translated by C. S. Smith and M. T. Gnudi, American Institute of Mining and Metallurgical Engineers, New York, 1942.

8. G. Agricola, *De re metallica*, translated by H. C. Hoover and L. H. Hoover, *Mining Magazine*, London, 1912; reprinted, Dover Publications, New York, 1950.

9. L. Ercker, *Treatise on Ores and Assaying*, translated by Anneliese Grünhaldt Sisco and Cyril Stanley Smith, University of Chicago Press, Chicago, 1951.

10. Biringuccio, *op. cit.*, p. xvi.

11. Agricola, *op. cit.*, pp. 1–3, footnote.

12. T. P. Sherlock, *Ambix*, **3**, 33–63 (1948).

13. Thorndike, *op. cit.*, Vol. V, pp. 617–651.

14. Stillman, *op. cit.*, p. 320.

15. Thorndike, *op. cit.*, Vol. V, p. 620.

16. Stillman, *op. cit.*, pp. 368–371.

17. F. Fritz, *Basilius Valentinus*, in G. Bugge, *Das Buch der grossen Chemiker*, Vol. I, Verlag Chemie, Berlin, 1929, pp. 125–141.

18. Stillman, *op. cit.*, p. 375.

19. Thorndike, *op. cit.*, Vol. VI, p. 238–253.

20. Sherlock, *op. cit.*, p. 63.

21. A. Libavius, *Alchemia*, Frankfurt, 1579, p. 1.

22. E. Darmstaedter, *Libavius*, in G. Bugge, *Das Buch der grossen Chemiker*, Vol. I, Verlag Chemie, Berlin, 1929, pp. 107–124.

23. *Ibid.*, pp. 119–120.

CHAPTER XI

CHEMICAL PRACTICE AND THEORY IN THE FIRST HALF OF THE SEVENTEENTH CENTURY

The emphasis by the iatrochemists on the use of chemical remedies continued to inspire men to study chemical reactions as the seventeenth century dawned. The rational path of investigation pointed out by Libavius was increasingly followed. As the number of available reagents increased, so too did the number of new compounds and the number of reactions studied. The emphasis was on practical laboratory operations, but theoretical speculation, so little developed in the previous century, became more frequent. As will be seen, the first steps in this direction were faltering and there was little unanimity of thought, but during the seventeenth century a pattern of chemical thinking emerged, and, by the end of the century, chemical philosophy was a flourishing and popular subject.

At this time, too, chemistry began to assume the position of an independent science. Those who followed it were followers of a new profession. Many were still members of other trained groups, but some would be called chemists today. Until this time, most of the men who took a deep interest in chemistry had been physicians, but, with increasing frequency, pharmacists began to work and publish in the field. They were particularly fitted to pursue the subject since they operated laboratories and carried on most of the preparation of iatrochemical remedies. Few physicians actually soiled their hands in laboratories, and so their interest in chemistry tended to be theoretical. The pharmacists, with their practical knowledge, became increasingly important in the development of chemistry. For the next two hundred years a large number of fundamental chemical discoveries were made by pharmacists or men with pharmaceutical training. This was particularly true on the continent of Europe. In England, chemical advances were made by a different type of investigator, the scientific amateur.

The Libavius tradition of practical chemistry lasted well into the new century. One of those who followed this tradition was the French pharmacist Jean Béguin (died about 1620). About 1604 he began to give lectures on chemistry to the general public and in 1610 he published his *Tyrocinium Chymicum,* "The Chemical Beginner." [1] The book became very popular and went through many editions. It is interesting to note that in it Béguin distinguished the viewpoints of the physicist, the physician, and the chemist toward the facts of nature.[2] This is definite evidence that the chemist was now recognized as an individual scientist.

Béguin's book contains almost no theory. It is a heterogeneous collection of recipes for the preparation of chemical remedies. Nevertheless, it shows in many ways how far the "kitchin cooks" had progressed. An interesting example is the description of the digestion of minium (lead oxide) with vinegar, and the distillation of the resulting crystals to produce a volatile substance that we now know is acetone. Béguin adds that if the receiver is "not very exactly luted on with the Retort, so great a fragrancy (filling the whole laboratory) will be lost as I doubt not but if the odours of all odourate Vegetables were gathered together, and mixed, it would far exceed them." [3] In the 1615 edition of his book, Béguin explains the reaction between antimony sulfide, Sb_2S_3, and mercuric sulfate by an almost modern equation.[4]

Another practical chemist, this time a physician, was Angelo Sala (1576–1637). In 1617 he described the preparation of copper vitriol ($CuSO_4 \cdot 5H_2O$) from weighed amounts of copper, spirit of sulfur (sulfuric acid), and water. He then decomposed the compound and found the same ingredients and in the same proportions as he had used in his original synthesis. This demonstrated the continued existence of the constituents in the salt, which ran counter to the old Aristotelian ideas, and also showed, as he stated, that the artificial and natural vitriols were the same.[5]

A far greater chemist than Béguin or Sala was Johann Rudolph Glauber (1604–1670).[6] He was self-taught in chemistry, and he wandered over much of Europe learning the methods in use in various

A. Le Fourneau auec son instrument de fer et son recipient. B. L'artiste qui de sa main droicte oste le couuercle, et de la gauche iette la matiere dedans C. la figure exterieure du vaisseau. D. La figure interieure. E. vn autre vaisseau qui est sur les chai

Fig. 9. Distillation apparatus of Glauber. (From French translation of Glauber's
***Furni Novi Philosophici.*)**

countries. At length he settled in Amsterdam, where he constructed an excellent laboratory. Most of his life was spent in chemical experimentation. He was one of the earliest industrial chemists and chemical engineers. In his *Furni Novi Philosophici,* "New Philosophical Furnaces" (Amsterdam, 1648–1650), he described much chemical apparatus and many chemical operations. In *Pharmacopoeia Spagyrica* (Nürnberg, 1654) he gave recipes for many iatrochemical medicines. In *Teutschlands Wohlfahrt,* "The Prosperity of Germany" (Amsterdam, 1656), he applied chemical principles in his elaborate recommendations for making Germany an economically self-sufficient country. His final illness and death probably resulted from his investigations on the chemistry of mercury and arsenic in poorly ventilated laboratories.[7]

Glauber was much interested in metallurgy and in the manufacture of acids, bases, and salts. Among other procedures, he prepared strong sulfuric acid and greatly improved the method of Libavius for the preparation of hydrochloric acid. His most famous recipe was for the treatment of ordinary salt with sulfuric acid, followed by distillation. The residue from the reaction contained sodium sulfate, a salt to which Glauber attributed marvelous powers. He himself called it *sal mirabile,* and it has since been known as Glauber's salt. Contrary to his usual custom, he made some attempt to keep the method of preparing this salt a secret, and his enthusiasm in extolling its virtues led to his being considered something of a charlatan by those who do not know of his other work.

More important for the history of chemistry was his great interest in salts in general. Since he had available the common mineral acids, he could treat a large number of metals and metal oxides with them to prepare neutral salts. He often obtained these in pure form and in large quantities. He was thus able to recognize that salts were made of two parts, one coming from an acid, the other from a metal or its earth (oxide). His studies further showed that neutral salts could react with each other to produce new salts: double decomposition. In the preparation of saltpeter (potassium nitrate) from nitric acid and *sal Tartari* (potassium carbonate), he used the evolution of carbon dioxide as an indicator for the neutral point. By such reactions he learned that different acids have different strengths. He expressed this fact in terms that showed that he was groping toward the idea of chemical affinity.

> As one metal is of a different nature from another, that such as are alike, love each other, and such as be unlike abhor and shun each other; and when there are divers Metals in one mass, and you would separate them, it is necessary that you do it by adding such a thing as is of affinity to the more imperfect part, and is at enmity with the perfect part. As for examp. Sulphur is a friend of all the Metals, save Gold, and that it hates; but yet it loves (even in imperfect Metals) one better than another.[8]

The terminology of love and hate is here essentially that of Empedocles 2100 years before; but, while the Greek philosopher thought of Love and Strife as physical bodies, it is clear that Glauber considered them to be forces.

Thus Glauber went beyond Libavius in his grasp of the nature of the inorganic reactions that he carried out. He also made observations in organic chemistry, preparing such substances as ethyl chloride, acetone, acrolein, and benzene, but the nature of these compounds was too complex to be understood by a seventeenth century scientist.

Even though Glauber was first of all a practical chemist, he had a greater theoretical understanding than his predecessors of the six-teenth century. Thus it is not surprising that his contemporaries who were more interested in theory should make striking changes in the long accepted ideas of the nature of matter. The chemist who most combined theory with practice in his work at this time was Jan Baptist Van Helmont (1577–1644). Although many of his theories were erro-neous, his contributions to the advance of chemistry were very great.[9]

Van Helmont was a wealthy physician who lived near Brussels. He spent most of his life in retirement, carrying out chemical experi-ments. He considered himself a *philosophus per ignem,* a philosopher by fire, which approximately signifies a professional chemist.

Van Helmont rejected strongly the Aristotelian idea of the four elements, since he felt that neither fire nor earth was a fundamental constituent of substances. Air was an element, but it could not be changed into any other form, and where it did exert any influence, as in aiding the burning of a fire, it was doing so only by a mechanical action. This left water as the basis of all chemical substances, and much of Van Helmont's experimental work was devoted to proving the importance of water in nature. Van Helmont was a follower of Paracelsus and accepted much of the latter's mysticism, but he did not stress the importance of the three principles, mercury, sulfur, and salt, very strongly.

The most famous attempt of Van Helmont to prove that water could be converted into other substances was his willow-tree experiment. This was an actual performance of the experiment suggested by Nicho-las of Cusa two hundred years before. Van Helmont planted a tree in a weighed amount of earth, watered it for 5 years, and then showed that, while the tree had gained 164 pounds, the weight of earth re-mained the same. To him, this proved that all parts of the tree had been formed from water. Of even greater chemical interest was his experiment with a weighed amount of sand. This was fused with excess alkali to form water glass, which liquefied when exposed to air, obviously a conversion of earth to water. The water could be recon-verted to earth by treatment with acid, and the amount of earth (silica) recovered was the same as had been used originally.

These experiments do not seem to us a very good demonstration of the elemental nature of water, but they illustrate two aspects of Van Helmont's work which show that his thinking was much closer to that of the modern chemist than had been the thinking of his predecessors. The first was the quantitative nature of his experiments. He used the

balance almost routinely. Stemming from this, and still more important, is the implicit assumption on his part that matter is not created
or destroyed in the changes that it undergoes. The law of conservation
of mass was not stated until much later, but Van Helmont and those
who followed him used the principle continuously. The use of the
balance no doubt caused a widespread acceptance of this principle,
for there would be little point in weighings if it were not true. The
instrument introduced by the assayers for purely practical purposes
was leading to important theoretical advances in chemistry.

Another significant advance resulted from Van Helmont's theory
of the elements. Air could not be converted to water, as many earlier
philosophers had thought, yet, when water evaporated, it gave rise to
an airlike substance. Many chemical reactions also liberated similar
substances. These could not be air, and so must represent a new class
of materials. The product of evaporation of water easily returned to
water, and so Van Helmont considered it to be a vapor. The other
substances were more permanent, and for them he found a new name.

> I call this spirit, unknown hitherto, by the new name of Gas, which
> can neither be contained by vessels, nor reduced into a visible body,
> unless the seed being first extinguished. But Bodies do contain this
> spirit, and do sometimes wholly depart into such a Spirit, not indeed
> because it is actually in those very bodies (for truly it could not be de-
> tained, yea the whole composed body should fly away at once) but it is
> a Spirit grown together, coagulated after the manner of a body. . . .[10]

The word "gas" was most probably derived from "chaos," which
Paracelsus had used as a generalized term for air. The use of this
new word never died out completely on the continent of Europe, but
in England Robert Boyle replaced it by the term "air," and it was not
until the nineteenth century that it was re-established in English.[11]

To Van Helmont, a gas was subtler than a vapor, but denser than
elementary air. The difference in properties between gases and vapors
lay in a different arrangement of sulfur, mercury, and salt in the
smallest parts.[12] Experimentally, Van Helmont prepared gas by a
number of different reactions, and frequently used the term *gas sylvestre*, "wild spirit," to designate it. Most of the specimens he prepared were actually carbon dioxide obtained from such sources as burning charcoal, fermenting grapes, or acids and salt of tartar (potassium
carbonate), but he also obtained impure samples of oxides of nitrogen,
sulfur dioxide, and hydrogen. He knew that his gases did not always
have the same properties, though he did not ascribe much importance
to this fact. He has been called the father of pneumatic chemistry.

As an iatrochemist, Van Helmont applied many of his ideas to living organisms. Following Paracelsus, he assumed the existence of an Archaeus to direct bodily reactions, but he generalized the concept by declaring that all reactions in life were controlled by "ferments," which were a sort of individual formative energy. This terminology continued in use until late in the nineteenth century. It cannot be said that Van Helmont's conception of ferments had much in common with the modern idea of enzymes, though this comparison is sometimes made. In spite of the rather mystical character of many of his biochemical theories, Van Helmont did carry out much practical work on the chemistry of body fluids, and so he helped to lay the groundwork for a scientific biochemistry.

Two of Van Helmont's prominent successors carried his ideas of a chemical mechanism of life much further than he himself had done. François de la Boe, whose name was Latinized to Sylvius (1614–1672), and Otto Tachenius (c. 1620–1690) were undoubtedly influenced by the mechanical theories of chemistry that developed by the middle of the century, which tried to simplify all chemical ideas. They were also acquainted with the practical discoveries of Glauber. As iatrochemists, they felt the need to explain all life processes in these modern terms, and so they reduced all reactions in the living body to the interaction of acids and alkalies. The impressive effervescence of carbonates with acids seemed enough to account for living forces. It was the violent conflict of antagonistic substances that produced life.[13] This actually was a revival of the old doctrine of contraries, but it was expressed in the then most modern language.

The pharmacists who prepared iatrochemical drugs were closer to the laboratory itself than were the iatrochemical physicians, and so were more concerned with the nature of the materials with which they worked than with devising all-embracing theories of life. They devoted much of their time to distillations, especially of plant and animal products. They believed that by this process they were "analyzing" the substances into their constituents. Since they obtained a volatile liquor, an inflammable substance, and a water-soluble residue in many cases, they were prepared to accept the three principles of Paracelsus: mercury, sulfur, and salt. They also found in many of their distillations that they obtained a heavier liquid and an insoluble solid, and so they added to the Paracelsan elements two more: phlegm and earth. The first three were the active principles; the latter two, the passive principles; and so arose a concept of five elements.[14] A whole series of pharmacists who gave public lectures on chemistry at the Jardin du Roi in Paris, Davidson, de Clave, Le Fèvre, Glaser, and Lémery, held to the basic belief in the five principles, although they differed greatly among themselves in their application of these principles to chemical theory.[15]

It can be seen that the first half of the seventeenth century was a period of increasing precision in practical chemistry. The importance of quantitative experiments was appreciated; the idea of the indestructibility of matter was intuitively realized; and the nature of acids, bases, and salts and of many of their reactions began to be understood. At the same time the theoretical development of chemistry was in a chaotic state. Nearly every chemist developed his own explanation of the fundamental structure of matter.[16] Most of the theories that were put forward at this time did not survive the century, but they played an important part in the history of chemistry nevertheless. They arose because the men of this age could not accept the theories that had been current for two thousand years, and by their variety they swept the older theories from the scene. Yet, they could fill the vacuum that was thus created for only a short time. New discoveries that poured from the laboratories demanded better explanations than could be offered by the mystical and occult forces of the Paracelsans on the one hand, or the oversimplified explanations of the more rationally inclined iatrochemists on the other. By clearing the ground, the varied and individualistic theories of this period opened the way for the corpuscular theory that followed them and that, in its gradual development, led to the ideas of modern chemistry.

REFERENCES

1. T. S. Patterson, *Ann. Sci.*, **2**, 243–298 (1937).

2. Hélène Metzger, *Les doctrines chimiques en France du début du XVIIe à la fin du XVIIIe siècle*, Vol. I, Les Presses Universitaires de France, Paris, 1923, pp. 39–40.

3. Patterson, *op. cit.*, p. 260.

4. *Ibid.*, p. 278.

5. R. Hooykaas, *Chymia*, **2**, 77–78 (1949).

6. P. Walden, *Glauber*, in G. Bugge, *Das Buch der grossen Chemiker*, Vol. I, Verlag Chemie, Berlin, 1929, pp. 151–172; Eva V. Armstrong and Claude K. Deischer, *J. Chem. Educ.*, **19**, 3–8 (1943).

7. Walden, *op. cit.*, p. 155.

8. Armstrong and Deischer, *op. cit.*, p. 5.

9. F. Strunz, *Van Helmont*, in G. Bugge, *Das Buch der grossen Chemiker*, Vol. I, Verlag Chemie, Berlin, 1929, pp. 142–150; J. R. Partington, *Ann. Sci.*, **1**, 359–384 (1936).

10. J. B. Van Helmont, *Oriatrike, or Physick Refined,* translated by J. C., London, 1662, p. 106.

11. Partington, *op. cit.,* p. 372.

12. Strunz, *op. cit.,* p. 147.

13. Metzger, *op. cit.,* p. 202.

14. *Ibid.,* p. 310.

15. *Ibid.,* pp. 20–97, 311–312; Clara de Milt, *J. Chem. Educ.,* **18,** 503–509 (1941).

16. Metzger, *op. cit.,* pp. 163–164.

THE SPREAD OF ATOMISTIC
THEORIES

The Aristotelian theory of form and matter led logically to the belief that every chemical change, with its resulting change in the properties of the substances involved, was actually a transmutation. The reaction products were completely new, and nothing of the old substance remained except, perhaps, some "virtue" or hidden quality. This idea was firmly held throughout the Middle Ages. Every individual substance was considered to be completely homogeneous and continuous.[1] The properties of material substances were due to "substantial forms and real qualities," which, in the Middle Ages, were believed to be actual entities attached to matter. A body was white because it contained the "form of whiteness," and this statement was felt to be a completely adequate explanation of the property.[2] Substances were endowed with personality; they loved and hated (affinity). These qualities later came to be called "occult." They were the special object of attack by seventeenth century physicists and chemists.

Even in the early Renaissance, men began to challenge some of these concepts. The first attacks came when the humanists began to translate the works of the Greek atomists. The first century B.C. poem of Lucretius, *De rerum natura,* which explained the Epicurean version of the atomic ideas of Demokritos, was first printed in 1473.[3] This reintroduced the concept of the void, or vacuum, in which were floating the minutest particles of substances, the atoms, endowed with shape and size, and in continuous motion. In 1575 appeared the first complete translation of Hero's *Pneumatica* (p. 34).[4] This was a less philosophical, more practical explanation of the behavior of matter, founded directly on the properties of gases. It did not assume a continuous vacuum. Undifferentiated particles were separated only by pores of varying sizes which permitted expansion and contraction of the gases. Hero was not attempting to present a complete picture of the nature of the whole cosmos. Though his theory, like that of Demokritos, considered matter to be particulate, it was far less comprehensive than the theory expounded by Lucretius.

These atomic ideas, at first expressed as theories only, began to receive experimental support from studies such as those of Béguin, Sala, and Van Helmont. As evidence accumulated that the same substance persisted through a series of chemical changes, it was natural to assume that minute atoms were the unchangeable parts that carried through all the steps. Van Helmont did not find this a necessary assumption, but a number of his contemporaries did.

Daniel Sennert (1572–1637) thought that the existence of the smallest individual particles, which he called "minima," was proved when vapor from spirits of wine penetrated writing paper, or when a large volume of vapor during distillation contracted to a small drop of liquid.[5] Joachim Junge, or Jungius (1587–1637), explained many reactions in atomic terms. He denied that the replacement of iron by copper in a copper sulfate solution was a transmutation, seeing in it only an exchange of atoms.[6] Many physicians, anti-Aristotelian in outlook, similarly used atomic explanations for the reactions that they observed.[7]

At first, an attempt was made to preserve at least a part of the older theory by dividing compounds into two classes, "natural" and "artificial." Natural compounds were those that resulted from true transmutations; artificial compounds, those that could be resolved into the substances from which they were made. As more and more experiments were performed, the number of artificial compounds became so great that the distinction had to be abandoned.[8]

These earlier atomists were usually professedly anti-Aristotelian, but they continued to endow their atoms with the forms and qualities of the Aristotelians. They made the idea of atoms familiar to the scientists of the day, but they did not attempt any new explanation of chemical properties.[9] The rationalists of the seventeenth century moved on to new concepts. Galileo (1564–1642) accepted the views of Hero, but he endowed his particles with motion, giving to motion an importance equal to size and shape in fixing the properties of atoms.[10]   This was the basis for the "mechanical philosophy" which completely altered the views of physicists and chemists in the seventeenth century.   At almost the same time, Francis Bacon (1561–1626), accepting a particulate theory of matter without accepting the Demokritan atoms as such, believed that heat was a form of motion and that science should strive to investigate "the discovery of forms," that is, to explain the properties of matter.[11]

The most influential atomic theories and attempts to explain nature in mechanical terms were those of Pierre Gassendi (1592–1655) and René Descartes (1596–1650).   Both men tried to establish a complete world system, after the manner of the Greek philosophers, but chemists took their ideas only from the parts that seemed applicable to chemical reactions, thus building up a new "mechanical" chemistry that went far toward banishing the occult forces from properties and reactions.

Gassendi was a convinced Epicurean and had written a life of Epicuros and an exposition of his philosophy.   He accepted the experimental proof of the existence of a vacuum which came from the work of Evangelista Torricelli (1608–1647),[12] who invented the barometer in 1643.   Gassendi considered that the atoms moved in this void.   He attempted to account for all the properties of matter by the size and shape of the atoms.   Heat was due to small, round atoms; cold, to pyramidal atoms with sharp points, which accounted for the pricking sensation of severe cold.   Solids were held together by interlacing hooks.[13]   There is a reminder here of the Platonic elements whose shapes accounted for their properties.   This aspect of atomism was stressed heavily by chemists in the following years.

Descartes did not believe in atoms as such, but rather in a continuous but infinitely divisible matter.[14]   No vacuum was possible, but the original particles of matter, by their own movement, were abraded into large particles of varying shapes.   These made up the "third element," terrestrial matter, which comprised chemical substances whose shapes were important, just as in the system of Gassendi.   The particles were infinitely divisible in theory, but actually, because of their relatively slow motion, they did not undergo very much change.   Between these particles were much smaller particles of the "second element," a swiftly moving, subtle matter that was the air element.   The interstices that remained were filled by extremely fine particles, also swiftly moving, of the "first element," fire, formed from the abraded particles of the other elements, and easily deformable, so that they filled all the remaining space and left no room for a vacuum. The motion of the third element was imparted by the more rapidly moving particles of the second element, and motion could account for many of the properties of bodies. Heat increased the motion of the second element, and so also of the third. Many of the properties of matter explained by Gassendi as due to physical shape were explained by Descartes as due to motion or relative rest. Even light was a form of motion of the subtle particles. The second element was termed "ether" by Descartes, and his concept of a subtle, all-pervasive particulate fluid underlay the later attempts to use this idea to explain the difficulties physicists found with light, heat, and electricity.[15]

The aim of these philosophers was to do away with all mysterious, occult, or personalized forces, and to explain nature on a mechanical basis. The greatest exponent of this mechanical approach to chemistry was the outstanding English investigator Robert Boyle (1627–1691).

Boyle was a representative of a type of scientist found especially in England during the next century and a half, the amateur investigator. Whereas the greatest contributions to chemistry on the continent of Europe came from pharmacists or men with pharmaceutical training, the major advances in England resulted from the work of men who pursued science as an avocation. They were independently wealthy, or they held positions that gave them ample time to carry on investigations and to develop new theories. As a result, they tended to advance the theoretical side of science, whereas the continental pharmacists were discovering new substances and new reactions.

The first important experimental work of Boyle was his study of the properties of air, which he published in *New Experiments Physico-mechanical, Touching the Spring of the Air and Its Effects* (1660). He applied the newly discovered air pump of Otto von Guericke (1602–1686), Burgomaster of Magdeburg, to produce a vacuum and study the physical behavior of air. These studies led to the enunciation of what is now usually called "Boyle's Law." They were so influential among his fellow scientists that the vacuum produced by the air pump became known as the *vacuum Boylianum*. The pump itself was built for him by his assistant, Robert Hooke (1635–1703), who later made important contributions of his own to science.

Boyle's work helped greatly to eliminate some of the old concepts of "sympathy" and "abhorrence" from physics. It gave a mechanical explanation of suction as resulting from pressure of the air,[16] and it indicated the path that Boyle was to follow in chemistry for the rest of his life. His main purpose was to present a mechanical picture of chemical reactions, to do away with all occult forms and qualities, and to explain the behavior of substances by analogy with a machine, specifically to consider the world as "a great piece of clockwork." [17]

One essential part of his plan was to clear away the old ideas, especially those of the Aristotelian elements and the Paracelsan principles, as well as the theory that bodies could be resolved into their ultimate parts by fire, that is, by destructive distillation. This task Boyle undertook in his most famous book, *The Sceptical Chymist,* published in 1661. In the form of a dialogue between supporters of the older theories and Carneades, the sceptical chemist (Boyle himself), he presented convincing arguments to destroy most of the former beliefs. The book was exceedingly influential in establishing the newer outlook among chemists of the seventeenth century. True to its title, however, the book did not present a substitute for the ideas which were cast aside. This has led some to believe that Boyle was a complete sceptic in science, performing experiments for their own sake and not attempting to evolve a unifying theory to explain his work. The extreme variety of his experiments and the apparently unsystematic order of their publication would seem to support this view. Actually it is far from being correct.

Boyle was guided throughout all his work by what he himself named the "corpuscular philosophy." He, like Hero, pictured air as fundamentally corpuscular, and his early experiments on its elasticity confirmed the picture. He knew the theories of Gassendi and Descartes, and he used certain aspects of each of them, but he built up his own view of the mechanical universe in which the fundamental qualities were matter and motion. His ideas were most fully explained in *The Origin of Forms and Qualities* (1666).

Boyle conceived of small, solid, physically indivisible particles that were the building blocks of nature. These were associated into larger groups which often acted as units through a number of chemical reactions. Size and shape of these units gave physical properties to substances, but their motion was equally important, and a change in motion resulted in a change in properties. Attraction and affinity were explained by the mutual fitting together of moving particles.[18]

The unifying principle in all the varied experiments that Boyle carried out was the attempt to use the idea of matter and motion to explain mechanically all chemical reactions and all physical properties and to discard all occult theories. In the course of his work,

Boyle, an expert experimenter, made numerous important discoveries and offered many important suggestions which were very stimulating to later chemists.

He worked out the method for isolation of phosphorus from hints given by its original discoverer, Brand,[19] and used this new substance in his studies on the chemistry of air.   He investigated acids and alkalies and the use of indicators.   He described many tests useful in qualitative analysis.[20]   Very influential among later chemists were his studies on the nature of fire and of calcination, which he interpreted in terms of his corpuscular theory.   He believed that fire was composed of small particles in rapid motion, for, like most of his contemporaries, he believed that motion accounted for heat.   He sealed various metals in glass flasks and heated strongly to convert them to their calces (oxides).   He then opened the flasks and weighed the product.   The increase in weight was attributed to fire particles that had penetrated the glass and combined with the metal.   Many chemists adopted this theory, and it was not conclusively refuted until his experiments were checked by Lavoisier.   This is an excellent illustration of the lengths to which the corpuscular theory could be carried.

Boyle also studied combustion in the open air, and recognized that part of the air was needed for the process to continue.   He thought of air as a mixture of a number of distinct sorts of particles: vapors of water and other exhalations, a peculiar substance that supported combustion, and the basic air particles that accounted for the "spring" (elasticity).   These last particles gave air its gaseous properties, but did not react chemically.   This recalls Van Helmont's idea of a gas. The first two kinds of particles accounted for all the reactions of air. These ideas were later extended by Hooke and Mayow.[21]

Although Boyle conceived of matter as entirely corpuscular, his ideas of elements were not at all modern.   He gave a definition of an element in the appendix to *The Sceptical Chymist* that has often been quoted as a forerunner of the ideas of Lavoisier:

> And to prevent mistakes, I must advertize You, that I now mean by Elements, as those Chymists that speak plainest do by their Principles, certain Primitive and Simple, or perfectly unmingled bodies; which not being made of any other bodies, or of one another, are the Ingredients of which all those call'd perfectly mixt Bodies are immediately compounded, and into which they are ultimately resolved.[22]

Actually, Boyle did not believe in elements in our sense of the word. To him the aggregates of the ultimate particles made up most known substances which could therefore be transmuted into almost any other substance by a rearrangement of the particles. In fact, Boyle still believed in the possibility of transmutation, and was interested in transmuting gold, not for alchemical reasons, but to prove his corpuscular theory.[23] His theories were fundamentally less advanced than those of many of his contemporaries. It was his experimental work, his arguments against Aristotelian and Paracelsan ideas, and his emphasis upon mechanical and corpuscular explanations that exerted such a great influence on later chemists.

The only important scientist who fully accepted Boyle's chemical ideas was Isaac Newton (1642–1727), who was much interested in chemistry and included a number of chemical queries at the end of his *Optics*.[24] Newton's theories of matter were essentially those of Boyle, though he did assume an attraction between particles that Boyle would probably have considered occult. Newton apparently also believed that the particles of material substances were not fundamental, and that transmutation was possible.[25]

This view of the non-elemental nature of the particles of matter was not held by most seventeenth century chemists. They followed Libavius in their definition of the aim of chemistry, which they believed to be to extract pure principles and to discover how these were combined in known compounds. Inevitably, this led to the idea that ultimate particles, elements, could be obtained. As the various corpuscular theories developed, it was natural to expect that indivisible particles of the elements, that is, atoms, should exist. These atoms could not change, and so, at last, the idea of transmutation was rejected, even by strict Cartesians.[26] It then remained only to account mechanically for the reactions and properties of these elements, for, whatever variations in theory were held by seventeenth century chemists, all were united in rejecting any occult explanations.

One of the most influential chemists of this period was Nicolas Lémery (1645–1715), an apothecary of Paris who gave public lectures on chemistry in the tradition of the Jardin du Roi, and who published a very popular textbook, the *Cours de chimie,* in 1675. The book was largely practical, and in its recipes for the preparation of chemical medicines it drew heavily on the work of the preceding pharmacist-chemists, especially Christofe Glaser.[27] When it did discuss theory, it was entirely atomistic in viewpoint. Lémery did not adhere specifically to any one theory, any more than did Boyle,[28] but he was less interested in motion and more in the shape of atoms. He explained physical and chemical properties by shape. Acids had sharp spikes on their atoms, accounting for the pricking sensation they exert on the skin. Alkalies were highly porous bodies into which the spikes of the acids penetrated and were broken or blunted in producing neutral salts.[29]

The explanations of Lémery were superficial, it is true, but they seemed reasonable and obvious even to non-chemists. Intelligent laymen had previously been turned away from chemistry by the vague and mystical explanations of the alchemists and iatrochemists. Now Lémery gave simple accounts of the natural world and popularized his theories in his lectures and textbook. The result was a widespread interest in chemistry on the part of the educated public. This increased the number of potential chemists for the future, and promoted fuller and more open discussion of chemical ideas. The effect on the further development of the science was great.[30]

At about this time, scientists themselves were organizing groups to meet and discuss the problems that they faced in their laboratories. At first, these were informal meetings at the homes of various scientists. Such were the private academies of Mersenne or Justel in Paris, or the group of which Boyle was a member that met at Oxford and in London, and that was known as the Invisible College. From these groups arose the formal organizations of the *Académie des Sciences* in Paris (founded in 1666) and the Royal Society in London (founded in 1662).[31, 32] International correspondence between such groups was a regular occurrence. The scientists, including of course the chemists, were able to discuss their work with their associates, submit to constructive criticism, and, finally, to publish their results in the journals that the new societies established. The importance of the relatively rapid publication of new discoveries that these journals made possible can hardly be overestimated.

The seventeenth century, then, resulted in a true chemical revolution, which was actually a part of the greater revolution of all the experimental sciences. The old, mystical doctrines were overthrown, the idea of atoms was firmly established, the experimental laboratory was given a new and more important place in science, and the chemists themselves were associated into strong and mutually helpful groups. The general public became aware of the progress and possibilities of the science. Although the phrase "Chemical Revolution" is usually applied to the work of Lavoisier and his associates at the end of the eighteenth century, it was the complete change in outlook during the seventeenth that prepared the way. There was still no unanimity of specific chemical theory,[33] but there was a general agreement as to the basic principles and methods to be used in finding the path of further progress.

REFERENCES

1. R. Hooykaas, *Chymia*, **2**, 68 (1949).
2. Marie Boas, *Osiris*, **10**, 415–417 (1952).
3. G. B. Stones, *Isis*, **10**, 444–465 (1928) .
4. Marie Boas, *Isis*, **40**, 38–48 (1949).
5. Stones, *op. cit.*
6. E. Block, *Isis*, **1**, 377–415 (1913).
7. Hooykaas, *op. cit.*, pp. 73–79.
8. R. Hooykaas, *Arch. Intern. Hist. Sci.*, **1**, 640–651 (1948).
9. Boas, *Osiris, op. cit.*, p. 427.
10. *Ibid.*, pp. 435–436.
11. *Ibid.*, p. 440; see also Marie Boas, *Isis*, **41**, 263–264 (1950).
12. J. R. Partington, *Ann. Sci.*, **4**, 245–282 (1939).
13. Boas, *Osiris, op. cit.*, p. 430.
14. *Ibid.*, pp. 442–460; Partington, *op. cit.*
15. Boas, *Osiris, op. cit.*, p. 500.
16. *Ibid.*, p. 422.
17. *Ibid.*, p. 486.
18. *Ibid.*, pp. 468–469, 483–484.
19. M. E. Weeks, *The Discovery of the Elements*, 5th ed., Journal of Chemical Education, Easton, Pa., 1945, pp. 41–49.
20. J. R. Partington, *A Short History of Chemistry*, 2nd ed., Macmillan and Co., London, 1948, p. 76.
21. Boas, *Osiris, op. cit.*, pp. 476–479.
22. Robert Boyle, *The Sceptical Chymist*, 2nd ed., London, 1680, p. 354.
23. T. S. Kuhn, *Isis*, **43**, 12–36 (1952).
24. Boas, *Osiris, op. cit.*, pp. 505–520.
25. Kuhn, *op. cit.*; R. J. Forbes, *Chymia*, **2**, 27–36 (1949).
26. Hélène Metzger, *Les doctrines chimiques en France du début du XVIIe à la fin du XVIIIe siècle*, Vol. I, Les presses universitaires de France, Paris, 1923, p. 246.
27. Clara de Milt, *J. Chem. Educ.*, **19**, 53–60 (1942).
28. Metzger, *op. cit.*, p. 293.
29. *Ibid.*, pp. 295–296.
30. *Ibid.*, pp. 248–249, 285–286.
31. Harcourt Brown, *Scientific Organizations in Seventeenth Century France (1620–1680)*, Williams and Wilkins, Baltimore, 1934.
32. Dorothy Stimson, *Scientists and Amateurs. A History of the Royal Society*, Henry Schuman, New York, 1948.
33. Metzger, *op. cit.*, pp. 273–274.

CHAPTER XIII

THEORIES OF THE

EIGHTEENTH CENTURY:

PHLOGISTON AND AFFINITY

D uring the second half of the seventeenth century and throughout most of the eighteenth, the attention of chemists came more and more to be centered on the problems of the nature of combustion and the forces that held chemical compounds together. At the same time, practical chemistry greatly increased the knowledge of elements and compounds; quantitative methods came to be accepted as essential to chemical investigation; and the whole new field of the chemistry of gases was opened up. The combination of all these factors made possible the foundation of modern chemistry by Lavoisier and the French school at the end of the eighteenth century.

As this period opened, the old concept of expressing the nature of a substance in terms of its properties had by no means been abandoned, though the idea of atomism had been almost universally accepted. Applied to the ideas of combustion, these concepts led to a belief in atoms of fire substance, but did little to alter the age-old ideas of what happened when a substance burned. Theories of the nature of this phenomenon had from earliest times been based on direct observation of a fire. It seemed self-evident that this was one of the most important changes that went on in nature, and many Greek philosophers had made fire the central point in their cosmologies. The changes of material bodies in fire always interested the alchemists, whether mystical or practical. The importance ascribed to sulfur, the principle of combustibility in the sulfur-mercury theory of metal composition, is sufficient evidence of this.

The most obvious fact in observing fire was that flame was escaping from the burning object. Something was being lost, and the relatively light ash left when an organic substance was consumed was further proof of this. Thus the inflammable principle, whatever it was, was naturally assumed to be escaping during combustion. This idea persisted as chemical theories grew more and more precise.[1]

The practical metallurgists of the Middle Ages knew quite well that when metals were heated they were converted to a heavier powder, the calx, but they probably did not bother to connect this with the burning of organic substances, since they were not interested in theoretical matters. They did not concern themselves with the conditions needed for combustion to take place.

Nevertheless, the idea gradually grew up that air was needed if combustion was to occur. The germ of this idea is found in the works of Paracelsus, who believed that air contributed something mysterious to life. This concept was made more specific by a Scottish alchemist, Alexander Seton (died 1604), called the Cosmopolite.[2] His book, *Novum Lumen Chymicum,* was published after his death by his follower, Michael Sendivogius (1556 or 1566–1636 or 1646), who added to it a tract, *De Sulphure.* In these works has been found the apparently specific source of the doctrine that air contains a vital spirit that nourishes life.[3] This vital spirit was identified with niter, by which was meant not the solid salt, but the essential spirit of niter that caused its violent reaction in gunpowder. This led directly into another ancient belief, stemming from the Aristotelian doctrine of the two exhalations from the earth. It was supposed that, as sulfur and niter were needed to produce the explosion of gunpowder, so a spirit of sulfur and a spirit of niter produced such natural phenomena as thunder, lightning, and earthquakes.[4] These things were generally accepted by scientists of the seventeenth century and were responsible for some of the experiments of Boyle on combustion. Thus, he tried to burn sulfur in a vacuum[5] and failed, proving the need for air. This need was recognized even earlier by Jean Rey (c. 1575–1645),[6] in 1630. John Mayow (1641–1679) in 1674 and especially Robert Hooke in his *Micrographia* of 1665 expressed very clearly the idea that some part of the air was necessary for combustion, but not the whole. Hooke believed that the nitrous particles existed in niter, but Boyle thought that they were only trapped in this salt.[7] It is easy for the modern reader to see in all these works more than the writers intended, for their ideas of chemical combustion were very vague, and they thought of the removal of inflammable material as a sort of solution rather than as a combination in the modern sense. Even Rey, who believed that part of the air combined with a metal during calcination, considered the combination an absorption analogous to that of water on sand when the two are mixed. Nevertheless, if these ideas had been accepted and studied by the active laboratory workers of the eighteenth century, chemical progress might have been more rapid. In actual fact, these theories were little noted at the time, and another explanation came to be generally accepted. This was the phlogiston theory.

In France and England the atomistic theories had led to an attempt to explain the universe in purely mechanical terms. This was quite satisfactory to the physicists, but the chemists, confronted with a vast and growing mass of confusing and individualized compounds and reactions, could not feel completely at ease in a clockwork universe. They did their best with the mechanical theories, but, when they were presented with a concept that grew out of the older chemical ideas of Van Helmont and that seemed to embrace many otherwise unrelated facts, they were quite ready to receive it. It was in Germany that the older ideas retained their greatest influence, and it was from Germany that the new theory emerged.

Johann Joachim Becher (1635–1682) resembled Van Helmont in many ways. He had similar, partly mystical ideas, and felt a great interest in organic compounds. To him, metals were only a by-product in the plan of the Creator, which was centered in organic life. Therefore, any explanation of combustion had to be based on the burning of organic substances. Becher accepted air, water, and earth as elements, but air, as Van Helmont had stated, could not take part in chemical reactions, and water had only its own specific properties. It followed, according to Becher, that the differences in chemical compounds resided in the different sorts of earth that composed them. He distinguished three kinds of earth: the vitreous, the fatty, and the fluid.[8] The first, corresponding to the Paracelsan salt, gave body to substances; the second, Paracelsan sulfur, gave combustibility; and the third, Paracelsan mercury, gave density and metallic luster. The second, or fatty earth, terra pinguis, was found particularly in animal or vegetable matter, and it left these bodies when they burned. It is clear that this theory of Becher was merely a restatement of older iatrochemical ideas, and by itself it would probably have exerted no more influence than many other contemporary theories.

It was, however, taken up by Becher's pupil, Georg Ernst Stahl (1660–1734), and made part of a unified theory that appealed greatly to other chemists. The explanation of combustion, at first merely a part of this generalized theory, eventually became the central doctrine of chemistry. As such it held sway until nearly the end of the eighteenth century.

Stahl was a physician, and mystically inclined, but he was also influenced by the strong metallurgical tradition of the German chemists which had been exemplified by the work of Agricola and Ercker. In his chemical theories he centered his attention on inorganic compounds rather than organic, as his master, Becher, had done.[9]

He accepted the existence of atoms, but, in addition to their mechanical properties, he endowed them with intrinsic ones. The particles of elementary substances were drawn to each other by a sort of Newtonian attraction. The resulting compounds were usually referred to as "mixts" at this period.[10] There were relatively few such simple mixts, and gold or silver were typical examples. The mixts could unite to more complex compounds, whose particles were still too small to be seen, and these compounds in turn could form aggregates whose particles were large enough to be visible.[11] The resemblance of these ideas to those of Boyle is clear.

The original elements could never be isolated, for they could not leave one mixt without entering another. Therefore, though each element had specific properties, these could be observed only in its compounds, and so the element could be known only by the effects it produced.[12] The elements of Stahl were the same as those of Becher. To the fatty earth, however, he gave the name phlogiston, from the Greek word for burned, or inflammable. The term had been used as early as 1606 by Hapelius, but not until the time of Stahl did it become common.[13]

Stahl, with his great interest in metals, centered more attention on phlogiston than Becher had done on his *terra pinguis*. He agreed with Becher that, when combustion occurred, the inflammable principle was lost. Thus, when a metal was heated, it lost phlogiston and was converted to the calx (the oxide, in our terms). The metal was therefore a more complex substance than the calx. Regeneration of the metal occurred when the calx combined with phlogiston once more. This was not necessarily a simple matter. The phlogiston lost from a metal was dispersed throughout the air, which was essential as the medium to carry away the phlogiston. Air thus retained the character of a mere mechanical aid to combustion which had been assigned to it by Van Helmont, but the established need for air if combustion was to take place was explained. Plants could absorb phlogiston from the air once more, and animals could obtain it from plants. Thus plant and animal substances were rich in phlogiston and could react with metallic calces to restore the phlogiston and convert them to metals again. The most useful substance for this purpose was charcoal, which was considered extremely rich in phlogiston.[14]

Since phlogiston was an elementary principle, its nature could be known only from its effects. Stahl concentrated his attention upon the chemical phenomena of combustion. In this field, the phlogiston theory supplied an excellent explanation for the then known facts. All the facts that are now considered under the head of oxidation-reduction were involved in this theory, though the explanation was essentially the reverse of our own. Where we consider a substance, oxygen, to be taken up, Stahl considered a substance, phlogiston, to be given off. In either case, the concept is one of the transfer of something from one substance to another. It was essentially this concept of a transfer that made the theory so useful and made it possible to include so many facts under its heading. It was thus the first great unifying principle in chemistry.[15] Its success accounted for the importance it assumed for eighteenth century chemists.

The inconsistencies of the theory at first were mostly its failures to account for physical changes. To Stahl these were unimportant. The fact that, when an organic substance burned, the apparent products weighed less than the original substance, while calcination of inorganic substances, recognized as the same process, led to increased weight in the products, was of so little importance to Stahl that he did not even mention it. If he considered the matter at all, he probably believed that phlogiston was weightless.[16] Phlogiston, after all, was a principle that could not be known directly, not a definite physical substance as we conceive one. Therefore Stahl and many of his successors felt no inconsistency in disregarding facts that did not fit into the chemical picture. It was only later when the idea of a chemical substance as a physical entity became accepted by the chemists that this point became crucial for the phlogiston theory.

Stahl's theory did not at once achieve acceptance by all chemists. The most influential chemist of his time, Hermann Boerhaave (1668–1738), did not even mention it in his lectures or in his famous textbook, *Elementa Chymia*, published in 1732. In this work Boerhaave, professor of medicine, botany, and chemistry at Leiden, set the pattern for chemical instruction in the first half of the eighteenth century.

Although he was not a phlogistonist, his ideas could be fitted into the pattern of the phlogiston theory, and the eventual fusion of the concepts of Stahl and Boerhaave, both drawing on the ideas of Van Helmont, Boyle, and other seventeenth century chemists, led to a chemical system from which Lavoisier could develop his brilliant new ideas.

Like Stahl, Boerhaave believed that air played only a mechanical part in chemical phenomena,[17] but he did not entirely exclude the possibility that it might, in some cases, play some part in certain reactions.[18] He thought of fire as a substance composed of fine particles that could penetrate other materials and alter the force of attraction that held them together.[19] He distinguished between fire as manifested in heat and fire manifested in combustion, a distinction not previously made. This opened the way for a consideration of fire as a material substance, a concept used by Lavoisier in developing his theory of caloric, and to later thermochemical ideas, such as Black's theory of latent heat.[20] Boerhaave believed that chemical reaction was essentially the same as solution. The solvent, or menstruum, usually a liquid, was composed of fine particles that pushed their way between the particles of dissolved substance. The atoms of each then remained suspended and related to one another as required by the affinities of each substance for the other.[21] Boerhaave here introduced the term affinity in the sense it retained for the next century.[22] From these ideas it was easy for Boerhaave to deduce that increased weight after calcination was due to the uptake of fire particles, which had weight, by the substance being calcined. This had been the explanation of Boyle, and its espousal by a second very influential chemist gave it great prestige. The idea that fire, heat, and light were material substances, originally suggested by the Cartesian idea of the ether and now supported by such strong authorities, became an accepted part of chemical thought until, in the nineteenth century, the concept of energy made it unnecessary.

The spread of the phlogiston theory and its almost complete acceptance by the middle of the eighteenth century coincided with a rapid accumulation of chemical facts. More and more chemists began to think of elements as substances just as material as any of the compounds with which they dealt in their laboratories. Both elements and compounds should obey the same laws, physical as well as chemical. It was no longer possible to think of abstract principles that could be made to fit any theory by disregarding inconvenient facts. It was thus impossible to ignore any longer the increase in weight of metals on calcination. As long as the part played by gases in chemical reactions was not understood, as long as air was assumed to be a substance that could not play a chemical role, the correct explanation of the increase could not be found. Nevertheless, a great amount of ingenuity was expended in attempts to find it.

The theory of Boyle and Boerhaave that fire particles were taken up during calcination satisfied many. Others confused density with absolute weight and assumed that the lower density of the calx actually indicated a loss of substance. Still others believed in the buoyancy of phlogiston, or assumed that it had a negative weight which caused an increase in weight of the calx when the phlogiston was lost. In the last days of the theory, when the part gases played in combustion was realized, it was sometimes assumed that, as phlogiston was lost, another substance with greater weight was taken up.[23] The disagreements among the phlogistonists, the accumulation of unsatisfactory theories, and the constant need to revise these theories as new facts were discovered made the fall of the phlogiston theory inevitable as soon as a more rational theory became available.

Side by side with the development of the phlogiston theory went the development of theories of affinity. The term itself dates back perhaps to Albertus Magnus, and crude, qualitative lists of the order of reactivity of metals toward various reagents had been given even in the writings of Geber,[24] but only when the occult forces of love and hate as an explanation of affinity had been banished by the mechanical theories of Boyle did it become possible for a more quantitative approach to give results. Even so, a further qualitative stage had to be passed, and the fundamental explanation of the actual cause of attraction between atoms remained unsatisfactory.

The wide acceptance of the physical theories of Newton could not but impress the chemists, and affinity began to be considered chiefly in terms of his ideas. Essentially, it was assumed that every particle of matter was endowed with a certain attractive force that uniquely caused all its chemical and physical reactions.[25] Although this theory was spectacularly successful when applied in astronomy and physics, it was in most cases too vague to apply to the special problems presented by individual chemical reactions.[26] The theories of Boerhaave on reaction and solution already discussed indicate how this concept of affinity was used to explain chemical behavior, but, in order to make the Newtonian concept generally useful, chemists felt the need to draw up tables of affinity that would express the reactivity of individual compounds toward each other, and that could, it was hoped, be used to predict the reactivity of other compounds in similar reactions. Such tables of necessity had to be based on actual experiments, and for this reason they were regarded with some suspicion by the atomic theorists of the period, who still felt it was better to reason abstractly than to test by experience.[27] Nevertheless, these tables typify the tendency of most chemists to use laboratory data as the true guide to further work, which became increasingly significant in the eighteenth century.

The first attempt to draw up such a table was made in 1718 by Etienne-François Geoffroy (1672–1731), usually called Geoffroy the Elder to distinguish him from his brother who was also a chemist. Geoffroy's basic idea was that "whenever two substances which have some disposition to unite, the one with the other, are united together and a third which has more affinity for one of the two is added, the third will unite with one of these, separating it from the other." [28] Geoffroy prepared a table with sixteen columns, each headed by the alchemical symbol for a chemical substance. In each column he listed the substances that were found by experiment to react with the substance at the head of the column. The order was such that each substance had a greater affinity for the parent material than any that stood below it in the column. Thus, in the first column, the heading was "acid spirits," and below were the symbols for fixed alkali salts (carbonates), volatile alkali salts (ammonium salts), absorbent earths (non-effervescing bases), and metallic substances.

> The fixed alkali salts are placed in the column immediately below the acid spirits, since I know of no substance which will separate these, once they are united, and on the other hand whenever one of the three types of substance below is united to acid spirits, it abandons its place in favor of fixed alkali salts which when added combine directly with the acid.

This type of table became very popular and reached its culmination in 1775 in the elaborate compilation of the Swedish chemist, Torbern Bergman (1735–1784). Bergman had contributed greatly to the development of quantitative analysis, and so knew the difference in reaction of many compounds in the "wet way" (in solution) and in the "dry way" (by fusion). He prepared tables of affinity resembling those of Geoffroy for fifty-nine substances in each of these two methods of reaction. He distinguished between "attraction of aggregation" in homogeneous substances, which resulted only in an increase in mass, and "attraction of composition" in heterogeneous substances, which resulted in compound formation. He distinguished two main types of this attraction: "single elective attractions," which are displacements; and "double elective attractions," which are double decompositions. His terminology persisted for many years. The compilation of these tables became more difficult as the number of known chemical compounds increased. In fact, Bergman estimated that to deter-

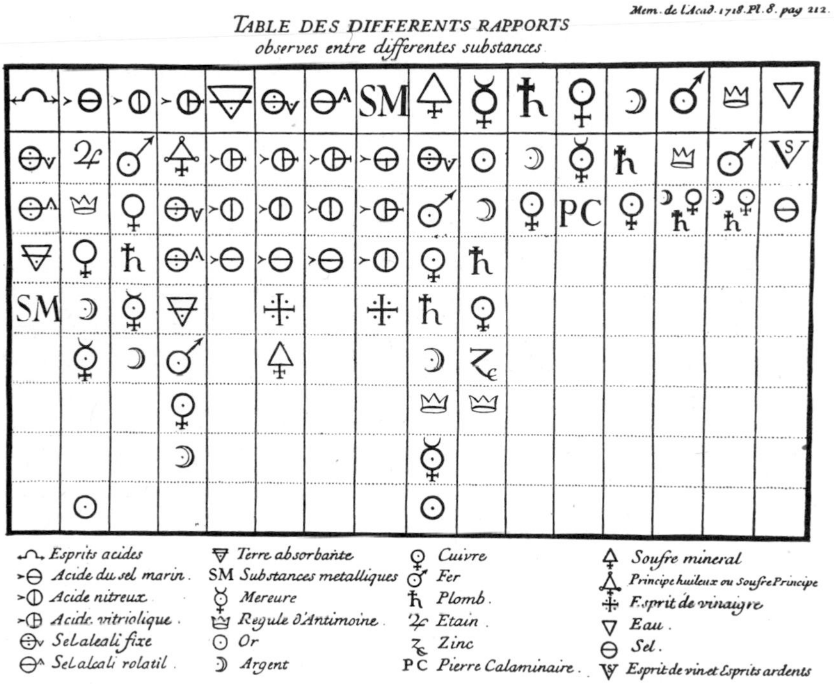

Mem. de L'Acad. 1718. Pl. 8. pag 212.

TABLE DES DIFFERENTS RAPPORTS
observes entre differentes substances

(alchemical affinity table — Geoffroy's Table of Affinities)

Legend:

- ⌐ *Esprits acides*
- ⊖ *Acide du sel marin.*
- ⊕ *Acide nitreux.*
- ⊕ *Acide nitriolique .*
- ⊖ᵥ *Sel alcali fixe*
- ⊖ᴬ *Sel alcali volatil .*
- ▽ *Terre absorbante*
- SM *Substances metalliques*
- ☿ *Mercure*
- ♘ *Regule d'Antimoine .*
- ☉ *Or*
- ☽ *Argent*
- ♀ *Cuivre*
- ♂ *Fer*
- ♄ *Plomb.*
- ♃ *Etain .*
- ⟋ *Zinc*
- PC *Pierre Calaminaire .*
- ♁ *Soufre mineral*
- ⚼ *Principe huileux ou Soufre Principe*
- ⚶ *Esprit de vinaigre*
- ▽ *Eau .*
- ⊖ *Sel .*
- ℣ *Esprit de vin et Esprits ardents*

Fig. 10. Geoffroy's Table of Affinities. (From *Mémoires de l'académie royale des sciences,* **1718, p. 212.)**

mine all the relations of the substances in his table would require over 30,000 separate experiments. A number of arbitrary assumptions were also needed. Bergman recognized that in some cases the amounts of reacting substances or the experimental conditions other than solution or fusion could affect the results of the reaction, but he thought that these differences were incidental and that the order of affinities was a true constant.[29]

The ideas of Bergman were popularized in the new dictionaries and encyclopedias of chemistry that began to appear in the eighteenth century, and that were probably the outgrowth of the wider interest in the science that developed from the work of such popularizers as

Lémery in the previous century. In turn, these works still further widened the general knowledge of the science. The first of these, the dictionary of P. J. Macquer (1718–1784), appeared in 1766 and discussed affinity from the viewpoint of Geoffroy, but, in the second, enlarged edition of 1778, the discussion was in almost the same terms as those of Bergman.[30] Guyton de Morveau (1737–1816) wrote a long article on affinity for the *Encyclopédie méthodique* in 1786, again giving essentially the ideas of Bergman.[31] These ideas were, therefore, widespread at the end of the century.

Their qualitative nature was obvious, and, as the quantitative spirit developed during the century, it was natural that attempts should be made to measure accurately the affinities of various substances. As early as 1700, Wilhelm Homberg (1652–1715) tried to measure the amount of base required to neutralize various acids.[32] C. F. Wenzel (1740–1793) in 1777 tried to determine the relative rates of solution of metals in acids,[33] and Richard Kirwan (1733–1812) in 1781 believed that the weights of bases required to saturate a known weight of acid were a measure of the affinity of the acid for the bases,[34] a refinement of the idea of Homberg. None of these methods gave very accurate or reproducible results, but the principles that they used were subsequently employed by Cavendish, Richter, and Wollaston in establishing the theory of chemical equivalents.

REFERENCES

1. J. C. Gregory, *Combustion from Heracleitos to Lavoisier,* E. Arnold and Co., London, 1934, pp. 43, 45.

2. John Read, *Humour and Humanism in Chemistry,* G. Bell and Sons, London, 1947, pp. 37–51.

3. H. Guerlac, *Actes septième congr. intern. hist. sci.,* Jerusalem, **1953,** pp. 332–349.

4. H. Guerlac, *Isis,* **45,** 243–255 (1954).

5. Robert Boyle, *New Experiments touching the Relation betwixt Flame and Air,* London, 1672.

6. Douglas McKie, *The Essays of Jean Rey,* E. Arnold and Co., London, 1951.

7. Douglas McKie, "Fire and the Flamma Vitalis," in *Science, Medicine and History. Essays on the Evolution of Scientific Thought and Medical Practice, Written in Honour of Charles Singer,* Vol. I, Oxford University Press, London, 1953, pp. 469–488.

8. Hélène Metzger, *Newton, Stahl, Boerhaave et la doctrine chimique,* Alcan, Paris, 1930, pp. 160–161.

9. *Ibid.,* p. 97.

10. *Ibid.,* p. 116.

11. *Ibid.,* pp. 121–124.

12. *Ibid.,* pp. 119–120.

13. J. H. White, *The History of the Phlogiston Theory,* E. Arnold and Co., London, 1932, p. 51.

14. Metzger, *op. cit.*, pp. 170, 177.

15. Walter Hückel, *Structural Chemistry of Inorganic Compounds*, translated by L. H. Long, Vol. I, Elsevier, New York, 1950, p. 8.

16. White, *op. cit.*, p. 56.

17. Metzger, *op. cit.*, pp. 240–241.

18. M. Kerker, *Isis*, **46**, 36–49 (1955).

19. Metzger, *op. cit.*, pp. 223–224.

20. *Ibid.*, p. 228.

21. *Ibid.*, pp. 280–289.

22. M. M. Pattison Muir, *A History of Chemical Theories and Laws*, John Wiley & Sons, New York, 1907, p. 381.

23. J. R. Partington and Douglas McKie, *Ann. Sci.*, **2**, 361–404 (1937); **3**, 1–58 (1938); White, *op. cit.*, pp. 59–92.

24. P. Walden, *J. Chem. Educ.*, **31**, 27–33 (1954).

25. Metzger, *op. cit.*, p. 73.

26. *Ibid.*, p. 50.

27. Hélène Metzger, *Les doctrines chimiques en France du début du XVIIe à la fin du XVIIIe siècle*, Vol. I, Les presses universitaires de France, Paris, 1923, p. 418.

28. E.-F. Geoffroy, *Mémoires de l'académie royale des sciences*, **1718**, 202–212.

29. T. Bergman, *N. Actes d'Upsal*, **3** (1775).

30. L. J. M. Coleby, *The Chemical Studies of P. J. Macquer*, George Allen and Unwin, London, 1938, pp. 39–41.

31. Muir, *op. cit.*, pp. 289–290.

32. Metzger, *Les doctrines chimiques*, etc., p. 413.

33. Muir, *op. cit.*, p. 383.

34. *Ibid.*, pp. 390–391.

LABORATORY DISCOVERIES

OF THE EIGHTEENTH CENTURY:

THE CHEMISTRY OF GASES

While the theories of chemistry developed slowly and were often incorrect, laboratory discoveries were made with increasing rapidity in the eighteenth century. This was chiefly the result of the increased appreciation of the importance of quantitative methods and the great number of new substances and reactions that became known. At the beginning of the century it was still possible for chemists to think of abstract principles as essentials of chemical elements; at the end, even heat and light were considered material.

Most of the major discoveries of the period were in the field of inorganic chemistry. Particularly in Sweden and Germany methods for qualitative and quantitative analysis of minerals reached a high state of development, and, as a result, new compounds and elements were constantly being found.

The older analytical procedures (the "dry way") were carried out at high temperatures and involved mostly fusions and distillations. Such methods continued to be used and became very useful on a small scale when the blowpipe became a common laboratory tool. This had first been used by Florentine glass blowers in 1660, but it was introduced into the analytical laboratory by the Swedish chemist A. F. Cronstedt (1722–1765). The Swedes became especially adept at handling it. Torbern Bergman used it extensively, and his student J. G. Gahn (1745–1818) was even more skillful with it.[1] Its most famous advocate was the Swedish master chemist of the next century, J. J. Berzelius.

At the same time, the use of reactions in solution (the "wet way") became increasingly important. Because of their greater convenience and adaptability such reactions permitted analyses to be performed more rapidly and accurately. Andreas Sigismund Marggraf (1709–1782) in Germany did much to extend the use of these methods,[2] though the work for which he is best remembered is his discovery of the possibility of producing sugar from beets. This discovery was first applied on a large scale in Napoleonic France.[3]

The greatest expansion of the wet method of analysis was due to Torbern Bergman. He was much interested in the composition of mineral waters and analyzed a great many. He introduced the practice of weighing precipitated salts rather than the more laborious method of isolating the free metals. His results were not always accurate, partly because he weighed his salts as crystals and did not heat to dryness.[4] The latter practice was introduced by the German chemist Martin Heinrich Klaproth (1743–1817), recognized as the best analyst of his period. He was the first to report the actual percentage composition as determined in analysis, instead of recalculating his values so that the sum would be exactly 100 per cent, as previous analysts had done. This permitted the discovery of errors in the analysis and also led in some cases to the recognition of new elements in the minerals analyzed.[5]

As a result of these laboratory methods, a considerable number of such new elements were isolated during the century. The definition of an element was not yet fixed, but no one doubted that these new substances were metals, and so the ancient doctrine of the seven metals was finally overthrown. The elements positively identified during the century were cobalt (1735), bismuth (1757), platinum, which was discovered in South America in 1740–1741 and was much studied because of its unusual properties, zinc (1746), nickel (1754), manganese (1774), molybdenum (1781), tellurium (1782), tungsten (1785), and chromium (1798). The oxides of zirconium, strontium, titanium, and yttrium were also recognized as new substances.[6] The isolation of the gaseous elements nitrogen, chlorine, hydrogen, and oxygen, which also took place in this century, will be discussed later.

The brilliant Swedish investigator Carl Wilhelm Scheele (1742–1786), besides his more famous work on gases, made valuable studies on the chemistry of manganese, molybdenum, tungsten, and arsenic. He discovered hydrofluoric acid and isolated many organic compounds, including hydrogen cyanide (whose taste he described), lactic, citric, and malic acids, and glycerol.[7]

G.-F. Rouelle (1703–1770), the teacher of Lavoisier in chemistry, introduced the name "base" for alkalies in 1754 and widened the concept of salts, which had previously meant neutral and soluble compounds. He gave the name salt almost its modern meaning by showing that when acids and "bases" reacted they could form acid, neutral, or basic salts, and that many true salts were insoluble. Thus the word salt finally lost the various mystical meanings that had been attached to it, though the acceptance of Rouelle's terminology was not rapid at first.[8]

During the eighteenth century, chemistry was acquiring its modern character. There was still no systematic nomenclature, and the theoretical basis of the phlogiston theory was still unsatisfactory, but the chemists of the day would feel more at home in a laboratory of the present day than they would have in any of their predecessors'.

The greatest advance in laboratory discoveries of the eighteenth century lay in the isolation and identification of gases as chemical individuals. This advance furnished the last pillar required to erect the new chemistry. Once the discovery had been made, the new developments came with a rapidity that showed how far chemistry had really come. In previous centuries each forward step had required many years before its full significance had been appreciated.

Near the beginning of the century an English clergyman with an interest in botany, Stephen Hales (1677–1761), investigated the amounts of "air" that were evolved from various substances by heating. In the course of this work he perfected the pneumatic trough to collect over water the gases that were formed. He probably obtained most of the common gases during his studies, but he did not realize that they differed chemically. To him they were all "air" with various incidental impurities. His discovery of the pneumatic trough, however, supplied an apparatus that was of great value to later workers in the field of gas chemistry.[9]

Boerhaave, influenced by the work of Hales, inferentially suggested that air might have some chemical function, as well as the purely physical one that most chemists of the day ascribed to it. Boerhaave's teachings were nowhere received with greater enthusiasm than in Scotland, and it was there that the full significance of his suggestion was at length realized.[10] In the middle of the century, Joseph Black (1728–1799) there made the studies that completely changed the understanding of the chemical nature of gases. He reported his results in his

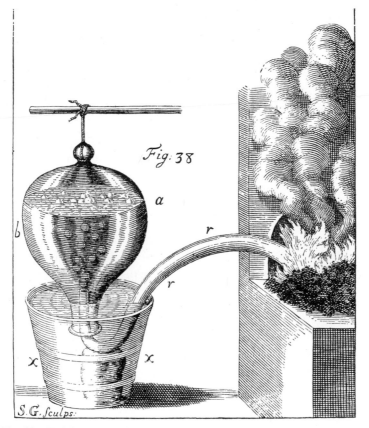

Fig. 11. Hales' pneumatic trough.   (From S. Hales, *Vegetable Staticks*.)

thesis for the degree of Doctor of Medicine at the University of Edinburgh.   The chemical part of the work was published in 1756 under the title *Experiments upon Magnesia Alba, Quick-lime, and Some Other Alcaline Substances.*   In this work he showed that magnesia alba (basic magnesium carbonate) lost a gas when it was heated and was thereby converted to "calcined magnesia," which gave with acids the same salts as magnesia alba, but without effervescence.   Treatment of the calcined magnesia with "alkali" (sodium or potassium carbonate) gave the original magnesia alba.   An analogous series of experiments with limestone gave quicklime and the same gas, and the quicklime could also be regenerated with alkali.   The gas was the *gas sylvestre* of Van Helmont, and Black named it "fixed air" because it was fixed in solid form by magnesia or lime.[11]

This work completely altered the thought of chemists. For the first time it was shown that a gas could combine chemically with a solid (be "fixed" by it) to produce a new compound with different properties, instead of being held by some indefinite physical force. The effect on Black's contemporaries is graphically described by his colleague, John Robinson, in the introduction to the printed version of Black's lectures on chemistry, published posthumously in 1803:

> He had discovered that a cubic inch of marble consisted of about half its weight of pure lime and as much air as would fill a vessel holding six wine gallons. . . . What could be more singular than to find so subtile a substance as air existing in the form of a hard stone, and its presence accompanied by such a change in the properties of the stone? [12]

This work finally eliminated the Van Helmont idea that a gas could not take part in chemical reactions, and so opened the way to a new approach to chemical substances.

In addition to his work on gases, Black laid the foundations for the science of thermodynamics that developed in the next century. Before his time even such great chemists as Boerhaave failed to distinguish between quantity and intensity of heat, the latter representing the concept of temperature. Black made this distinction and then went on to develop the important ideas of specific heat and latent heat. He observed that when mercury at 150° was mixed with water at 100° the resulting temperature was only 120°. Mercury became "less warm" by 30° while the water became warmer by 20°. Each substance attracted its own particular quantity of heat, its specific heat.

Black measured the input of heat into a quantity of ice that was melting, and observed that the temperature did not change until all the ice had melted. In freezing, an equal amount of heat was evolved. He noticed the similar effect of latent heat of evaporation. These observations were made about 1760 and were incorporated in his lectures and in discussions with friends, but were not published until after his death. However, James Watt (1736–1819) used the ideas in developing his steam engine.[13]

Once the work of Black had established that gases were as much chemical and physical individuals as solids or liquids, and as it was realized that different gases existed, their study proceeded rapidly. In 1766 a wealthy and eccentric English scientist, Henry Cavendish (1731–1810), published a study on the properties of inflammable air (hydrogen) and fixed air. Hydrogen had been obtained incidentally by a number of earlier workers, and Boyle had described its inflammability in 1670,[14] but it had not previously been characterized as an individual substance. Cavendish obtained it by the action of dilute acids on zinc, iron, and tin, measuring the amounts given off by similar amounts of different metals. He determined the specific gravity with a fair accuracy by two different methods. The remarkable properties of this gas led him to suggest that it might be pure phlogiston, for, like most of his contemporaries, Cavendish was a phlogistonist. He then applied the same methods to a study of the properties of fixed air, which he obtained from different sources. These investigations represented the first application of quantitative methods to gases and showed that their physical properties were as significant as their chemical properties.[15]

In 1772 Daniel Rutherford (1749–1819), a student of Black, eliminated from ordinary air all the gases that could be removed by respiration or combustion. He recognized that the residue was a new gas, which he called "mephitic air." [16] At almost the same time Cavendish and also Scheele obtained this gas, our nitrogen, though they did not publish their results. Cavendish, who had a passion for quantitative measurement, determined its specific gravity and the amount required to prevent combustion. All three men determined the approximate proportions of oxygen and nitrogen in ordinary air, though they did not yet clearly realize the nature of oxygen.[17]

Responsible for the isolation and characterization of more gases than any of his contemporaries was Joseph Priestley (1733–1804), dissenting clergyman, and, with Cavendish, the chief of the amateur chemists of his time. Priestley was completely untrained in chemistry and did not even begin his chemical investigations until he was thirty-eight years old. The chance fact that he resided next to a brewery from which a large supply of carbon dioxide could be obtained led him to study this gas, with the practical result that in 1772 he invented soda water. His claim to fame rests on firmer ground, however, for during the next five years he studied a large number of gases that had previously been entirely unknown. By using mercury in the pneumatic trough he was able to obtain several gases whose solubility in water had prevented other chemists from isolating them.

One of the first gases that Priestley studied was "nitrous air" (nitric oxide), which he prepared by treating metals with "spirit of nitre" (nitric acid). The production of a brown, soluble gas when this was mixed with "common air" interested him greatly. He observed that, when air was used up in combustion or respiration, the amount of brown gas it formed with nitrous air was decreased. He therefore assumed that the amount of such brown gas was a measure of the "relative purity" of the air. He built an apparatus, the eudiometer (from two Greek words meaning "measure of goodness of air"), to determine this purity. He did not, of course, know that he was actually measuring the amount of oxygen in the air, but later this reaction was of great value to him when he did isolate oxygen.[18]

Besides nitric oxide, carbon monoxide, sulfur dioxide, hydrogen chloride, and ammonia were first isolated and characterized by Priestley. In all his work he was a strong supporter of the phlogiston theory. He explained all his results in terms of it. Since he was far more skillful in laboratory manipulations than in theoretical reasoning, his explanations were not always consistent.

In 1774 Priestley obtained a large burning glass and began to study the gases evolved when a number of substances were subjected to the high heat that this instrument could produce. Among the substances that he studied were *mercurius calcinatus per se* and the "red precipitate," both of which were mercuric oxide, though their identity was not generally known. The action of heat on this substance had been reported early in 1774 by Pierre Bayen (1725–1798), but the French chemist did not recognize the gas he obtained as a new substance.[19] Priestley obtained a large amount of gas from this reaction, and for some time he was greatly puzzled as to its nature. In 1775 he studied the gas more thoroughly, and by applying his nitric oxide test he found that it was "even purer" than common air. It supported combustion very strongly, and animals lived longer in it than in common air. It was obviously a new gas, and, since Priestley believed that air that no longer supported combustion had become completely phlogisticated, he named it "dephlogisticated air." [20] In his later studies, Priestley discovered that green plants gave off dephlogisticated air in the light. This observation, confirmed and extended by Jan Ingenhousz (1730–1799) and Jean Senebier (1742–1809), was the basis for all later studies of photosynthesis.[21]

The brilliant work of Priestley on oxygen was actually preceded by the discovery of this gas by Scheele. The Swedish pharmacist in his short life discovered an amazing number of important compounds, some of which have already been mentioned. His classic study of manganese compounds in 1774 led to the discovery of chlorine, which he called dephlogisticated marine acid, for he was also a supporter of the phlogiston theory. For several years prior to this he had been studying oxygen, which he called "fire air." His book, *Chemische Abhandlung von der Luft und dem Feuer,* in which he described his results was not published until 1777, and so the first credit for the discovery of oxygen went to Priestley. It is now recognized that Scheele and Priestley discovered this gas independently.[22]

This new gas, which its discoverers tried so hard to fit into the phlogiston theory, was the final link in the chain of evidence that once and for all overthrew the theory. It supplied the conclusive evidence needed by Lavoisier in establishing the new theory. Scheele died before he could appreciate the new work, and Priestley, though he lived until 1804, never completely abandoned the theory of Stahl, though in his last years he recognized that time might prove him to be wrong.[23] Within twenty years after the discovery of oxygen, chemistry became basically what it is today.

REFERENCES

1. E. G. Ferguson, *J. Chem. Educ.*, **17,** 557 (1940).

2. J. M. Stillman, *The Story of Early Chemistry,* D. Appleton and Co., New York, 1924, p. 438.

3. *Ibid.,* pp. 441–442.

4. Ferguson, *op. cit.,* p. 557; Stillman, *op. cit.,* pp. 445–452.

5. Ferguson, *op. cit.,* p. 560.

6. M. E. Weeks, *The Discovery of the Elements,* 2nd ed., Journal of Chemical Education, Easton, Pa., 1934, pp. 346–349.

7. Stillman, *op. cit.,* p. 460.

8. G.-F. Rouelle, *Mémoires de l'académie royale des sciences,* **1754,** 572–588.

9. Stillman, *op. cit.,* pp. 461–463; H. Guerlac, *Arch. intern. hist. sci.,* **4,** 393–404 (1951).

10. M. Kerker, *Isis,* **46,** 36–49 (1955).

11. Stillman, *op. cit.,* pp. 465–466.

12. Quoted by John Read, *Humour and Humanism in Chemistry,* G. Bell and Sons, London, 1947, p. 185.

13. William Ramsay, *The Life and Letters of Joseph Black, M.D.,* Constable and Co., London, 1918, pp. 38–46.

14. Stillman, *op. cit.,* pp. 361–363.

15. *Ibid.,* pp. 473–475.

16. *Ibid.,* p. 476.

17. Weeks, *op. cit.,* pp. 34–35.

18. Stillman, *op. cit.,* pp. 486–488.

19. E. W. J. Neave, *Ann. Sci.,* **7,** 144–148 (1951).

20. Stillman, *op. cit.,* pp. 490–494.

21. J. Priestley, *Experiments and Observations on Different Kinds of Air,* Vol. 3, Thomas Pearson, Birmingham, 1790, pp. 293–296, 304.

22. Stillman, *op. cit.,* p. 458.

23. P. J. Hartog, *Ann. Sci.,* **5,** 45–48 (1941).

CHAPTER XV

Lavoisier and the Foundation

of Modern Chemistry

In the latter half of the eighteenth century, confusion in chemical thought was at its height. The number of known chemical facts had increased enormously, but the phlogiston theory had failed to keep pace with them. Chemists were, in general, convinced of the material nature of atoms and their specific, individual properties, but everyone sought to explain reactions by a personal interpretation of the theory of Stahl. It was the work of Antoine Laurent Lavoisier (1743–1794) that resolved this confusion and placed chemistry on an essentially modern basis. This step is often called the Chemical Revolution.*

Lavoisier was the chief exception among continental chemists to the generalization that most had received pharmaceutical or medical training. He resembled the English amateur chemists such as Boyle or Cavendish. He came from a wealthy family that reached the ranks of the French aristocracy during his lifetime. He increased his wealth by membership in the *Ferme générale,* an organization of financiers that leased from the government the right to collect taxes on many essentials of commerce. He was a man of tremendous energy, most of which he devoted to public causes. Throughout his life he was a

---

* The complete writings of Lavoisier have been listed and annotated by Duveen and Klickstein.[1] An excellent critical survey of the biographical material on Lavoisier is presented by Guerlac.[2]

member of many boards, commissions, and societies that strove to improve political, social, and economic conditions in France, a France enmeshed in governmental inefficiency that approached chaos as the Revolution neared. He was a notable economist whose suggestions might have done much to stave off or moderate the Revolution if they had been accepted. At the height of the Reign of Terror he was guillotined along with the other *Fermiers généraux* whom the hysterical mob held responsible for many of their ills.[3]

In spite of his multitude of duties, Lavoisier remained throughout his life deeply devoted to science. His wealth made it possible for him to equip an outstanding laboratory. He made it a point to spend a definite amount of time in scientific work and to use the best apparatus obtainable.[4] His clarity of insight and his method of planning and executing his experiments led him to an understanding of natural phenomena that was shared by few of his contemporaries.

Lavoisier was trained in science by some of the best scientific minds in France. Even at the beginning of his career he realized the importance of exact scientific measurement. His first experimental study, on the nature of gypsum, begun at the age of twenty-one, involved the quantitative determination of the amount of water lost when the mineral was heated and the amount regained when it set as plaster of Paris.[5] He made a geological tour of France at twenty-four, during which he carried out repeated studies of the specific gravity of the waters of various localities by means of accurate hydrometers built to his own design.[6] All his experiments were performed after a careful review of the literature and detailed advance planning of what he hoped to accomplish and how he intended to do it. He shared with many of his contemporaries the realization of the importance of the balance, but he went far beyond most of them, for they used quantitative measurements chiefly in the analysis of minerals, but he used them to demonstrate fundamental laws of nature. Although his studies lay chiefly in the field of chemistry, his approach was essentially that of the physicist.[7]

His first important researches were designed to test long accepted beliefs that still remained to be proved or disproved positively. The truth of the old Greek idea of the interconvertibility of water and earth, given new support by the authority of Van Helmont and Boyle, needed a definite experimental test, and Lavoisier supplied it. He showed by quantitative measurements that the amount of solid material found in water that had been heated for 101 days had been dissolved from the glass of the vessel in which the water was heated and that the water itself was unchanged. This finally disposed of the ancient idea of interconversion.[8] Although the compound nature of water was not yet understood, the results of this experiment no doubt contributed to Lavoisier's later interest in the constitution of water and his formulation of a concept of elements.[9]

As a young man Lavoisier made an intensive study of the problem of lighting the streets of a city at night. In the course of a thorough consideration of all phases of this problem, he devoted much attention to the combustion of fuels in lamps. The interest thus aroused in combustion may have led him into this field, in which he was interested all his life. In 1772 he began a series of very important studies of combustion and calcination that led directly to his formulation of the new chemistry. In that year he and a group of other chemists showed that a diamond could be burned in air if enough heat was used. The best means available at that time for getting high temperatures was a large burning glass. With this instrument, great heat could be applied locally at a desired spot, either in the presence or absence of air.[10]

At the same time that he was burning the diamond, he was familiarizing himself with the results of the study of gases which had occupied so much of the time of eighteenth century chemists. He was well acquainted with the work of Hales that showed that gases could be contained in chemical materials and could be evolved from them. He even used apparatus described by Hales in some of his early studies.[11] Somewhat later he learned of the work of Black, which he greatly admired. His appreciation of the value of quantitative measurement was increased by his understanding of the importance of Black's experiments. Even more important was his realization, resulting from the studies of Hales and the work of Black on fixed air, that gases could combine chemically or be released from compounds by chemical reactions. Lavoisier also knew of the studies on gases by Cavendish and Priestley in England. He was thus in a position to study the phenomena of combustion with a wealth of information at hand. It has frequently been pointed out that he made no new discovery of compounds or reactions. His great genius lay in his ability to see the essential weaknesses of the older theories and to combine the available facts into a new and more correct, comprehensive theory.

Following his experiments on the diamond, Lavoisier turned to a study of the products of combustion of phosphorus and sulfur. Late in 1772 he announced to the Academy of Sciences that when phosphorus burned it combined with air and produced "acid spirit of

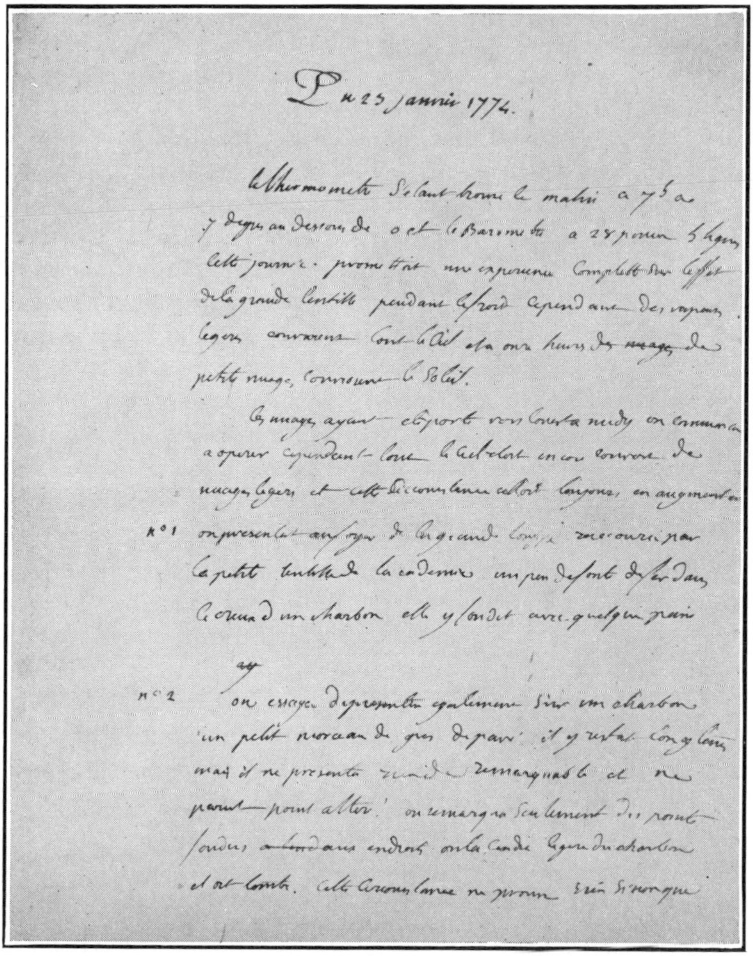

Du 25 janvier 1774.

Fig. 12. Page from the laboratory notebook of Lavoisier relating to experiments with the burning glass. (Courtesy of Denis I. Duveen.)

phosphorus" (phosphoric acid), which weighed more than the original phosphorus. Sulfur underwent a similar reaction and produced "vitriolic acid." Thus Lavoisier extended Black's observation on chemical combination of gases in a manner that was, at this time, entirely unexpected. Even more surprising, however, was the fact that at this early stage of his work he realized that calcination of metals was a phenomenon analogous to the burning of phosphorus and sulfur, and involved a combination with air.[12]

He next began an important series of experiments with tin and lead. First he showed that Boyle was wrong in believing that the gain in weight when they were calcined came from absorption of fire particles. When tin was calcined in sealed vessels, it was partly converted to the calx (oxide), but there was no gain in weight until the vessel was opened. When this was done, air could be heard rushing in. There was no doubt that the increase in weight when a calx was formed came from a combination of the metal with air. At first Lavoisier was uncertain as to whether the combination was with the fixed air of Black (carbon dioxide) or with ordinary air or some part of it. He strongly suspected that this last was the case. He noted that heating a calx with charcoal resulted in the formation of the metal and fixed air, which he positively identified.[13]

In October, 1774, Priestley visited Paris and in a conversation with Lavoisier told of his work with the red precipitate and of the surprising results that he obtained by heating it. It has been claimed that Lavoisier at once realized that this was closely connected with his own work. It seems more probable that at this time the connection was not obvious to either man. It was only later that Priestley's more accurate work was seen to fit into Lavoisier's theories.[14]   Nevertheless, by April, 1775, Lavoisier had repeated the experiments of Bayen and Priestley and was ready with a preliminary report. He showed that reduction of red precipitate with charcoal produced mercury and fixed air, and so red precipitate was a true calx. Then he used the burning glass to heat red precipitate alone, and confirmed Priestley and Bayen as to the production of mercury and a new gas, not fixed air. Thus the "pure" portion of air was probably the part that combined with metals during calcination.[15]

These results were extended in 1776 and 1777. The paper that Lavoisier had contributed to the *Mémoires* of the Academy of Sciences in 1774 was not published until 1778. Such a delay in publication was quite usual for this journal. Lavoisier took advantage of it and revised his paper, including his newer results and ideas, just before the volume was published. He was now convinced that only a part of the common air combined with metals, and so he realized that such air was a mixture of two substances. The purer part was used in respiration and in calcination of metals. The residue he called *mofette*. Later he named it "azote" from the Greek for "without life," and in 1790 Chaptal named it nitrogen. It will be recalled that Rutherford had first named it mephitic air.

Further experiments with the pure air, which he now called "eminently respirable air," showed that it combined with charcoal when this substance was heated with a calx, and that the fixed air thus produced could only be a compound of charcoal and the eminently respirable air.

Experiments on animals conducted at about this time convinced Lavoisier that the respirable air combined with carbon in the body, specifically in the lungs, as he thought, giving off heat just as it did in the laboratory. The source of animal heat was thus explained, though not the mechanism of its production. Nevertheless, this was a fundamental step in the development of biochemistry.

The combustion of phosphorus and sulfur was now seen to be the result of a combination of these elements with eminently respirable air, and Lavoisier believed that this gas entered the composition of all acids. In November, 1779, he suggested for it the name oxygen (*principe oxygine*) from the Greek words meaning "to form an acid." [16]

Lavoisier was now ready to make a direct attack on the phlogiston theory.* He did this in a paper submitted to the Academy in 1783 and published in 1786 in which he pointed out the many weaknesses of that theory. The difficulties thus raised could be avoided if it was recognized that, in every combustion, combination with oxygen occurred, with evolution of heat and light.[19]

The final step required for the completion of Lavoisier's theory was an understanding of the composition of water. This step was now taken in England. Cavendish had noticed in 1766 that his "inflammable air" burned in common air, but he did not identify the product. In 1781 Priestley noticed a dew condensing in the vessels in which such combustion occurred. Cavendish repeated Priestley's experiments and collected the dew that resulted. He showed that it was pure water, but he also observed that an' acid was formed when a mixture of inflammable air and common air (containing nitrogen) was exploded by an electric spark. He delayed publication of his results while he studied this reaction. He found that sparking mix-

---

* Dorfman [17] has pointed out that strong criticism of the phlogiston theory had come from the Russian poet and scientist Mikhail Vasil'evich Lomonosov (1711–1765) at an earlier time. His ideas were published in the *New Commentaries of the St. Petersburg Academy* for 1750,[18] a periodical that was known to Lavoisier, since he quoted from a paper by Richman in the same volume. Dorfman believes that Lavoisier was influenced by the ideas of Lomonosov, whose criticisms were based on physical reasoning. Since Lavoisier approached the subject from a chemical point of view, he did not acknowledge his awareness of the ideas of Lomonosov.

tures of common air with the proper amounts of inflammable air used up all but a small bubble of gas, and nitric acid was formed. The small bubble of gas was identified in 1894 as argon. The remarkable observation of this small quantity of inert gas is a tribute to the experimental skill of Cavendish.

Since Cavendish believed that inflammable air was almost pure phlogiston, and that oxygen was dephlogisticated air, he explained the formation of water as due to liberation of this compound from both gases during the phlogistication of the dephlogisticated air. Lavoisier learned of these experiments in 1783, though they were not actually published until 1784. He at once realized their significance and arrived at the correct explanation: that water was a compound of inflammable air and oxygen. He repeated the experiments and drew his conclusions in 1783, but he published the work fully only in the *Mémoires* of the Academy for 1781, which appeared in 1784. The confusion arising from the various delays in publication, as well as certain misdatings of some journals and the fact that Priestley, Watt, Cavendish, Monge, and Lavoisier all worked on the composition of water at about the same time, has given rise to considerable amount of controversy over actual priorities. The situation was not helped by the fact that the various investigators often knew of each other's work, a fact not always acknowledged. The so-called "water controversy" involved the supporters of the claims of the various workers and often produced rather violent arguments.[20] Whatever the actual priorities may have been, there is no doubt that the best experimental proof of the composition of water was given by Cavendish, and that the correct explanation was first proposed by Lavoisier. The name hydrogen for inflammable air was proposed in the new nomenclature system of de Morveau, and it means "to form water."

The work of Lavoisier had now brought to chemistry an order and system that it had never possessed, but the method of naming chemical substances remained in the wildest confusion. The old alchemical terms, which bore no relation to actual composition, still designated the materials with which Lavoisier worked. Only by the exercise of sheer memory could a student learn the names of the constantly increasing number of substances with which he dealt. This was a problem that was felt very forcibly by Guyton de Morveau (1737–1816), originally a phlogistonist, but an early convert to Lavoisier's system. In 1782 he published a paper on methods that should be employed to systematize chemical nomenclature. Lavoisier was naturally interested in any project to bring order to the science, and so he joined de

Morveau in his work. Two other converts to Lavoisier's theories, Claude Louis Berthollet (1748–1822) and A. F. de Fourcroy (1755–1809), also collaborated in working out the new concepts. Their results appeared in a book, *Méthode de nomenclature chimique,* published at Paris in 1787. This volume contained the principles for naming chemical compounds which are essentially those in use today. Every substance should have a definite name. The names of simple substances should express their characters when possible, and the names of compounds should indicate their composition in terms of their simple constituents. Thus the method of naming acids and bases from their elements, and salts from their constituent acids and bases, was proposed. The system was so simple and expressive that it was adopted by chemists everywhere. Translation of the book into all leading languages soon followed.[21] With the subsequent spread of Lavoisier's system of chemistry, the new nomenclature became firmly entrenched even in such scientific outposts as America then was.[22]

The theory of Lavoisier was now complete, and there existed a new language in which to express it. A considerable group of French chemists, closely associated with Lavoisier, had accepted the new ideas, but most of the rest of the scientific world was still struggling to reconcile the many discrepancies of the phlogiston theory. Therefore, Lavoisier determined to prepare a textbook of chemistry based on the new principles. It was to break sharply with the older tradition of chemical textbooks and to give the future generations of chemists a new foundation upon which to build. He began to plan the book between 1778 and 1780.[23] It appeared in Paris in 1789, the famous *Traité élémentaire de chimie,* which is to chemistry what Newton's *Principia* is to physics.[24]

In this book Lavoisier described in considerable detail the experimental basis for his rejection of phlogiston and for his new theory of combustion in which oxygen held the central position. His view was essentially that of a modern chemist. Thus he wrote: "Chemistry, in subjecting to experiments the various bodies in nature, aims at decomposing them so as to be able to examine separately the different substances which enter into their composition." From this definition he was able to draw up a "table of simple substances belonging to all the kingdoms of nature, which may be considered the elements of bodies." He admitted that this was an empirical list which was subject to revision as new facts were discovered, but, based as it is on sound chemical principles, it is considered the first true table of chemical elements.

In spite of his remarkable understanding of chemical phenomena, Lavoisier was still a child of his time and so could not break away completely from the ideas of his contemporaries. The concept of heat as a form of motion which had prevailed when the corpuscular theory was first introduced had now given way to the idea that heat and light were material substances. The rejection of the old "occult principles" had gone so far that everything was considered to be material. Lavoisier agreed with this idea and therefore headed his table of elements with light and with heat, which he called "caloric." In actual fact, caloric retained some of the properties of phlogiston, which Lavoisier was rejecting by its former name. Thus he believed that oxygen gas was a compound of the oxygen principle with caloric, and that, when the gas united with a metal, caloric was given off, appearing as the heat of the reaction. This view of the nature of heat and the idea that all acids contained oxygen, were the two most serious errors in Lavoisier's system of chemistry. These errors created difficulties for chemists until well into the next century.

Once past caloric, the table of elements given in the *Traité* is correct and shows great insight into the nature of both acid and basic oxides. Lavoisier even recognized the fact that the fixed alkalies potash and soda were probably compounds whose elementary principles were still unknown.

The *Traité* contains further concepts of the greatest importance. It has been seen that from the beginning of the seventeenth century the idea of the conservation of matter had been assumed implicitly by many chemists. It had even been stated explicitly by Lomonosov, but most of his works remained unknown to the West and did not influence the progress of scientific thought in this respect.[25] Lavoisier for the first time stated this concept effectively and showed how it could be applied in chemistry. In discussing the fermentation of sugar to alcohol he pointed out that "nothing is created in the operations either of art or of nature, and it can be taken as an axiom that in every operation an equal quantity of matter exists both before and after the operation." Following this principle, he was able to write what was clearly the forerunner of a modern chemical equation:

"must of grapes = carbonic acid + alcohol"

He himself recognized the significance of this statement, for he wrote:

We may consider the substances submitted to fermentation, and the products resulting from that operation, as forming an algebraic equation, and, by successively supposing each of the elements in this equation unknown, we can calculate their values in succession and thus verify our experiments by calculation and our calculation by experiment reciprocally. I have often successfully employed this method for correcting the first results of my experiment and to direct me in the proper road for repeating them to advantage.[26]

The importance of the *Traité* in the history of chemistry cannot be overemphasized. Its influence spread rapidly. Translations into all important languages quickly followed, and it ran through many editions. With few exceptions (most notably Priestley) all important chemists became converted to the new ideas, and the science of chemistry entered upon a century of almost unbelievable progress.

Although Lavoisier lived only five years after the publication of his treatise, and they were years of the greatest social and political turmoil during which scientific activities were difficult to pursue, he continued his chemical work in many ways. The studies on animal respiration that he had begun with the mathematician P. S. Laplace (1749–1827) and that he continued with a young colleague, Armand Séguin (1765–1835), now proved that combustion of carbon compounds to carbon dioxide and water with oxygen was the true source of animal heat, and that, during physical work, oxygen consumption increased.[27] This work was fundamental to the studies of Voit and Rubner in Germany in the late nineteenth century, the basis of the modern science of nutrition.

In the course of his work, Lavoisier studied a number of carbon compounds and devised the method of burning them in oxygen and determining the carbon dioxide and water formed, the method that is still the basis of organic analysis. His quantitative results were very inaccurate, however.[28]

Lavoisier was connected with another project that played an important part in the development of chemistry as an independent science. Prior to 1778 there was no distinct chemical journal. All chemical research had to be presented in journals that also published material in other sciences. Some of the disadvantages under which authors suffered are indicated by the long delays in publication of many of Lavoisier's own papers in the *Mémoires* of the Academy. In 1778 Lorenz von Crell (1744–1816) founded the first purely chemical periodical, the *Chemisches Journal,* which survived until 1781. In 1784 it resumed publication as the *Chemische Annalen,* usually called Crell's *Annalen* to distinguish it from those later published by Poggendorf and by Liebig. Crell's journal was published until 1803, and many important papers appeared in it.[29]   In 1787 Pierre August Adet (1763–1832), who had been associated with Lavoisier in publishing the *Méthode de nomenclature chimique,* attempted to found a French chemical journal.   In this he was unsuccessful, but in April, 1789, Lavoisier, de Morveau, Monge, Berthollet, de Dietrich, Hassenfratz, and Adet joined to publish the first number of the *Annales de chimie,* a journal which has survived until today and in which a large number of the most important papers in the history of chemistry have appeared.[30]

Such were the chemical activities that were cut short when Lavoisier at the age of fifty was guillotined on May 8, 1794.   It can only be surmised what he might have accomplished if he had been allowed to continue his scientific work, but what he actually completed was enough to give France a superiority in chemistry which she held for many years, and to set chemistry on a course that allowed it to develop its potentialities in ways whose results are still not entirely realized.

REFERENCES

1. Denis I. Duveen and Herbert S. Klickstein, *A Bibliography of the Works of Antoine Laurent Lavoisier, 1743–1794,* Wm. Dawson and Sons and E. Weil, London, 1954.

2. H. Guerlac, *Isis,* **45,** 51–62 (1954).

3. Douglas McKie, *Antoine Lavoisier, Scientist, Economist, Social Reformer,* Henry Schuman, New York, 1952.

4. M. Daumas, *Chymia,* **3,** 45–62 (1950).

5. McKie, *op. cit.,* p. 61.

6. Ya. G. Dorfman, *Lavoisier,* Akademiya Nauk, S.S.S.R., Moscow, Leningrad, 1948, pp. 59–66 (in Russian).

7. *Ibid.,* p. 7.

8. McKie, *op. cit.,* pp. 81–90.

9. A. N. Meldrum, *Isis,* **19,** 330–363 (1933); **20,** 396–425 (1934).

10. McKie, *op. cit.,* pp. 97–101.

11. H. Guerlac, *Arch. intern. hist. sci.,* **4,** 393–404 (1951).

12. McKie, *op. cit.,* pp. 101–102.

13. *Ibid.,* pp. 103–113.

14. Sidney J. French, *J. Chem. Educ.,* **27,** 83–89 (1950).

15. McKie, *op. cit.,* pp. 122–125.

16. *Ibid.,* pp. 132–139.

17. Dorfman, *op. cit.,* pp. 182–184.

18. M. V. Lomonosov, *Novi Comentarii Academiae Scientiarum Imperialis Petropolitanae,* **1750,** 206–229.

19. McKie, *op. cit.,* pp. 147–158.

20. *Ibid.,* pp. 159–174; see also Sidney M. Edelstein, *Chymia,* **1,** 123–127 (1948).

21. McKie, *op. cit.,* pp. 263–274.

22. Denis I. Duveen and Herbert S. Klickstein, *Isis,* **45,** 278–292, 368–382 (1954).

23. M. Daumas, *Arch. intern. hist. sci.*, **3,** 570–590 (1950).

24. McKie, *op. cit.,* pp. 274–275.

25. B. N. Menshutkin, *Russia's Lomonosov,* Princeton University Press, Princeton, N. J., 1952, pp. 116–118.

26. McKie, *op. cit.,* pp. 274–288.

27. *Ibid.,* pp. 347–353.

28. J. M. Stillman, *The Story of Early Chemistry,* D. Appleton and Co., New York, 1924, p. 528; Moritz Kohn, *Anal. Chim. Acta,* **5,** 337 (1951).

29. II. Kopp, *Geschichte der Chemie,* Vol. 3, F. Vieweg und Sohn, Braunschweig, 1848, p. 163.

30. McKie, *op. cit.,* pp. 304–306.

THE LAWS OF ATOMIC

COMBINATION

The work of Lavoisier at last gave a satisfactory solution to the problem of combustion that had absorbed the attention of many chemists for hundreds of years. At the same time it showed the value of quantitative methods and defined the task of chemistry in clear terms. In the light of these new insights, chemists could turn to other problems with which they had been concerned, confident that these too would yield to the new approach. The major problems at the beginning of the nineteenth century concerned the composition of pure compounds and the nature of affinity. They were attacked with vigor, and striking results were soon obtained.

Realization of the importance of quantitative methods led at this time to attempts to apply mathematics to chemistry as it had been so successfully applied to physics at an earlier period. The mathematics of quantitative analysis was of the simplest kind, and most of the theoretical concepts developed at this period did not require any extensive mathematical knowledge. Nevertheless, the idea that it was not only possible, but also necessary, to determine definite numerical values for the forces and quantities involved in chemical reactions was an important step forward.

The attempts by Homberg, Wenzel, and Kirwan to give such numerical values to the forces of affinity were not very successful, as has been pointed out. This type of experiment was repeated by Jeremias

Benjamin Richter (1762–1807), who in 1792 published at Breslau the first volume of his *Anfangsgründe der Stöchyometrie* (Outlines of Stoichiometry, or the Art of Measuring Chemical Elements).[1] Like Homberg and Kirwan, he believed that he could obtain an accurate measure of affinity by determining the different amounts of acid that would neutralize a given quantity of base, and vice versa. He summed up his results in a table that showed the number of parts of sulfuric, muriatic, and nitric acids required to neutralize 1000 parts of the bases potash, soda, volatile alkali (ammonia), baryta, lime, magnesia, and alumina. Richter further pointed out that, when two neutral salts react by double decomposition, the products are also neutral. This meant that, when *AB* reacted with *CD* to form *AC, BD* would also have to be formed, and it would be possible to calculate the compositions of *AC* and *BD* if those of *AB* and *CD* were known. This, of course, was an application of the law of the conservation of matter. To describe the field of his study, Richter coined the word stoichiometry, from the Greek meaning to measure something that cannot be divided. It can be seen that he had actually expressed the law of constant proportions: the proportions of the elements in a compound are constant, and for any compound of two elements the proportion by weight is also encountered in other compounds containing the same element.[2] Richter's neutralization table was essentially the first table of equivalents.

Unfortunately, Richter's style was very involved, and his preoccupation with mathematics was so great that he attempted to deduce various questionable mathematical relationships from the numerical values that he determined. His work, therefore, did not appeal to other chemists and did not exert much influence at the time it was published. In 1802, Ernst Gottfried Fischer (1754–1831) translated Berthollet's French work on the laws of affinity into German. He added to it Richter's table, which he simplified into a true table of equivalents, though this term was not yet used. The table follows. It shows the acids and bases familiar at this time. In it the number given for each acid means the weight of the acid required to saturate the weight of base indicated by the number given with it.

Practical proof of the law of constant proportions was supplied by the work of a French chemist who taught at Madrid, Joseph Louis Proust (1754–1826). In 1799 Proust showed that the composition of copper carbonate was fixed, no matter how it was prepared and whether it occurred naturally or was prepared by synthesis.[4] For the next nine years he devoted himself to purifying and analyzing various

Bases		Acids	
Alumina	525	Fluoric	427
Magnesia	615	Carbonic	577
Ammonia	672	Fatty	706
Lime	793	Muriatic	712
Soda	859	Oxalic	755
Strontia	1329	Phosphoric	979
Potassia	1605	Formic	988
Baryta	2222	Sulfuric	1000
		Succinic	1209
		Nitric	1405
		Acetic	1480
		Citric	1683
		Tartaric	1694 [3]

compounds to support his belief in the law of constant proportions. During this time he was engaged in a famous controversy with his fellow countryman Berthollet, who had collaborated with de Morveau and Lavoisier in the work on chemical nomenclature.

Berthollet approached the problem of chemical composition from his studies on affinity, described in his two books *Recherches sur les lois de l'affinité* (Paris, 1801), and the more famous *Essai de statique chimique* (Paris, 1803). Berthollet pointed out that the assumptions made by Bergman in compiling his tables of elective affinity were not completely valid. Affinity was not an absolute force, since, besides the affinities that acted between the various substances, the amounts of the reactants could influence the direction of a reaction. He stated: "When a substance acts on a combination, the subject of combination divides itself between the two others not only in proportion to the energy of their respective affinities, but also in proportion to their quantities." [5] This is actually a statement of the law of mass action, a fact not recognized for more than another half-century. Berthollet performed a valuable service in pointing out the limitations of the older ideas of elective affinity, but he carried his theories much further and was led into a serious error.

He believed that chemical affinity was a force akin to gravity, and he felt that any type of combination between substances was an expression of this same force. There was no fundamental difference between solution and chemical combination, and so the law of constant proportions was only a special case of the general law of affinity. He believed that the composition of a compound would vary unless some particular factor such as solubility exerted an influence. If a combination containing definite proportions of its constituents happened to be the least soluble form of combination, this form would always precipitate from solution and a substance of apparently constant composition would result. Berthollet believed that this was only an accidental effect.

It was this view that brought Proust and Berthollet into conflict and led to much analytical work. Proust paid particular attention to the purity of his compounds. He was able to show that many of the analyses cited by Berthollet in support of his position were faulty because impure compounds or mixtures had been used. He also distinguished between solutions and chemical reactions. "The solution of ammonia in water is to my eyes not at all like that of hydrogen in azote which produces ammonia." [6]

By 1808 Proust's opinion had prevailed and the law of constant composition was accepted by almost all chemists. In disregarding the theories of Berthollet they not only disregarded the theory of mass action, and thus had to wait many years before the study of chemical equilibrium could begin, but they also disregarded the nature of many complex crystalline substances whose composition actually was variable because of substitutions in the crystal lattice. It was perhaps fortunate for the chemistry of his time that Proust worked with simple substances that obeyed the law of constant composition, for it was necessary to build on this law before the nature of more complex compounds could be understood. Eventually it was recognized that there had been truth in the ideas of Berthollet even in regard to variable composition. This fact was acknowledged by Kurnakov in 1914, when he suggested that alloys and other compounds of indefinite composition be called "berthollides," while the ordinary compounds should be called "daltonides" after John Dalton.[7]

The theories of Richter, Berthollet, and Proust directed the thinking of chemists toward the concept of chemical compounds as we consider them today, but they did not depend on any real atomic theory. The development of a quantitative atomic theory that gave meaning to the law of constant composition was the work of John Dalton (1766–1844) of Manchester. He had been to some extent anticipated in his ideas by the Irish chemist William Higgins (1766–1825),[8] who in 1789 published a book embodying the concept of atomic combination and the law of multiple proportions. His ideas did not reach the majority of chemists. Only the theories of Dalton gave the atomic explanation of the laws of constant and multiple proportions a basis that permitted them to be generally accepted.

Dalton was interested in meteorology and the composition of the atmosphere. In attempting to explain to himself many of the physical properties of gases he at first assumed that the atoms, by now believed by almost everyone to be the smallest particles of matter, were of the same size for all different substances. He found it impossible to reconcile the behavior of gases with this assumption and so was led to think of atoms as varying in size. He regarded them as dense spheres of different dimensions, each surrounded by an atmosphere of heat (caloric) which repelled other atoms. In keeping with the quantitative spirit of the time, and because the concept of variable size was so important to his thinking, he attempted to determine the numerical values for the differences in size or, more accurately, in weight.

In order to do this, he had to make certain assumptions as to the nature of chemical combination. His ideas were based more on physical than on chemical properties, and so he made the simplest assumption of chemical composition possible. Unless there was reason to assume otherwise, he believed that a compound of two substances (a binary compound) would contain one atom of each of the two constituents. Thus, water was a compound of one atom of hydrogen and one of oxygen, ammonia one of hydrogen and one of nitrogen, and so on. If this assumption was valid, the results of chemical analysis at once gave a method for determining the relative weights of atoms. The analyses of water available to him showed that it contained $85\frac{2}{3}$ parts of oxygen and $14\frac{1}{3}$ parts of hydrogen. If the weight of hydrogen was taken as unity, the relative weight of oxygen became 6. Similarly, analysis of ammonia gave 80 parts of nitrogen and 20 parts of hydrogen. The relative weight of an atom of nitrogen was thus 4. In this way, Dalton was able to draw up the first table of atomic weights, which he presented as a supplement to a paper on the absorption of gases by water, read to the Literary and Philosophical Society of Manchester in 1803 and published in 1805.[9] He did not explain there how he derived the table, and the values he gave were changed in later versions, but the principle remained the same.

In 1804 the Scottish chemist Thomas Thomson (1773–1852), a very active popularizer of chemistry, visited Dalton and learned the details of his atomic theory. Thomson was so impressed by what he heard that he became an ardent advocate of the Dalton theory. He was later accused by Higgins of deliberately suppressing the contributions of the latter. There is no doubt that the enthusiastic support of Thomson did much to make the work of Dalton well known to other chemists, so that it became the basis for later work on the application of the atomic theory to chemistry.[8]

In 1807 Thomson published his five-volume *System of Chemistry* in which he explained Dalton's theory, and in 1808 Dalton himself brought out *A New System of Chemical Philosophy,* one of the classics in the history of chemistry. In these works the atomic theory was developed in detail and many of its applications were discussed.

Dalton still clung to the assumption that the majority of compounds were binary. He knew, however, that more than one compound of some elements existed, and so he assumed that ternary compounds, the next simplest to picture, could also exist. In these, one atom of one element was united to two of the other. Thus, variability of chemical composition was explained, but it was not the continuous variability of Berthollet. The old philosophical principle of discontinuity received a quantitative theoretical basis, and the law of multiple proportions was presented. This law followed so essentially from Dalton's theory that he did not even express it as a distinct principle. He merely used it as an obvious part of the development of the theory.[10]

Dalton devised a set of symbols to express his theory. Their graphic nature probably helped in its acceptance. They were circles, since his atoms were spherical, and they contained various lines, dots, or letters to represent the atoms of different elements. Thus hydrogen was ⊙, nitrogen ⊘, oxygen ○, and carbon ●. Water became ⊙○ with an "atomic" weight of $1 + 7 = 8$; ammonia ⊙⊘, "atomic" weight 6; "carbonic oxide" ○● ; and the ternary carbonic acid ○●○ . Sugar was supposed to consist of one atom of alcohol and one of carbonic acid, and was therefore given the septenary formula .

Erroneous though Dalton's theory was in many respects, chiefly because of its rigid, arbitrary assumptions, it presented to chemists a number of new and important concepts. It gave a precise, quantitative basis to the older, vague idea of atoms; it gave to the concept of elements a specificity that had previously been lacking; it explained the discontinuity in the proportions of elements in compounds as expressed in the laws of constant and multiple proportions; and it suggested that the arrangement of the atoms in a compound could be represented schematically in such a way as to indicate the actual structure of the compound. Many of the developments of chemistry in the nineteenth century resulted from the expansion of these ideas.

At the same time, it should be noted that the theory gave no indication of any single standard for determining atomic weights, since the relative weights of the atoms varied, depending on whether the compound in which they were found was binary, ternary, or of some other degree of complexity. There was no distinction between atoms and molecules in the modern sense. The theory was more suggestive than positively informative. Dalton himself never modified his rigid ideas, but in the hands of other chemists the implications of the theory were gradually developed.

Thomas Thomson and his friend, the English physician and chemist, William Hyde Wollaston (1766–1828), presented confirmation of the law of multiple proportions in 1808, the year in which Dalton published the *New System*. Thomson showed that oxalic acid combined with potash and strontia to form two sets of salts, one of which contained twice as much base as the other.[11] Wollaston confirmed the existence of these salts and also proved the existence of "quadroxalate of potash" ($KHC_2O_4 \cdot H_2C_2O_4$).[12]

These experiments attracted the attention of a young Swedish scientist, Jöns Jacob Berzelius (1779–1848), who later became the most influential chemist of the first half of the nineteenth century. Berzelius had been interested in the work of Wenzel and Richter and had begun a series of analyses of various minerals and salts before he learned of the work of Thomson and Wollaston and, through this, of Dalton's theory. He determined to devote most of his attention to quantitative analysis in order to test the laws of chemical combination and to determine the various atomic weights.

Berzelius was a brilliant chemist, and in the course of his analytical work (which was not always of the highest degree of accuracy) he described many new reactions and substances.[13] Among his discoveries were the new elements selenium (1818), silicon (1823), titanium (1825), and many new minerals.[14] More important, by 1812 he had performed such a great number of analyses that he had firmly established the law of multiple proportions in the minds of most chemists.[15]

Berzelius recognized that one atom of an element might combine with varying numbers of atoms of other elements, and that two atoms could combine with three or five of another element, but he could not tell whether two atoms could combine with two, four, or six other atoms. As long as the concept of molecules and molecular weight did not exist, no difference could be recognized between the formulas (as we now write them) HO or H_2O_2. As a result, the formula assumed to be correct had to be deduced individually for each compound, often by analogy with other compounds that behaved in a similar way.

In his later work Berzelius made much use of two generalizations in determining the atomic weights of the elements. The first of these was the rule announced in 1819 by Pierre Louis Dulong (1785–1838) and Alexis Thérèse Petit (1791–1820) that the product of the atomic weight and specific heat for an element is constant.[16] Although this law is now known to be an approximation, it was very useful in deciding whether the correct atomic weight of an element should be its equivalent weight or some multiple of this.

The second principle employed by Berzelius was the law of isomorphism, announced by his student, Eilhard Mitscherlich (1794–1863), in 1820.[17] This stated that when two substances crystallized in similar forms they usually had analogous formulas. If the number of atoms of an element in one compound was known, the number of atoms of a similar element in an isomorphous compound could be deduced. These methods served Berzelius well, but they were not sufficiently general to give absolute assurance of the atomic weights he sought so earnestly to establish.

A more satisfactory method, but one which was applicable only to gases, rested on the law of combining volumes discovered by the French chemist Joseph Louis Gay-Lussac (1778–1850). In 1805, working with the great naturalist Alexander von Humboldt (1769–1854), Gay-Lussac had redetermined the fact, first observed by Cavendish, that hydrogen and oxygen united in the proportions 2:1 to form water. He went on to study such relationships in other gases, and by 1809 he was able to announce that the ratios of the volumes of reacting gases were small whole numbers.[18] Thus, ammonia combined with equal volumes of fluoboric acid (BF_3), muriatic acid, and carbonic acid to form "neutral salts," while fluoboric and carbonic acids combined with 2 volumes of ammonia to form "subsalts." Data of other authors showed that 1 volume of nitrogen and 3 of hydrogen were combined in ammonia, and that oxides of nitrogen were known that consisted of 1 volume of nitrogen combined with $\frac{1}{2}$, 1, and 2 volumes of oxygen. Dalton never accepted these results of Gay-Lussac, but Berzelius used them wherever possible.

Although Berzelius used the law of combining volumes, he never extended it to its final conclusions, and so was never able to make the distinction between atoms and molecules in gaseous reactions. This step was taken in 1811 by the Italian, Amadeo Avogadro (1776–1856), but his ideas were neglected for nearly fifty years. Avogadro took up an assumption that had been considered—but rejected—by Dalton: that equal volumes of different gases contained the same number of particles. From this he immediately deduced that the ratio of the densities of two gases such as oxygen (1.10359) and hydrogen (0.07321) represented the ratio between the masses of their particles, that is, their atomic weights, which in this particular case came out 15.074 to 1. This showed that the equivalent weight of oxygen of about 8, which was often used by other chemists, was not the atomic weight.

Avogadro then distinguished between what he called "integral molecules," our molecules, and "elementary molecules," our atoms. He assumed that atoms of a simple gas could combine with each other, and, in reaction with another gas, these resulting integral molecules could split apart and form new integral molecules of different composition. Thus, "the molecule of water will be comprised of half a molecule of oxygen with one molecule, or what is the same thing, two half molecules of hydrogen." [19] A similar hypothesis was proposed by the French physicist Ampère (1775–1836) in 1814.

If the Avogadro hypothesis had been accepted, chemists would have been spared half a century of confusion. At the time of its appearance, however, few facts were known that confirmed it, and Berzelius could not conceive of two like atoms uniting together. He therefore disregarded it, and the great weight of his authority discouraged other chemists from investigating it more thoroughly. In 1832 J. B. A. Dumas (1800–1884), who succeeded Berzelius as a great leader of chemical thought, studied the vapor densities of sulfur, phosphorus, arsenic, and mercury. He did not realize that these vapors had an anomalous structure, and so he felt that his results discredited Avogadro's theory. With such influential opposition as that of Berzelius and Dumas there was little likelihood that chemists would accept the theory until hopeless confusion forced them to do so.

With the exception of his disregard of Avogadro, Berzelius used the methods available with great skill and intuition. In 1814 he was able to draw up a table of atomic weights that was surprisingly accurate.[20] The table was twice revised. In the 1826 version the atomic weights for almost all the elements were close to those used today. Only for silver, sodium, and potassium did Berzelius use values double those of today.

In spite of the ingenuity with which Berzelius drew up his table, most contemporary chemists felt that there was little theoretical basis for his values. They believed that it was far safer to use numbers that could be determined by direct analysis. This was especially the view of Wollaston, who introduced the term "equivalent weight" to express the combining ratios of the elements. He drew up a table of equivalents from all the analytical data available to him and designed a synoptic scale of chemical equivalents that was a sort of chemical slide rule.[21] This appealed widely to chemists, and the atomic weights of Berzelius were almost entirely replaced by equivalent weights. For a long time the names atomic and equivalent were confused, and the various possible values for equivalent weights derived from different compounds of the same element added to the confusion. The particular numerical value chosen by any chemist was largely a matter of his individual preference and might be determined by some particular theory that he adopted.

This fact is well illustrated by the history of Prout's hypothesis. The English physician William Prout (1785–1850) in 1815 and 1816 published two anonymous papers in which he suggested that the atomic weights of many elements were whole multiples of the atomic weight of hydrogen, taken as unity. He supported the theory by data from inaccurate analyses and expressed the opinion that hydrogen might be the prime matter of the ancients, from which everything else was formed.[22] Thomson was much impressed by this theory and later published a book [23] containing a number of analyses that he adapted to fit Prout's hypothesis. He did not consider this in any way wrong, for he believed that the theory was correct and the analyses were in error. Berzelius did not approve of such treatment of analytical results, and made the caustic comment: "The greatest consideration which contemporaries can show to the author is to treat his book as if it had never appeared." [24]

In spite of the confusion over atomic and equivalent weights, the fact that numerical calculations could be applied to chemical equations and that each element was recognized as having certain fundamental characteristics greatly systematized chemistry. This systematization was rendered even more pronounced when Berzelius introduced modern chemical symbols. Whereas the reform in nomenclature of de Morveau and his collaborators had made it easier to think in chemical terms, the reform in chemical symbols that Berzelius proposed in 1814 [20] permitted a visualization of chemical reactions in the simplest and most effective way.

76

Name.	Formel.	O=100.	H=1.
Unterschwefl. Säure	Ṡ	301,165	48,265
Schweflichte Säure	S̈	401,165	64,291
Unterschwefelsäure	S̈̇	902,330	144,609
Schwefelsäure	S̈̈	501,165	80,317
Phosphorsäure	P̈̇	892,310	143,003
Chlorsäure	C̈̈l	942,650	151,071
Oxydirte Chlorsäure	C̈̈̇l	1042,650	167,097
Jodsäure	J̈̇	2037,562	326,543
Kohlensäure	Ċ	276,437	44,302
Oxalsäure	C̈	452,875	72,578
Borsäure	B̈̈	871,966	139,743
Kieselsäure	S̈i	577,478	92,548
Selensäure	S̈̇e	694,582	111,315
Arseniksäure	Ä̶s	1440,084	230,790
Chromoxydul	C̈r	1003,638	160,845
Chromsäure	C̈r	651,819	104,462
Molybdänsäure	M̈o	898,525	143,999
Wolframsäure	Ẅ	1483,200	237,700
Antimonoxyd	S̈b	1912,904	306,565
Antimonichte Säure	S̈b	1006,452	161,296
	S̈̇b	2012,904	322,591
Antimonsäure	S̈̇b	2112,904	338,617
Telluroxyd	T̈e	1006,452	161,296
Tantalsäure	T̈̇a	2607,430	417,871
Titansäure	T̈i	589,092	94,409
Goldoxydul	Ȧu	2586,026	414,441
Goldoxyd	Ä̶u	2786,026	446,493
Platinoxyd	Ṗt	1415,220	226,806
Rhodiumoxyd	R̈	1801,360	228,689

Fig. 13. Examples of the chemical symbols and atomic weights of Berzelius. (From *Jahresbericht über die Fortschritte der physischen Wissenschaft*, 1828, p. 76.)

Berzelius suggested that the initial letter of the Latin name of the element be used as its chemical symbol. When the names of elements began with the same letter, the next distinctive letter of the name was to be added. At first he suggested that oxygen be indicated by a dot placed over the symbol of the element with which it was combined, so that SO_3 was to be written $\overset{..}{S}$, but this part of his system did not survive very long. He also noticed that two atoms of an element often reacted as a unit, and he later suggested that such a double atom be represented by a bar drawn across the symbol of the element, so that H_2 became $\overline{H}$. These barred atoms survived longer and underwent various modifications by other chemists, but eventually they too were abandoned.

The formulas of Berzelius were a great improvement over those previously proposed not only because of their simplicity and because they could be set in ordinary type, but also because they stood for definite weights of the element. They thus contributed to the quantitative approach to chemistry that was growing so important.

Two major errors in the system of Lavoisier remained, and elimination of these began at this time. The idea that caloric was a definite substance began to give way as the physicists, who had never entirely abandoned the kinetic theory of heat of the seventeenth century, began to study the relationships of the various forms of energy.[25] This development will be discussed in detail in connection with the rise of physical chemistry.

More purely chemical were the views of Lavoisier on acids. Impressed by the importance of oxygen, he believed that all acids contained this principle, and he even used this idea in choosing a name for the substance. As early as 1789 Berthollet had shown that hydrocyanic acid and hydrogen sulfide did not contain oxygen. These acids were so weak that many did not consider them to be true acids, and so the faith of Lavoisier and his followers was not shaken.[26] Decisive proof came in the case of chlorine. This existed in the strong muriatic acid, and so was supposed to be the oxide of an element, murium. Gay-Lussac and his collaborator Louis-Jacques Thenard (1777–1857) made a long study of muriates in 1809 and produced evidence that they contained no oxygen. They were too strongly influenced by the views of Lavoisier to accept their own evidence, and so it was left to the brilliant English investigator Humphry Davy (1778–1819) to prove in 1810 that chlorine was an element in its own right.[27] When Gay-Lussac studied hydriodic acid in 1813, he admitted the correctness of Davy's views. Thus Davy gave the deathblow to Lavoisier's theory of the composition of acids.

An actual understanding of the essential nature of acids came from the work of Graham and Liebig later in the century. Thomas Graham (1805–1869) showed that ortho-, pyro-, and metaphosphoric acids were distinct substances which, in his formulation, contained three, two, and one molecules of water, respectively, water that could be replaced by a corresponding number of equivalents of a base.[28] Justus Liebig (1803–1873) generalized this in his theory of polybasic acids,[29] showing that organic acids existed that could combine with various equivalents of bases. He therefore assumed that acids were compounds of hydrogen, and that this hydrogen could be replaced by metals. This did away with the need to write acids by the dualistic system of Berzelius, in which they were represented as composed of water and an acid radical. Proper importance was given to hydrogen itself. In 1839, on the basis of his electrochemical studies, John Frederick Daniell (1790–1845) abandoned the dualistic method of writing the formulas of salts in an early application of a form of the ionic theory (see p. 208).

The work of the first two decades of the nineteenth century had now defined elements and compounds as chemical individuals, had given them specific quantitative properties, and had supplied a convenient method for expressing chemical relationships. It was inevitable that the same chemists who had performed this work should attempt to solve the old problem of affinity. The remarkable discoveries then being made in the field of electricity seemed to offer hope of such a solution. The beginnings of the science of electrochemistry must therefore be considered.

REFERENCES

1. J. R. Partington, *Ann. Sci.*, **7**, 173–198 (1951).

2. Walter Hückel, *Structural Chemistry of Inorganic Compounds*, Vol. 1, p. 18, translated by L. H. Long, Elsevier Press, New York, 1950.

3. This table became widely known through its reproduction in C. L. Berthollet, *Essai de statique chimique*, Vol. 1, p. 136, Demonville et Sœurs, Paris, 1803.

4. J. L. Proust, *Ann. chim.*, **32**, 26–54 (1799).

5. C. L. Berthollet, *Recherches sur les lois de l'affinité*, Paris, 1801, Article 2, section 9.

6. J. L. Proust, *J. phys.*, **63**, 369 (1806).

7. N. S. Kurnakov, *Bull. Acad. Sci. St. Petersburg*, **1914**, 321–338.

8. E. R. Atkinson, *J. Chem. Educ.*, **17**, 3–11 (1940).

9. John Dalton, *Mem. Literary Phil. Soc. Manchester*, [2] **1**, 271–287 (1805).

10. M. E. Pattison Muir, *A History of Chemical Theories and Laws*, New York, J. Wiley & Sons, 1907, p. 83.

11. T. Thomson, *Phil. Trans.*, **98**, 63–95 (1808).

12. W. H. Wollaston, *ibid.*, **98**, 96–102 (1808).

13. W. McNevin, *J. Chem. Educ.*, **31**, 207–210 (1954).

14. M. E. Weeks, *The Discovery of the Elements*, 2nd ed., Journal of Chemical Education, Easton, Pa., 1934, p. 350.

15. Muir, *op. cit.*, p. 90.

16. P. L. Dulong and A. T. Petit, *Ann. chim.*, **10**, 395–413 (1819).

17. E. Mitscherlich, *Abhandl. kgl. Akad. Wiss. Berlin, 1818–1819*, **1820**, 427–437.

18. J. L. Gay-Lussac, *Mém. soc. Arcueil*, **2**, 207–234 (1809).

19. A. Avogadro, *J. phys.*, **73**, 58–76 (1811).

20. J. J. Berzelius, *Ann. Philosophy*, **3**, 362–363 (1814).

21. *Ibid.*, **6**, 321–330 (1815); **7**, 111–113 (1816).

22. W. H. Wollaston, *Phil. Trans.*, **1814**, 1–22.

23. T. Thomson, *An Attempt to Establish the First Principles of Chemistry*, Baldwin, Craddock and Joy, London, 1825.

24. J. J. Berzelius, *Jahresber. Fortschr. phys. Wiss.*, **6**, 78 (1827).

25. H. T. Pledge, *Science since 1500*, Philosophical Library, New York, 1947, p. 141.

26. R. E. Oesper, *J. Chem. Educ.*, **23**, 162 (1946).

27. H. Davy, *Phil. Trans.*, **100**, 231–257 (1810).

28. T. Graham, *ibid.*, **1833**, 253–284.

29. J. Liebig, *Ann.*, **26**, 113–189 (1838).

ELECTROCHEMISTRY AND

CHEMICAL AFFINITY

The scientific study of electrical phenomena began seriously in the seventeenth century. After Otto von Guericke between 1660 and 1670 constructed a machine in which static electricity was produced by rubbing a ball of sulfur with the hand, physicists began an intensive investigation of this new branch of their science. It was actively studied throughout the eighteenth century. In 1729 Stephen Gray (1666 or 1667–1736) [1] showed that metals could conduct current away from its source. This suggested that electricity was a fluid, an idea that fitted well into the concepts of imponderable fluids so popular at this time. Even after heat and light ceased to be placed in this class, electricity continued to be compared to a fluid. In 1734 C. F. de C. Du Fay (1692–1739) distinguished two types of electricity, which he called "vitreous" and "resinous," according to whether they were produced by rubbing glass or resin. Benjamin Franklin (1706–1790) gave these their modern names of positive and negative electricity. The polarity of electrical effects was thus established.

In 1745 von Kleist discovered a primitive condenser, which was rediscovered and first announced by Pieter van Musschenbroek (1692–1761) of Leiden. It became known as the Leiden jar and was an essential piece of laboratory equipment of the time. It consisted of a small flask held in the hand while an electrical charge was applied to a wire that passed into the flask. [2]

By means of such static machines and condensers a certain number of chemical reactions could be produced. Cavendish and Priestley used electric sparks to cause the combination of hydrogen or nitrogen with oxygen. In 1789 A. Paets van Troostwijk (1752–1837) and J. R. Deimann (1743–1808) decomposed water with a large static machine. They did not notice the separation of hydrogen and oxygen at different poles in this experiment. In no case at that time was it possible to produce a current strong or continuous enough to permit a significant study of chemical reactions.[3] This situation changed completely at the end of the eighteenth century.

In 1786 Luigi Galvani (1737–1798), professor of surgical and anatomical operations at the University of Bologna, was studying a nerve-muscle preparation of a frog leg. A copper hook on which the muscle hung was placed on an iron support. The muscle twitched. Galvani was much impressed by this event and studied it in considerable detail. Since he was a biologist, he centered his attention on the muscle, in which he believed the electricity arose. His fellow countryman, Alessandro Volta (1745–1827), professor of natural philosophy at the University of Pavia, being a physicist, sought the cause of the electrical effect in the metals. He soon found that the electricity arose at their junction. The muscle served merely as an indicator. He then tried placing a number of metal junctions together and found that the effect was multiplied. In 1800 he reported his results to Sir Joseph Banks (1743–1820), President of the Royal Society of London, and they were published in the *Philosophical Transactions*.[4]

Volta built up a long column consisting of alternate plates of copper and tin, or silver and zinc, joined by a disc of paper or leather soaked in a saline solution. This was the Voltaic pile, the first true battery, and from it came a continuous current whose effects could be increased by merely increasing the size and number of alternating metal plates.

Almost at once chemists began to use this new apparatus to produce chemical reactions. Banks showed Volta's letter to his friend William Nicholson (1753–1815), founder of *Nicholson's Journal of Natural Philosophy, Chemistry, and the Arts*, in which many of the scientific papers of the time were published. Nicholson and Anthony Carlisle (1768–1840) studied the decomposition of water with the pile, and shortly after the publication of Volta's report they described the electrolysis of water solutions of various salts with liberation of hydrogen at one pole of the pile and oxygen at the other.[5]

In 1803 Berzelius and William Hisinger (1766–1852) performed a similar experiment and found that, when salts are decomposed during

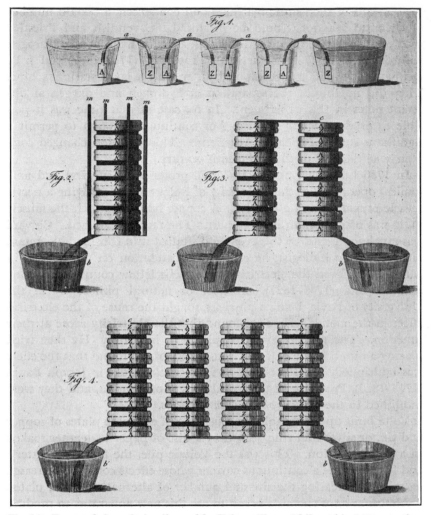

Fig. 14.   Forms of the voltaic pile used by Volta.   (From *Philosophical Transactions of the Royal Society*, 1800, p. 431.)

electrolysis, bases are found at the negative pole and acids at the positive, indicating that acids and bases carry opposite charges.   This observation made a great impression on Berzelius.   It probably led to his later electrochemical theory of affinity.

The most striking experimental results in this field were obtained by Humphry Davy at the Royal Institution in London, where he was professor of chemistry.   Davy began work on electrolysis almost as soon as Volta's results appeared. He constructed a battery of over 250 metallic plates, one of the most powerful then available. Using this apparatus he found that he could not isolate the components of alkali salts from water solutions. He therefore tried the electrolysis of fused solids, with spectacular results. In November, 1807, he was able to announce the isolation of potassium and sodium as metals.[6] The extreme reactivity of these elements greatly impressed contemporary chemists. Davy went on to isolate barium, magnesium, calcium, and strontium by similar methods.[7] He used potassium to reduce boric acid to boron. This reductive method was much used by later chemists in the preparation of various metals. Davy found that, when mercury was present as the oxide, electrolytic production of the metals with formation of amalgams proceeded very easily. Berzelius applied this reaction to ammonium salts and obtained ammonium amalgam, confirming the basic character of ammonia. The name ammonium was proposed to indicate the analogy of this substance to the metals.

These chemical reactions studied in the first two decades of the nineteenth century profoundly influenced the thinking of chemists, but their ideas had a purely qualitative character. Recognition of the quantitative aspects came from the later studies of Michael Faraday (1791–1867), whom Davy had chosen as his assistant at the Royal Institution, and who succeeded him there. Faraday's investigations in the field of electricity were chiefly physical, and he is best known for his discovery of electromagnetic induction. His chemical work was also extremely important. His greatest chemical discovery, announced in 1832–1833, was that in electrolysis the amount of substance decomposed is proportional to current strength and time, and that the weight of substance deposited is proportional to the equivalent weight of the substance.[8] This discovery supplied an independent method for determining equivalents, but it was not immediately adopted by chemists, since Berzelius refused to accept it.

Faraday sought a better system of terminology for the electrochemistry of his day. He turned to William Whewell (1794–1866), a classical scholar and historian of science, who suggested the names still in use today: electrode, anode, cathode, ion, anion, cation.[9]

It was inevitable that the force of electricity (or the "electric fluid") that produced such startling experimental results should become an important part of chemical theory. Since electrolysis broke up chemical compounds, it was an obvious step to assume that electricity must be concerned in some way in affinity, which so occupied the thoughts of chemists.

As early as 1800, William Cruikshank (1745–1800) assumed that the electrical fluid, a chemical substance like caloric, combined with oxygen or hydrogen when they were liberated at the electrodes.[10]   Davy suggested that chemical substances became electrically charged when they approached each other and that compounds were held together by neutralization of these charges.[11]

It remained for Berzelius to formulate a more precise theory of chemical affinity in electrical terms and, by the weight of his authority, to impose this dualistic theory on all chemistry.   Berzelius was especially impressed by the opposite charges at the two poles of an electrolysis apparatus, and by the attractions and repulsions they exerted. The old doctrine of opposites had never lost its appeal to scientists, and this made easy the acceptance of a new "physics of contraries."

Berzelius assumed that every atom had both a positive and a negative charge, that is, was polarized.   The only exception was oxygen, the most electronegative element.   All the others could be arranged in a series such that they were electropositive to those above them and electronegative to those below.   At the bottom of the table stood potassium, the most electropositive element.   It is apparent that there was always an excess of either positive or negative electricity on each atom. In the formation of chemical compounds there was neutralization of positive and negative charges (often with liberation of light or heat, analogous to sparking across a condenser), but the resulting compound was not necessarily neutral, since the unequal charges did not have to neutralize each other exactly.   Thus, sulfur, electropositive with respect to oxygen, could combine with it to form the binary compound sulfur trioxide, SO_3, in which the negative charge predominated, leaving the compound as a whole electrically negative.   Similarly, potassium and oxygen combined to give the oxide K_2O (or KO as Berzelius wrote it), which retained a positive charge.   Therefore the oxides of sulfur and potassium would combine to the ternary salt, potassium sulfate, written $KO \cdot SO_3$.   This was still not neutral, since it could unite with aluminum sulfate to form alum, $KO \cdot Al_2O_3 \cdot 4SO_3$, and this in turn could add water of crystallization by a similar process.[12]

This theory fitted the facts of electrolysis well and gave an explanation of the forces of affinity that held salts together.   In fact, Berzelius believed that he had at last explained the cause of affinity.   There were certain experimental facts that did not fit into the theory, though these tended to be disregarded.   For example, the actual compounds SO_3 and K_2O were not electrically charged.   The theory had still more serious defects.   It made it impossible to accept Avogadro's theory in which two similarly charged atoms of hydrogen, oxygen, or nitrogen were united with each other. This difficulty became more evident with later developments of organic chemistry and was one of the chief factors in the downfall of the dualistic theory. As long as chemists dealt mostly with acids, bases, and salts, however, the theory served well enough, and, in a modified form, it is still essentially a part of our explanation of the nature of polar compounds.

The most serious theoretical objection to the theory lay on purely physical grounds. Berzelius made the error of confusing the roles of current intensity and current quantity.[13] This is reminiscent of the similar confusion with respect to heat which was cleared up by Black in the previous century. It was this error that also prevented Berzelius from accepting Faraday's law of electrochemical equivalents. This error was clear to physicists of his day, but not to chemists, who at this time tended to disregard physics and who often had little training in it. The apparent simplicity of the dualistic theory and its easy explanation of many chemical facts gave it first place in the thinking of chemists.

Berzelius was by no means backward in advocating his chemical beliefs. He had contributed so much to chemistry in the years prior to 1830 that he was respected by everyone. In addition he had published a textbook of chemistry that went through five editions between 1808 and 1848, and that was everywhere accepted as the standard chemical reference. He published an annual report on the progress of chemistry, the famous *Jahresbericht über die Fortschritte der physischen Wissenschaft,* from 1821 to 1849. In this he stated frankly his opinions of the work of other chemists. As he grew older, he grew more and more concerned with the preservation of the theories he had done so much to establish in his younger days. The great influence that he exerted tended to oppose chemical progress. Toward the end of his life he was engaged in many controversies, in most of which he supported what eventually proved to be the losing side. Even in these controversies, however, his opposition often resulted in stimulating better research. Few chemists have been as influential in their day as Berzelius.

A survey of the progress of chemistry from the time of Lavoisier through the first quarter of the nineteenth century reveals astonishing advances. Never before had there been such a reorganization and systematization of the science. All sciences showed a similar advance, but chemistry responded to special conditions and perhaps advanced most rapidly as a result.

An important factor was the completely international character of science at this time. The numerous new journals and the extensive correspondence between scientists were factors, and the sense of being a scientist was not impeded by nationalistic feelings. Certain characteristics distinguished the scientists of the leading countries, and contact between them fertilized and advanced science. Such contact was remarkably free. The best example of this is the fact that in 1813 Davy was able to visit France and travel through the laboratories as a guest of French chemists, though England and France were in the midst of the Napoleonic wars. It is difficult to visualize a comparable situation today.

Among the special factors that favored chemistry at this time, two stand out clearly. For the first time, chemistry was fully recognized as a profession in its own right. No longer were chemists trained as pharmacists or physicians before they undertook chemical investigations. Professors of chemistry became more common in the universities, and many prominent chemists, especially in France, established private laboratories in which they gave chemical instruction.

Even more important, perhaps, was the close connection between technical and theoretical chemistry. It is probable that never before or since has it been so close, for never before had there been such a brilliant group of contributors to chemical theory who were also practical technical chemists. At this time there was no distinction between "pure" and "applied" chemistry in the minds of chemists. Lavoisier was chiefly responsible for supplying the French government with explosives of good quality, and solved many other technical problems for his countrymen. Berthollet was active in the French dyeing and bleaching industries. Gay-Lussac contributed his tower to the sulfuric acid manufacturers. Davy invented the miner's safety lamp. Many important industries expanded from the laboratory or the apothecary shop under the influence of the Napoleonic wars and the Continental Blockade. Production of beet sugar increased. The Leblanc process for producing soda was discovered. In fact, large-scale chemical industry may be said to have begun at this time.

Although there were many favorable factors to account for the progress of chemistry, there were unfavorable factors as well that prevented full utilization of the new discoveries. Mention has been made of the disregard of physics in the dualistic theory of Berzelius. This was not an isolated case. Up to this period, chemistry and physics were not clearly distinguished as separate sciences. Boyle and Lavoisier were physicists in many respects. Now that chemistry was making such rapid progress, largely by means of qualitative theories and simple quantitative methods, chemists began to neglect physics. This in turn alienated the physicists, who neglected chemistry in developing their own science. The results were not entirely harmful, for chemistry had to accumulate a tremendous amount of purely factual material before the larger generalizations could be made, and there was work enough for the chemists for many years to come. Closer cooperation between chemists and physicists might have saved some time for both. As it was, however, most chemists turned to the development of organic chemistry by chemical methods that eventually, to the great surprise of many physicists, were found to give an essentially correct view of the physical structure of organic compounds. The slow development of physical chemistry gradually brought the two sciences together once more.

REFERENCES

1. I. Bernard Cohen, *Isis,* **45,** 41–50 (1954).

2. W. F. Magie, *A Source Book in Physics,* McGraw-Hill Book Co., New York, 1935, pp. 403–405.

3. E. W. J. Neave, *Ann. Sci.,* **7,** 395–398 (1951).

4. A. Volta, *Phil. Trans.,* **1800,** 403–431. A facsimile reproduction is given in *Isis,* **15,** 129–157 (1931).

5. W. Nicholson (and A. Carlisle), *Nicholson's Journal,* **4,** 179–187 (1800).

6. H. Davy, *Phil. Trans.,* **98,** 1–44 (1808).

7. H. Davy, *ibid.,* **98,** 333–370 (1808).

8. M. Faraday, *ibid.,* **1833,** 23–52; **1834,** 77–122.

9. A. W. Richeson, *Isis,* **36,** 160–162 (1946); S. M. Edelstein, *ibid.,* **37,** 180 (1947).

10. W. Cruikshank, *Nicholson's Journal,* **4,** 187–191 (1800).

11. H. Davy, *Elements of Chemical Philosophy,* J. Johnson and Co., London, 1812, p. 164.

12. J. J. Berzelius, *Essai sur la théorie des proportions et sur l'influence chimique de l'électricité,* Méquignon-Marvis, Paris, 1819.

13. W. Hückel, *Structural Chemistry of Inorganic Compounds,* translated by L. H. Long, Elsevier Press, New York, 1950, Vol. 1, pp. 30–32; R. G. Ehl and A. J. Ihde, *J. Chem. Educ.,* **31,** 226–232 (1954).

THE DEVELOPMENT

OF ORGANIC CHEMISTRY:

THE RADICAL AND

UNITARY THEORIES

Technologists, pharmacists, physicians, alchemists, and chemists had worked with substances we now class as organic ever since men began to manipulate the materials of nature. At first, animal and vegetable tissues and fluids were used as such. Gradually, certain substances, such as sugar or alcohol, were purified and used for their special properties. During the Middle Ages, compounds such as ether or acetone were accidentally obtained, but they were never considered to belong to any special category.

As knowledge of chemical facts increased, it was recognized that the products of living organisms were far less stable and far more reactive than most mineral compounds. A three-way distinction arose. The mineral substances were relatively simple; the pure products extracted from living matter, since they were not themselves living, were considered a class of especially complex chemicals; and the actual fluids and tissues of animals and vegetables ("organized beings") were classed as "organic." Bergman first expressed this distinction between inorganic and organic substances in 1780, and Berzelius in his textbook first spoke of "organic chemistry," although by this he chiefly meant what would today be called biochemistry.[1]

Before organic compounds could be studied, analytical methods applicable to them had to be developed. Lavoisier first described such a method, burning the compounds in oxygen under a bell jar and attempting to determine the water and carbon dioxide formed. Gay-Lussac and Thenard greatly improved this method by burning the sample in a combustion tube with an oxidizing agent—at first potassium chlorate (1810) and later copper oxide (1815). Berzelius carried out organic analyses with great care, but he was more interested in obtaining atomic weights than in perfecting a practical method for analyzing new compounds. It required eighteen months for Berzelius to perform twenty-one analyses of seven organic acids. Credit for perfecting organic analysis and making it a routine procedure belongs to Justus Liebig. By 1831 he had described the method which remained standard until it was modified by the introduction of microanalysis in the twentieth century. With the development by Dumas of his method for nitrogen analysis in organic compounds in 1833, organic chemistry possessed the basic analytical techniques upon which the great advances in this science were made.[2]

As a result of his analytical work, Berzelius by 1814 recognized that organic compounds obeyed the law of constant composition. He wished to fit these compounds as completely as possible into the laws of chemistry that had developed from the study of inorganic substances, but he did not believe that this could ever be done completely. Like most chemists of his time, even the great systematizer thought that the products of a living organism were controlled by a special "vital force" exerted by life itself that gave distinctive properties to organic compounds. The ordinary laboratory methods were not believed to be entirely applicable to these substances, and so it was thought improbable that they would ever be prepared in the laboratory. This view was weakened when Chevreul explained the nature of fats, as will be seen, and it received its first major challenge in 1828 when Friedrich Wöhler (1800–1882) found that ammonium cyanate could be transformed into urea, a typical product of the animal body.[3] New syntheses continually weakened the position of the vitalists, and even Berzelius gradually changed his views.[4] With the development of the concept of conservation of energy in the middle of the century it was seen that there was no place for a life force. When Marcellin Berthelot (1827–1907) in 1860 published his *Chimie organique fondée sur la synthèse,* in which he showed the possibility of total synthesis of all classes of organic compounds from the elements carbon, hydrogen, oxygen, and nitrogen, the doctrine of vitalism was generally abandoned by chemists.

The first important step in clarifying the nature of organic compounds was the development of the concept of radicals. Guyton de

Morveau, in the book on nomenclature, spoke of the "radical of an acid" as "the simple substance of each acid which modifies the oxygen." Lavoisier accepted this term. He believed that in inorganic compounds a simple radical was united to oxygen, whereas in organic substances a complex radical composed of carbon and hydrogen was similarly united.

The concept of the radical was extended by the work of Gay-Lussac on hydrogen cyanide and cyanogen.[5] He showed that the cyanide radical, a union of carbon and nitrogen, passed unchanged through a series of reactions closely analogous to those of chlorine or iodine. It was, in fact, "a body which, though compound, acts the part of a simple substance in its combinations with hydrogen and metals." This concept of a radical as a group of atoms that reacted as a unit became a basic idea in the development of organic chemistry.

While Gay-Lussac was thus revealing the possibility that radicals could be transferred as if they were elements, Michel Eugène Chevreul (1786–1889), the only noted centenarian in the history of chemistry, was carrying on his remarkable studies on the composition of natural fats. This work began in 1813 and was summarized in his book *Recherches chimiques sur les corps gras d'origine animale,* published in Paris in 1823. In spite of their early date, these studies have a surprisingly modern character. Chevreul noted that soaps formed by saponification of fats gave rise to crystalline substances when they were treated with acids. He purified these by recrystallization and was among the first to use constancy of melting point as a criterion of purity. He identified a large number of these organic acids, from butyric to stearic, and showed their relationship in the fats to glycerol, which had first been isolated by Scheele. Chevreul also isolated cetyl alcohol (which he called ethal) and cholesterol from some of his fat mixtures. As a result of his work it became clear that a fat was merely a compound of an organic acid with glycerol, a type of union at least formally analogous to an inorganic salt, and that in saponification the glycerol was replaced by an inorganic base. "In this hypothesis, saponification is only the decomposition of a fatty salt by a salifiable base which takes the place of the anhydrous glycerine." Chevreul here indicated strongly that inorganic and organic compounds reacted according to the same laws. He also revealed the fundamental structure of a great class of natural compounds, one of the earliest steps in systematizing biochemistry. The importance of his work has not always been fully appreciated.

In 1823 Liebig studied salts of fulminic acid and published analyses of these in the *Annales de chimie*,[6] of which Gay-Lussac was editor. At almost the same time Wöhler took up the study of the cyanates. When his paper was published in the *Annales*,[7] Gay-Lussac noticed the surprising fact that the analysis of the two sets of salts was the same. This discovery brought Liebig and Wöhler together in a friendship and collaboration that lasted throughout the lives of these two great chemists and resulted in many important discoveries.

A similar case of compounds having the same empirical composition and different properties came with the discovery of butylene by Faraday in 1825 and its comparison with ethylene. In 1830 Berzelius noticed the identity in analysis of tartaric and racemic acids. He had hesitated to accept these relationships, but he now gave up the idea that for every definite chemical composition there was only one compound with one definite set of properties. He recognized that the arrangement of atoms could differ in compounds, resulting in different sets of properties, and he introduced the term "isomerism" (from the Greek, "composed of equal parts") to identify this phenomenon.[8]

The task of the organic chemist was now becoming clearer. It was necessary to identify the various complex groups, or radicals, which passed through different reactions, and to find the relationships among these groups that would explain the facts of isomerism. When possible, the reactions should be related to analogous inorganic reactions.

In 1828 Dumas and Polydore Boullay (1806–1835) attempted to explain the reactions of alcohol by assuming that it was a hydrate of ethylene, C_4H_4. They used the equivalent weight of carbon as 6, so that their formula is the same as the present one, C_2H_4. They ascribed to ethylene an alkaline character and assumed that it formed compounds in the same way as ammonia.[9] Thus, alcohol was $C_4H_4 \cdot H_2O$, ether was $2C_4H_4 \cdot H_2O$, and ethyl chloride was $C_4H_4 \cdot HCl$, just as ammonium chloride was $NH_3 \cdot HCl$.

The strongest support for the radical theory came from the joint work of Liebig and Wöhler on the oil of bitter almonds (benzaldehyde).[10] They carried through a large number of reactions with this substance and showed that in all of them the group $C_{14}H_{10}O_2$ remained unchanged. Owing to Liebig's failure to understand the concept of atomic weight, his formulas are double those used today, and we write this radical C_7H_5O. This radical was named "benzoyl" since it was the radical of benzoic acid, and Liebig and Wöhler adopted the now common termination "yl" from the Greek word *hyle* meaning material.

Berzelius, with his strong desire for order and system, accepted the ideas of Liebig and Wöhler enthusiastically. He added a note to their paper in which he designated the benzoyl radical as Bz and wrote benzoic acid BzO, bitter almond oil BzH, chlorobenzoyl BzCl, and benzamide $BzNH_2$. He called attention to the ethylene radical of Dumas and Boullay, which he named etherin, and showed that this too could give rise to a series of compounds.

With the weight of experimental evidence so strong, and with the very influential support of Berzelius for the radical theory, chemists began to look for radicals in every compound. Liebig explained the nature of alcohol and ether in terms of the radical ethyl: [11] ether is the oxide of ethyl, $C_4H_{10}O$, and alcohol its hydrate, $C_4H_{10}O \cdot H_2O$. This neglect of atomic weights further shows how little Liebig understood their significance. Dumas and E. M. Peligot (1811–1890) worked on wood alcohol and described its radical, methyl. As more and more attempts were made to find new radicals, confusion began to appear.

It was not long before Berzelius realized that he had been premature in accepting the benzoyl radical as a unit. It contained oxygen, the most electronegative element, and the center of his system, as it had been of Lavoisier's. Oxygen could not be considered a relatively unimportant part of a radical. Berzelius now assumed that all radicals had to be composed of carbon and hydrogen, and that such radicals could then unite with oxygen. Thus the dualistic system could be preserved. Benzoyl was $C_{14}H_{10}$. As time went on and new compounds and reactions were discovered, Berzelius was compelled to invent more and more complex radicals to account for the new advances.[12] Soon no one else accepted his ideas, though he himself never abandoned them.

By 1837 it seemed to many chemists that the radical theory was the final answer to the mysteries of organic chemistry. In that year Dumas and Liebig, extending the concept of Lavoisier and his school, published a triumphant paper [13] in which they called radicals the elements of organic chemistry. "In mineral chemistry the radicals are simple; in organic chemistry, the radicals are compound; that is all the difference. The laws of combination and of reaction are otherwise the same in these two branches of chemistry."

Even while Dumas and Liebig were writing these words, however, the discoveries in Dumas' own laboratory were showing that organic chemistry was not quite as simple as this distinction made it appear. In 1834 Dumas announced the results of his study of the action of chlorine on alcohol, with the formation of chloral and chloroform. He showed that the halogens could replace hydrogen in an organic compound with the elimination of an equal volume of halogen acid from the molecule.[14] He referred to his discovery as the "law of substitution" and later named it metalepsy. Dumas did not at once realize the full consequences of his theory, but they were recognized almost immediately by his student Auguste Laurent (1808–1853).[15] Laurent began to study the replacement of hydrogen by chlorine, bromine, and nitric acid in various aromatic compounds. In the course of this work he isolated naphthalene and suggested the name "phene" (Greek meaning "to illuminate") for benzene, which he found in illuminating gas. Although the name did not persist for the hydrocarbon itself, it has been retained in the name of the phenyl radical and in phenol.

Between 1835 and 1840 Laurent repeatedly stressed the idea that hydrocarbons were a "fundamental radical" from which various "derived radicals" could be obtained by substitution reactions. These derived radicals still had essentially the same properties as the fundamental radicals from which they were prepared.

This theory at once aroused Berzelius, to whose dualistic thinking it was inconceivable that electronegative chlorine could replace electropositive hydrogen without completely altering the compound. His vehement attacks alarmed Dumas, who in 1838 declared that his theory of substitution was nothing more than an empirical discovery. He added, "I am not responsible for the gross exaggerations with which Laurent has invested my theory." [16]

Laurent continued to accumulate evidence in support of his views. As he extended and generalized his theory, he antagonized most of the prominent chemists of his time. In addition to Berzelius, Liebig and even Dumas attacked him bitterly. In particular the enmity of Dumas increased as he and Laurent engaged in polemics over the question of priority. Laurent was not at all averse to stating his claims, but his outspokenness had very unfavorable results for him. Dumas by this time had become the most influential chemist in France, and so also in the French Academy of Sciences. In this body was centralized all French science. It controlled all professional advancement for French scientists through its ability to choose the occupants of the important chairs in French universities. Only in Paris were there adequate laboratories. For much of his professional life, Laurent was exiled to provincial universities, and even when he came to Paris he was never able to obtain a satisfactory position. He died at an early age from tuberculosis contracted from the unhealthful laboratory in which he was forced to work.

In spite of these difficulties, Laurent greatly advanced the theoretical ideas of contemporary organic chemistry. As a result of his work, supported eventually by the studies of Dumas on the chlorination of acetic acid and the properties of the resulting trichloroacetic acid, chemists began gradually to accept a unitary theory, in distinction to the dualistic theory of Berzelius. Laurent called his version of the unitary theory the "nucleus theory," since he now called his fundamental radicals "nuclei." He classified all organic compounds in terms of these nuclei and the derived nuclei obtained from them. This classification was adopted by Leopold Gmelin (1788–1853) in his massive textbook of chemistry. In turn it was taken over by Friedrich Beilstein (1838–1906) when he prepared his famous *Handbook of Organic Chemistry*. Thus Laurent's classification of organic compounds has come down to the present, though his rather cumbersome system of names for the various classes has never been adopted by any other chemist.

Dumas eventually accepted the unitary theory, calling it the theory of types. Dumas believed that "there exist in organic chemistry certain types which remain unchanged even when the hydrogen which they contain is replaced by equal volumes of chlorine, bromine, or iodine." [17]

Another version of the unitary theory was proposed by Charles Gerhardt (1816–1856), who collaborated with Laurent in the last years of his life, and who also incurred the enmity of Dumas and the powerful conservatives of the Academy of Sciences. As a result, Gerhardt, like Laurent, was never able to obtain an adequate laboratory for his work. Gerhardt wrote formulas for organic compounds based on a theory of residues. These residues had the same composition as the radicals that the older chemists had assumed were capable of free existence. To Gerhardt the residues were wholly imaginary, useful only to explain organic reactions. They were assumed to be "paired" or "copulated" to build up organic compounds. Gerhardt explicitly stated that his formulas never represented the actual constitution of compounds, but only their reactions. Consequently, the same compound might have different formulas when it took part in different reactions. Gerhardt did not believe that the true constitution of organic compounds could ever be discovered.

In 1843 Gerhardt adopted the so-called "two volume system" in which atomic weights of volatile compounds agreed with the weights of two volumes of hydrogen instead of four, or H_2O instead of H_4O_2, which Liebig had used as his standard and which had resulted in formulas double those now used. Laurent accepted this suggestion of his friend, and went on to distinguish quite clearly between atoms and molecules in the sense of Avogadro. It was only his unpopularity and early death that prevented chemists from accepting his ideas and so realizing the full significance of Avogadro's hypothesis ten years earlier than they actually did.[18]

By about the middle of the nineteenth century, the confusion in organic chemistry had begun to clear somewhat. Although the chemists of the time were not aware of it, they were ready for the decisive steps that would lead to the structural theory of organic compounds. They had already resolved the complicated substances with which they dealt into functional groups, whether these were called radicals, nuclei, or residues. They saw clearly that these groups did not obey the dualistic laws that appeared to be applicable to inorganic compounds. They did not yet see how the radicals themselves were composed.

Such a failure followed logically from the way in which the theories of organic compounds had developed. With the acceptance of the radicals as "organic elements," and more particularly with the appearance of the unitary theory, chemists temporarily lost interest in the old problem of the nature of chemical affinity. They were too busy studying the reactions of organic compounds and attempting to devise schemes of classification in terms of these reactions. The confusion as to equivalent, atomic, and molecular weights caused many investigators to lose interest in atoms as such, and, until this confusion was cleared up, there could be little hope of understanding how atoms were united to one another. It was not until chemists began to ask how the radicals were constructed that they again became interested in atoms. It is not a coincidence that the solution of the problem of chemical constitution was accompanied by a recognition of the value of Avogadro's hypothesis and a gradual return to the question of the nature of affinity.

REFERENCES

1. E. Hjelt, *Geschichte der organischen Chemie*, F. Vieweg und Sohn, Braunschweig, 1916, p. 22.
2. M. Kohn, *Anal. Chim. Acta,* 5, 337–344 (1951).
3. F. Wöhler, *Poggendorfs Ann.,* 12, 253–256 (1828).
4. J. Jacques, *Rev. hist. sci. et leur applications,* 3, 32–66 (1950).
5. J. L. Gay-Lussac, *Ann. chim.,* 95, 136–231 (1815).
6. J. Liebig, *Ann. chim.,* 24, 294–317 (1823).

7. F. Wöhler, *ibid.*, **27**, 196–200 (1824).

8. J. J. Berzelius, *Jahresber. Fortschr. phys. Wiss.*, **11**, 44–48 (1832).

9. J. B. A. Dumas and P. Boullay, *Ann. chim. phys.*, **37**, 15–53 (1828).

10. F. Wöhler and J. Liebig, *Ann.*, **3**, 249–282 (1832).

11. J. Liebig, *ibid.*, **9**, 1–39 (1834).

12. W. Prandtl, *Humphry Davy, Jöns Jacob Berzelius,* Wissenschaftliche Verlagsgesellschaft M.B.H., Stuttgart, 1948, pp. 218–219.

13. J. B. A. Dumas and J. Liebig, *Compt. rend.*, **5**, 567–572 (1837).

14. J. B. A. Dumas, *Ann. chim. phys.*, **56**, 113–150 (1834).

15. Clara de Milt, *Chymia*, **4**, 85–114 (1953).

16. J. B. A. Dumas, *Compt. rend.*, **6**, 647, 699–700 (1838).

17. J. B. A. Dumas, *Ann.*, **32**, 101–119 (1839); **33**, 179–182 (1840); *Compt. rend.*, **8**, 609–622 (1839).

18. M. Daumas, *Chymia*, **1**, 59 (1948).

CHAPTER XIX

ORGANIC CHEMISTRY FROM THE THEORY OF TYPES TO THE STRUCTURAL THEORY

Although Gerhardt did not believe in the reality of radicals, many chemists not only accepted the fact of their physical existence but also tried to isolate them in the free state. The first to feel that he had accomplished this was Robert Bunsen (1811–1899), who began his career as an organic chemist but attained his greatest reputation later in the fields of inorganic and physical chemistry. From 1839 to 1843 Bunsen studied the reactions of the unpleasant-smelling and poisonous cacodyl compounds, derivatives of cacodyl oxide, $C_4H_{12}As_2O$. When he treated cacodyl chloride with zinc he obtained what he considered to be the free cacodyl radical, $C_4H_{12}As_2$, now written $(CH_3)_2As \cdot As(CH_3)_2$.[1] This discovery was taken as the strongest evidence for the existence of free radicals.

In 1849 Hermann Kolbe (1818–1884) electrolyzed potassium acetate and obtained a gas that he believed was free methyl, though it was actually ethane.[2] At about the same time Edward Frankland (1825–1899) treated ethyl iodide with zinc and isolated free "ethyl," actually butane.[3] As a result of such studies, chemists began to abandon the older type theories and to attempt to find at least the position of the radicals in the organic molecules. They did not yet look more deeply into the structure of the radicals themselves. Working chiefly on the principle of analogy, they began to approach the modern structural formula.

Charles Wurtz (1817–1884) was a pupil and friend of Dumas, yet he remained an admirer of the work of Laurent and Gerhardt. He adopted and used ideas from all three men. In 1849 he discovered the primary amines,[4] which he called methyl and ethyl amide. Wurtz recognized that they were derivatives of ammonia in which a hydrogen had been replaced by methyl or ethyl, but he did not develop this idea. His work was taken up by A. W. von Hofmann (1818–1892), who conclusively proved the relation of the amines to ammonia by successively replacing all the hydrogens by organic groups, preparing primary, secondary, and tertiary amines, and then going on to obtain the quaternary ammonium salts.[5] Hofmann assigned these compounds to an "ammonia type."

At about the same time, A. W. Williamson (1824–1904) showed that ethers could be prepared by treating the potassium salt of an alcohol with an alkyl iodide.[6] This showed that Liebig's hydrate theory of the structure of alcohols was incorrect, and permitted the formulation of a "water type." These types were usually represented as shown in the accompanying formulas. It can be seen that this was a true

$$\left.\begin{matrix} H \\ H \\ H \end{matrix}\right\} N \qquad \left.\begin{matrix} C_2H_5 \\ H \\ H \end{matrix}\right\} N \qquad \left.\begin{matrix} C_2H_5 \\ C_2H_5 \\ H \end{matrix}\right\} N \qquad \left.\begin{matrix} C_2H_5 \\ C_2H_5 \\ C_2H_5 \end{matrix}\right\} N \qquad \left.\begin{matrix} C_2H_5 \\ C_2H_5 \\ C_2H_5 \\ C_2H_5 \end{matrix}\right\} NI$$

ammonia type

$$\left.\begin{matrix} H \\ H \end{matrix}\right\} O \qquad \left.\begin{matrix} C_2H_5 \\ H \end{matrix}\right\} O \qquad \left.\begin{matrix} C_2H_5 \\ C_2H_5 \end{matrix}\right\} O$$

water type

approach to a structural formula, though Hofmann and Williamson, thinking of the analogy in a formal sense, did not, of course, realize this.

Gerhardt generalized the "new type theory"[7] by introducing the hydrogen type, which included the hydrocarbons, and the hydrogen chloride type, which included ethyl chloride. These are shown in the accompanying formulas.

$$\left.\begin{matrix} H \\ H \end{matrix}\right\} \qquad \left.\begin{matrix} C_2H_5 \\ H \end{matrix}\right\} \qquad \left.\begin{matrix} C_2H_5 \\ C_2H_5 \end{matrix}\right\} \qquad \left.\begin{matrix} H \\ Cl \end{matrix}\right\} \qquad \left.\begin{matrix} C_2H_5 \\ Cl \end{matrix}\right\}$$

| hydrogen | ethane | butane | hydrogen chloride | ethyl chloride |

hydrogen type   hydrogen chloride type

On the basis of such types, Williamson and Gerhardt wrote acetic acid as a member of the water type:

$$\left.\begin{array}{l} C_2H_3O \\ H \end{array}\right\} O$$

and so foresaw that it should be possible to prepare the compound

$$\left.\begin{array}{l} C_2H_3O \\ C_2H_3O \end{array}\right\} O$$

This would be an "anhydrous acid," an acid anhydride in modern terms. Gerhardt actually prepared such compounds in his laboratory. The formulas of the organic chemist had begun to have predictive value instead of being useful only for purposes of classification. This was the first clear evidence of the approach to the structural theory, in which the prediction of possible reactions is a most important feature.

Kolbe probably brought type formulas closer to structural formulas than did any chemist before Kekule, who gave the modern explanation of structure, and their work was actually overlapping. Kolbe persisted in the use of equivalent weights, $C = 6$ and $O = 8$, until 1870, so that in his formulas C_2 is always equal to C, and O_2 to O in modern usage. This often required that he add an extra OH group to bring his oxygens out at the right number and gives to his formulas a strange appearance, but they are actually very close to the modern ones.

In 1850 he recognized that the acetyl group consisted of a methyl united with another carbon which was the true "point of attack of the binding power of oxygen, chlorine, etc." [8] Somewhat later he formulated the fatty acids as derivatives of carbonic acid which he wrote as the dibasic acid $2HO,C_2O_4$.[9] He replaced one HO (and an O to preserve the equivalent balance) by methyl, which he wrote C_2H_3, to obtain the monobasic methyl carbonic acid, or acetic acid, $HO,(C_2H_3)C_2O_3$. Here he recognized the existence of a special group (carboxyl) that characterized the formulas of all the fatty acids. He further saw that if he replaced the "HOO" group of his acetic acid by H to give $\left.\begin{array}{l} C_2H_3 \\ H \end{array}\right\} C_2O_2$ he obtained the formula for acetaldehyde, and replacement of the H in this formula by another methyl group gave acetone: $\left.\begin{array}{l} C_2H_3 \\ C_2H_3 \end{array}\right\} C_2O_2$. The relations of acids, aldehydes, and ketones were thus made clear, and the carbonyl group was recog-

nized as an entity.   From his formulations it was easy to give a structure for alcohol, which Kolbe wrote as

$$HO \left\{ \begin{array}{c} C_2H_3 \\ H_2 \end{array} \right\} C_2,O$$

This formula permitted the visualization of new classes of alcohols,
obtained by replacing one or both the hydrogens within the brackets
by radicals.   Kolbe predicted the existence of what he called "singly
and doubly methylated" alcohol:

$$HO \left\{ \begin{array}{c} C_2H_3 \\ C_2H_3 \\ H \end{array} \right\} C_2,O \qquad HO \left\{ \begin{array}{c} C_2H_3 \\ C_2H_3 \\ C_2H_3 \end{array} \right\} C_2,O \ ^{[10]}$$

The first secondary alcohol, isopropyl, was prepared by Charles Friedel
(1832–1899) in 1862, and the first tertiary alcohol, tertiary butyl, by
Alexander Mikhailovich Butlerov (1828–1886) in 1864.   Again it can
be seen that these approximations to the modern structural formula
had predictive value.

Kolbe's student and collaborator Frankland went beyond the ideas
of his master.   His studies on metallo-organic compounds showed that,
in the case of nitrogen, phosphorus, arsenic, and antimony, an atom
of these elements always combined with three or five organic radicals.
Zinc, mercury, and oxygen combined with two.   This led him in
1852 [11] to the discovery that "no matter what the character of the
uniting atoms may be, the combining-power of the attracting element,
if I may be allowed the term, is always satisfied by the same number
of these atoms."   This term, combining-power, was variously expressed
by his contemporaries as atomicity or affinity units.   The name valence
was introduced by C. W. Wichelhaus (1842–1927) in 1868.   Thus a
concept of the utmost importance to chemistry in general was first
utilized in an attempt to clarify the nature of organic compounds.   It
served once more to direct the attention of organic chemists to the
problem of affinity, as the term "affinity units" suggests.   For the time
being, little attention was paid to the cause of valence, but the idea of
a limited number of valence centers and their possible orientations
led to many important advances.

Organic chemistry had now reached the point at which the inner
constitution of the radicals could be considered.   Almost simultaneously this problem was attacked independently by Friedrich August
Kekule (1829–1896) in Germany, and Archibald Scott Couper (1831–

1892) in Paris, to which he had come from Scotland to work in the laboratory of Wurtz.

Kekule found the solution to the old puzzle in the recognition of the atomicity of carbon. In 1858 he showed that carbon was "tetratomic," that is, had four "affinity units" by which it could unite with four monatomic elements like hydrogen and two diatomic elements like oxygen. The decisive step was the recognition that a carbon atom could use one of its affinity units to unite with another carbon atom, and that each would then have three units to combine with other atoms. In this way chains of carbon atoms could be built up, and a carbon skeleton became the basis for organic compounds.[12] In his textbook of organic chemistry published in 1861, Kekule was able to define the science in the modern way as the chemistry of carbon compounds. All traces of vitalism disappeared with this statement, though vitalism itself was by no means dead. The carbon chain theory gave an explanation for the law of homology that Gerhardt had introduced when he showed that a long series of similar compounds such as alcohols or acids differed from each other only by the increment of CH_2.

Couper developed essentially the same theory as Kekule[13] and expressed his affinity bonds by lines as is done today instead of by a diagrammatic representation, which Kekule at first used, and which was not as convenient for a visualization of the actual structure. Couper's work remained unnoticed, but in 1861 Alexander Crum Brown (1838–1922) at the University of Edinburgh, and in 1864 Wurtz in Paris, used essentially the modern graphic formulas.

A. M. Butlerov espoused the cause of the new theory with great enthusiasm and worked out many of the consequences. He stressed strongly the fact that there was but one formula for a given compound, instead of the various formulas that Gerhardt and others had used, depending on the various reactions of compounds. Butlerov introduced the term "chemical structure" in 1861 at a chemical meeting at Speyer in Germany. His textbook of organic chemistry, published in Russian in 1864 and translated into German in 1868, was the first book that actually used the new formulas throughout. It did much to popularize the new theory.[14]

The nature of aliphatic compounds was now satisfactorily explained, but the structure of aromatic substances remained a mystery. This was dispelled by Kekule in 1865.[15] His remarkable power of visualizing the structure of carbon skeletons in organic compounds was perhaps due to his early training in architecture. At any rate, in an idle moment he pictured to himself a carbon chain bending and uniting with itself to form a ring. From this he deduced the structure of benzene and the nature of the whole system of aromatic compounds. When his student Wilhelm Körner (1839–1925) showed that the number of isomeric trisubstituted benzenes derived from each of the disubstituted benzenes indicated the *ortho-, meta-,* or *para*-structures of the latter,[16] the essential reference compounds needed to determine the structures of more complex organic compounds became available.

A few further concepts made possible most of the later developments in structural chemistry. Crum Brown in 1864 wrote a double bond for ethylene, and Lothar Meyer (1830–1895), noted for his later work on the periodic table, referred to it as "unsaturated" in a book published in the same year. Emil Erlenmeyer (1825–1909) in 1862 recognized the triple bond in acetylene. Butlerov in 1876 gave examples of tautomerism, and in 1885 its theory was independently developed by Peter Conrad Laar (1853–1929) of Hanover, who suggested the name for this phenomenon.[17] Kekule believed that carbon was always quadrivalent, but evidence of its divalence gradually accumulated, especially in America. The studies of John Ulric Nef (1862–1915) at Chicago at the end of the nineteenth century finally proved the existence of the divalent state. In 1900 Moses Gomberg (1866–1947), who was born in Russia but carried out his scientific work at the University of Michigan, prepared compounds containing trivalent carbon.[18] The idea of the constant quadrivalence of this element was finally abandoned.

The formal structural theory made no allowance for the influence of neighboring groups on the reactivity of the various parts of organic molecules. V. V. Markovnikov (1838–1904), a student of Butlerov, was once asked, "Why is it that chlorine in acetyl chloride is so different from that in ethyl chloride?"[19] To answer such questions he studied the effect of various groupings on the position taken by the halogen and hydrogen of a halogen acid when it saturated a double bond. Markovnikov's rule,[20] which embodied the results of his studies, was the earliest forerunner of the extended studies on the effect of electron structure on organic reactions which have occupied much of the first half of the twentieth century.

Kekule, like the other chemists of his day, made no attempt to explain the forces that held atoms together, but his architectural sense led him to picture the valence bonds as definite and concrete. This idea was extended by Jacobus Henricus van't Hoff (1852–1911)[21] and J. A. Le Bel (1847–1930),[22] who pictured the four bonds as uniformly directed in space. Van't Hoff considered the carbon atom to be tetrahedral, and both used geometrical ideas in their work.

This extension of structural ideas into three dimensions permitted an explanation of the findings of Louis Pasteur (1822–1895). In 1848 [23] he had studied isomeric salts of tartaric acid, which rotated the plane of polarized light in opposite directions. He found that crystals of these optically isomeric salts were mirror images of each other. Van't Hoff and Le Bel independently and within two months of each other showed that when a carbon atom has four different groups around it, that is, is asymmetric, a new type of isomerism is possible. In such compounds, the two isomers had structures that were mirror images of one another, and these isomers actually showed the type of opposite rotation that Pasteur had observed. Van't Hoff further showed that when the molecule contained a double bond, as in fumaric and maleic acids, another type of isomerism, cis-trans isomerism, existed. The application of these ideas was largely due to the work of Johannes Adolf Wislicenus (1835–1902), who popularized this new field of stereochemistry.

The most important practical use of stereochemical ideas was the explanation of the structure of the isomeric sugars given by Emil Fischer (1852–1919). His work furnished the basis for all carbohydrate chemistry. Other stereochemical ideas of importance were the strain theory of Adolf Baeyer (1835–1917),[24] which explained the stability of ring compounds in terms of the distortion of their valence bonds from the normal angles of the tetrahedral carbon atom, and the theory of steric hindrance of Victor Meyer (1848–1897), which showed that large groups substituted in organic compounds could prevent reactions on neighboring carbon atoms simply because of their size.[25] At the end of the nineteenth century, W. J. Pope (1870–1939) showed that asymmetric compounds of nitrogen, sulfur, and selenium could be prepared. Alfred Werner (1866–1919) found complex compounds of platinum, cobalt, and similar elements that also showed optical isomerism. Thus, stereochemistry was a general phenomenon, not restricted to carbon compounds.

On the basis of the theoretical concepts that have been described, chemists have been able to elucidate the structures of some of the most complex of the naturally occurring organic compounds, and to synthesize hundreds of thousands of previously unknown substances with absolute certainty as to their constitution. It is probable that the development of organic chemistry within the last one hundred years represents the most remarkable use of logical reasoning of a non-quantitative type that has ever taken place. The men who developed this field were usually not well trained in physics, and the intense preoccupation with organic chemistry during the nineteenth century tended to widen the breach between chemists and physicists that had begun at the end of the eighteenth century. Nevertheless, physical chemistry of the modern type had its beginnings at this same time. For most of the century the workers in the two branches held somewhat apart. A certain antagonism existed between those who followed the logic of mathematics and those who pursued the logic of organic chemistry. It has been the task of the twentieth century to bring these two essentially inseparable branches together once more.

REFERENCES

1. R. Bunsen, *Ann.*, **31**, 175–180 (1839); **37**, 1–57 (1841); **42**, 14–46 (1842); **46**, 1–48 (1843).
2. H. Kolbe, *ibid.*, **69**, 257–294 (1849).
3. E. Frankland, *J. Chem. Soc.*, **2**, 265 (1849).
4. C. A. Wurtz, *Compt. rend.*, **28**, 223–226 (1849).
5. A. W. von Hofmann, *Phil. Trans.*, **1851**, 357–397.
6. A. W. Williamson, *Phil. Mag.*, **37**, 350–356 (1850).
7. C. Gerhardt, *Ann. chim.*, **37**, 285–342 (1853).
8. H. Kolbe, *Ann.*, **75**, 211–239 (1850).
9. H. Kolbe, *ibid.*, **101**, 257–265 (1857).
10. H. Kolbe, *ibid.*, **113**, 293–332 (1860).
11. E. Frankland, *Phil. Trans.*, **142**, 417–444 (1852).
12. A. F. Kekule, *Ann.*, **106**, 129–159 (1858).
13. A. S. Couper, *Compt. rend.*, **46**, 1157–1160 (1858).
14. H. M. Leicester, *J. Chem. Educ.*, **17**, 203–209 (1940).
15. A. F. Kekule, *Ann.*, **137**, 129–196 (1865).
16. W. Körner, *Gazz. chim. ital.*, **4**, 305–446 (1870).
17. P. C. Laar, *Ber.*, **18**, 648–657 (1885).
18. M. Gomberg, *J. Am. Chem. Soc.*, **22**, 757–771 (1900).
19. H. M. Leicester, *J. Chem. Educ.*, **18**, 54 (1941).
20. V. V. Markovnikov, *Ann.*, **153**, 259 (1870).
21. J. H. van't Hoff, *Arch. néerl. sci.*, **9**, 445–454 (1874).
22. J. A. Le Bel, *Bull. soc. chim., France*, **22**, 337–347 (1874).
23. L. Pasteur, *Compt. rend.*, **26**, 535–538 (1848).
24. A. Baeyer, *Ber.*, **18**, 2269–2281 (1885).
25. V. Meyer, *Ber.*, **27**, 510–512, 1584–1592 (1894).

CHAPTER XX

THE SYSTEMATIZATION OF

INORGANIC CHEMISTRY

While the great development of organic chemistry was taking place, a smaller number of chemists continued to devote themselves to the older discipline of inorganic chemistry. Some of these men also worked in the new field of physical chemistry, and, as has been seen, many of the advances of organic chemistry had a wider significance for chemistry as a whole. As a result of all these factors, the foundations for great progress in general chemistry were laid during the nineteenth century.

New elements were discovered in increasing numbers. During the first half of the century, the standard chemical methods of the time were employed, particularly by Berzelius and his students. The isolation of sodium and potassium by Davy supplied a powerful tool for the isolation of new metals, owing to the great reactivity of these alkali metals. The disadvantage of their use was that metals prepared with their help were seldom very pure. Berzelius used fusions of metal oxides with potassium to isolate crude silicon (1824), zirconium (1824), titanium (1825), and thorium (1828). A. A. Bussy (1794–1882) obtained magnesium (1831) and beryllium (1828), also isolated at the same time by Wöhler. Hans Christian Oersted (1777–1851), the Danish physicist best known for his discovery of the magnetic effect of the electric current, obtained aluminum in 1825, and Wöhler repeated the isolation in 1827. Almost all these metals were obtained in purer form later in the century, often by the use of electrolytic methods.[1]

During the same period most of the platinum metals were discovered and the halogen family was completed with the exception of the violently reactive fluorine, which was not obtained free until 1886, when Henri Moissan (1852–1907) used an electrolytic method for its isolation.[2] A beginning was made in unraveling the complexities of the rare earths, but the early studies, chiefly by Johann Gadolin (1760–1852), Carl Gustav Mosander (1797–1858), and Berzelius, were not extended until nearly the end of the century, when Carl Auer von Welsbach (1858–1929) and others isolated a number of rare earths.

The discovery of a new element by purely chemical methods required that a relatively large amount of the element be present in the mixture from which it was to be isolated. Many of the more uncommon elements were present in minerals in such small amounts that, when their presence was not suspected, there was little likelihood of finding them. This situation was greatly changed by the discovery of spectroscopic analysis in 1859. In that year, Bunsen, who had now turned away from organic chemistry, undertook a systematic study of the effects produced by various elements on the color of a flame. He worked with the physicist Gustav Robert Kirchhoff (1824–1887). This was the first important example of the collaboration of scientists in such fields since the work of Lavoisier and Laplace on calorimetry.

A. S. Marggraf in 1758 had noticed the colors that sodium and potassium salts produce in a flame. In 1822 the astronomer Herschel (1792–1871) observed the bright lines and dark spaces in the spectra from such flames. Bunsen and Kirchhoff built a new instrument, the spectroscope,[3] with which to map these lines accurately. They showed that each element had characteristic lines that were not affected by the presence of other elements. Minute traces of an element were sufficient to give its characteristic spectrum. This work furnished a new tool of unprecedented sensitivity for indicating the presence of new elements in different minerals. Bunsen quickly applied it in the discovery of the new alkali metals cesium (1860) and rubidium (1861), which he named from the beautiful blue and red lines in their respective spectra.

Not only were new elements discovered frequently during this period, but also the accuracy of determination of their equivalent or atomic weights was improved. The most careful work in this field was done by Jean Servais Stas (1813–1891) in Brussels. The precision and attention to minute details that characterized his work have seldom been exceeded. In spite of the confusion in the minds of most chemists as to the significance of the values determined by Stas, his numerical data were accepted as extremely accurate. They seemed to give the deathblow to Prout's hypothesis, for very few of the combining weights were whole numbers.

When Avogadro put forward his hypothesis there were hardly enough facts available to make a thorough test of its validity. This was one of the important reasons for its long neglect. As the needed facts accumulated, the lack of an adequate theory to explain them created an almost unbelievable confusion. Attempts such as those of Gerhardt and Laurent to resolve this confusion did not succeed, and by 1860 the situation was so bad that nearly every chemist was using his own method of writing formulas. In his textbook of organic chemistry, Kekule devoted nearly a whole page to the various formulas then suggested for acetic acid, nineteen in all.[4]

Wishing to clear up this confusion, Kekule decided that a meeting of chemists from all countries should be called to attempt to find agreement on disputed points. His friend Carl Weltzien (1813–1870) agreed to organize a congress of chemists at Karlsruhe, and Wurtz joined them as one of the sponsors. This meeting, the first International Chemical Congress, assembled on September 3, 1860.[5] The members, with one exception, did not come prepared to do more than discuss the general problems of chemistry. As might have been expected, their discussion did not lead to any positive decisions. The one exception was Stanislao Cannizzaro (1826–1910), professor of chemistry at the University of Genoa. Cannizzaro was thoroughly familiar with the hypothesis of his countryman Avogadro, and he had used it regularly in his chemical course at Genoa. He had published an account of this course in the official journal of the University of Pisa,[6] and he brought reprints of this paper with him to Karlsruhe.

During the Congress he spoke strongly in favor of Avogadro's hypothesis, especially as it had been used by Gerhardt, and at the end of the session, when the chemists were leaving for home apparently in as great confusion of mind as when they had come, his friend Angelo Pavesi of the University of Pavia distributed his reprints. In his paper Cannizzaro reviewed the historical development of the concept of atoms and molecules, starting from the hypothesis of Avogadro, and showing how various parts of this had been accepted by Berzelius, Dumas, and Gerhardt, but that it had been accepted completely by no one. He then went on to show the results of a complete acceptance, so that atomic weights were referred to the weight of half a *molecule* of hydrogen taken as unity, or to the density of hydrogen taken as 2, so that the weights of the molecules were all represented by the weight of one volume. In this way Cannizzaro was able to give a correct table of the molecular weights of many compounds. The few apparent exceptions to the rule that the vapor densities of gases could be used in determining the molecular weights fell into line after Henri Sainte-Claire Deville (1818–1881) showed that at high temperatures many compounds could dissociate into their constituents, which could then exist together in the vapor.[7]

The ideas of Cannizzaro soon began to spread. The most influential convert to the Avogadro hypothesis was Lothar Meyer. In 1864 he published his book *Die modernen Theorien der Chemie und ihre Bedeutung für die chemische Statik* at Breslau. The book was based on the ideas explained by Cannizzaro, and it became very popular. It was not long before almost all chemists accepted the distinction between atoms and molecules and the modern table of atomic weights based on this distinction.

With new assurance, organic chemists could now build up their complex structures on the basis of the clear and logical rules of the behavior of atoms and molecules. The inorganic chemists had no such positive assurances. It was obvious that there were relations between the various elements, but there was no overall generalization that told how many elements to expect, or how to predict as yet undiscovered elements and their properties. Yet a body of empirical facts had accumulated that appeared to offer hope of systematization, and several attempts had been made to achieve one.

The first attempt to generalize the relations between the elements became possible only when a considerable number had been discovered. Early in the nineteenth century enough were known to permit the recognition among them of certain groups that were obviously characterized by the analogous reactions of their members. The halogens, the alkali metals, and the platinum group showed these analogies clearly. At the same time, the atomic weights determined by Berzelius gave a set of numerical values in terms of which some classification might be sought.

Johann Wolfgang Döbereiner (1780–1849) undertook such a classification in 1829 when he noted that there were often three members in a group with similar chemical properties.[8] Among such "triads" were chlorine, bromine, and iodine; calcium, strontium, and barium; sulfur, selenium, and tellurium; iron, cobalt, and manganese; and several others. In every case, the atomic weight of the middle member of the triad was approximately the arithmetic mean of the weights of the other two elements. Dumas extended these observations, but the theory had value only as a method of classification. As long as the confusion as to atomic and equivalent weights continued, no further classification in terms of these properties was possible.

After the clarification of this problem by Cannizzaro there were several attempts to use the atomic weights as a basis for systematization. In 1862 and 1863 the French geologist A. E. Béguyer de Chancourtois (1819–1886) arranged the elements in the order of their atomic weights as a spiral around a cylinder. He pointed out that the halogens fell in a straight line on the side of this "telluric helix." His work remained unnoticed. John Alexander Reina Newlands (1837–1898), after arranging the elements according to atomic weight, observed that elements belonging to the same group usually appeared on a horizontal line when a new column was started with every eighth element. Newlands, who had had musical training, called this the "law of octaves." His arrangement was received with some ridicule. Nevertheless, the idea of periodic repetition was implicit in the arrangements of both de Chancourtois and Newlands.

As happened so often with the statement of important chemical theories in the nineteenth century, the periodic law was announced almost simultaneously from the independent work of two men, the German Lothar Meyer, and the Russian Dmitriĭ Ivanovich Mendeleev (1834–1907). Both developed their ideas while preparing textbooks. Meyer's *Modern Theories of Chemistry* contained the germ of his theory, and he expanded his ideas until in 1868 he had drawn up his table in nearly final form. He did not publish it until 1870,[9] after Mendeleev's version had already appeared.[10] Mendeleev had been writing his famous textbook, *Principles of Chemistry* (St. Petersburg, 1868–1870), which ran through many editions in Russian, German, English, and French. It was while systematizing his ideas for this book that Mendeleev devised his periodic table. Following publication of the Russian paper that described it, a German translation appeared almost at once.[11] It is possible that Meyer modified his version somewhat after seeing the form used by Mendeleev, and it is also likely that the later version of Mendeleev was influenced by the publication of Meyer's table. There is no doubt that both men are equally entitled to the honor of the discovery, and each acknowledged this.

Both arranged the elements in the order of increasing atomic weight and noted the periodic recurrence of properties in families of elements. Meyer was particularly struck by the periodicities of physical proper-

Ueber die Beziehungen der Eigenschaften zu den **Atomgewichten** der Elemente. Von D. Men d e l e j e f f. — Ordnet man Elemente nach zunehmenden Atomgewichten in verticale Reihen so, dass die Horizontal-reihen analoge Elemente enthalten, wieder nach zunehmendem Atomge-wicht geordnet, so erhält man folgende Zusammenstellung, aus der sich einige allgemeinere Folgerungen ableiten lassen.

				Ti = 50	Zr = 90	? = 180
				V = 51	Nb = 94	Ta = 182
				Cr = 52	Mo = 96	W = 186
				Mn = 55	Rh = 104,4	Pt = 197,4
				Fe = 56	Ru = 104,4	Ir = 198
			Ni = Co = 59	Pd = 106,6	Os = 199
H = 1				Cu = 63,4	Ag = 108	Hg = 200
	Be = 9,4	Mg = 24	Zn = 65,2	Cd = 112	
	B = 11	Al = 27,4	? = 68	Ur = 116	Au = 197 ?
	C = 12	Si = 28	? = 70	Sn = 118	
	N = 14	P = 31	As = 75	Sb = 122	Bi = 210 ?
	O = 16	S = 32	Se = 79,4	Te = 128 ?	
	F = 19	Cl = 35,5	Br = 80	J = 127	
Li = 7 Na = 23	K = 39	Rb = 85,4	Cs = 133	Tl = 204
	Ca = 40	Sr = 87,6	Ba = 137	Pb = 207
	? = 45	Ce = 92		
	?Er = 56	La = 94		
	?Yt = 60	Di = 95		
	?In = 75,6	Th = 118 ?		

1. Die nach der Grösse des Atomgewichts geordneten Elemente zeigen eine stufenweise Abänderung in den Eigenschaften.

2. Chemisch-analoge Elemente haben entweder übereinstimmende Atom-gewichte (Pt, Ir, Os), oder letztere nehmen gleichviel zu (K, Rb, Cs).

3. Das Anordnen nach den Atomgewichten entspricht der *Werthigkeit* der Elemente und bis zu einem gewissen Grade der Verschiedenheit im chemischen Verhalten, z. B. Li, Be, B, C, N, O, F.

4. Die in der Natur verbreitetsten Elemente haben *kleine* Atomgewichte

Fig. 15.   First form of Mendeleev's periodic table.   (From *Zeitschrift für Chemie*, 12, 405 (1869).)

ties such as atomic volumes, whereas Mendeleev devoted most of his attention to the periodicity of chemical properties. Both left vacant spaces where an element should fit into a family group but where such an element was not yet known. This was a great advance over previous attempts, in which such spaces had not been left. Mendeleev was bolder in speculation than Meyer. He ventured the statement that, if the atomic weight of an element caused it to be placed in the wrong group of the table, the value must be incorrect. Meyer was reluctant to take such a step.[12] In most instances Mendeleev was cor-rect in applying this rule, but in the case of iodine and tellurium, the order of atomic weights is actually reversed. This could not be explained until the discovery of isotopes.

In a still more important respect Mendeleev placed more confidence in the table than did Meyer. He was so impressed with the periodicity of the elements that he felt able to predict the chemical and physical properties of the elements that should occupy the vacant places in his table.[13] In particular he selected three vacancies to discuss in detail. These spaces lay below the elements boron, aluminum, and silicon. Using the Sanskrit prefix *eka,* meaning one, he named his hypothetical substances eka-boron, eka-aluminum, and eka-silicon. He gave their approximate atomic weights, valences, and the types of compounds they would form. It was an astonishing example of confidence, and the vindication resulted in final acceptance of the periodic law.

For some time after the two versions of the table had appeared, chemists failed to pay much attention to them. Then, in 1874, Lecoq de Boisbaudran (1838–1912) discovered a new element spectroscopically[14] and named it gallium. Mendeleev showed that it was the eka-aluminum he had predicted.[15] Table 1 shows the close agreement between predicted and observed properties.

TABLE 1

Eka-aluminum	Gallium
Predicted	*Observed*
Atomic weight: about 68	Atomic weight: 69.9
Metal of specific gravity 5.9; melting point low; nonvolatile; unaffected by air; should decompose steam at red heat; should dissolve slowly in acids and alkalies.	Metal of specific gravity 5.94; melting point 30.15; nonvolatile at moderate temperatures; not changed by air; action of steam unknown; dissolves slowly in acids and alkalies.
Oxide: formula Ea_2O_3; specific gravity 5.5; should dissolve in acids to form salts of the type EaX_3; the hydroxide should dissolve in acids and alkalies.	Oxide: formula Ga_2O_3, specific gravity unknown; dissolves in acids forming salts of the type GaX_3; the hydroxide dissolves in acids and alkalies.
Salts should have a tendency to form basic salts; the sulfate should form alums; the sulfide should be precipitated by H_2S or $(NH_4)_2S$. The anhydrous chloride should be more volatile than zinc chloride. The element will probably be discovered by spectroscopic analysis.	Salts readily hydrolyze and form basic salts; alums are known; the sulfide is precipitated by H_2S and by $(NH_4)_2S$ under special conditions. The anhydrous chloride is more volatile than zinc chloride. Gallium was discovered with the aid of the spectroscope.

Shortly afterward, in 1879, Lars Fredrik Nilson (1840–1899) discovered scandium,[16] which was shown by Per Theodore Cleve (1840–

1905) to be eka-boron.[17]   In 1885 Clemens Alexander Winkler (1838–1904) isolated germanium.[18]   For a time there was doubt as to the exact position of this element in the periodic table, but at length Winkler showed from the physical properties that this was eka-silicon. The comparison of physical properties was particularly convincing, as Table 2 shows.

TABLE 2

	Eka-silicon	Germanium
Atomic weight	72	72.32
Specific gravity	5.5	5.47
Atomic volume	13	13.22
Valence	4	4
Specific heat	0.073	0.076
Specific gravity of dioxide	4.7	4.703
Molecular volume of dioxide	22	22.16
Boiling point of tetrachloride	Under 100°	86°
Specific gravity of tetrachloride	1.9	1.887
Molecular volume of tetrachloride	113	113.35

After these convincing demonstrations, the table was generally accepted and its importance in systematizing inorganic chemistry and limiting the number of possible elements was recognized.   Ever since, it has been a fundamental building block of chemistry.

The table was not perfect in its original form, nor could it be markedly improved until in the twentieth century it was discovered that it was actually based on values more fundamental than atomic weights. For example, besides the misplaced elements iodine and tellurium, the rare-earth group did not fit well into the table.   Nevertheless, it seemed that all valence groups fell in a logical order, and there was no room for any new families of elements.   Therefore, the surprise was great when a new family was actually discovered.   John William Strutt, Baron Rayleigh (1842–1919), in 1892 found that the gas prepared by removing all other known gases from nitrogen of the air had a greater density than nitrogen prepared from its compounds.[19] William Ramsay (1852–1916) suspected that some new gas might be present.   By passing atmospheric nitrogen over red-hot magnesium he removed the nitrogen, leaving a small amount of a nonreacting gas. This recalled the experiment of Cavendish in 1785 (p. 144).   Cavendish had passed an electric spark repeatedly through a mixture of oxygen and nitrogen from air, and after removing the reacted gases had found a residue of gas "not more than $\frac{1}{120}$ part of the whole." [20]   Lord Rayleigh repeated the experiment and confirmed the results of Cavendish. Working with large amounts of air, Rayleigh and Ramsay [21] in 1895 isolated the new gas and showed that it did not combine with any other element. The gas was named argon. Ramsay then looked for a larger source of such an inert gas. He learned that certain minerals that contained uranium also contained quantities of a gas that had been examined by W. F. Hillebrand (1853–1925) in America, and that he had decided was nitrogen. Ramsay obtained some of this gas and found that it was not nitrogen, nor was it argon. Spectroscopic examination gave the astonishing result that it showed a spectral line identical with one that had been observed in 1868 in the spectrum of the sun by the astronomers P. J. C. Janssen (1824–1907) and J. N. Lockyer (1836–1920). Lockyer had decided that it was due to a new element, not known on earth, which he named "helium." Ramsay had now found this element on earth.[22]

There seemed to be no place for these new elements in the periodic table, but at length Ramsay ventured to suggest that they formed a new family, the zero group, in the table, that is, they had a valence of zero. Search for the other members of the group soon led to their discovery: krypton, neon, and xenon, all in 1898. They were obtained by fractional distillation of liquid air. The last member of the family, radon, was isolated from thorium by Lord Rutherford (1871–1937) in 1900.[23] He first called it "emanation." It was finally identified as a member of the inert-gas family by Rutherford and Frederick Soddy (1877–   ).

The systematization of organic and inorganic chemistry was almost complete by the end of the nineteenth century, and both branches had advanced chiefly by purely chemical methods. The progress that had been made in physical chemistry during the century had had relatively little influence on the rest of chemistry. The tremendous discovery of atomic structure, with which the twentieth century opened, not only served to give a new direction and a new impetus to inorganic and organic chemistry but also united them more closely with physical chemistry. The three branches were once more brought together in this work.

REFERENCES

1. M. E. Weeks, *The Discovery of the Elements*, 2nd ed., Journal of Chemical Education, Easton, Pa., 1934, pp. 128–179.

2. H. Moissan, *Compt. rend.*, **102**, 1543–1544 (1886).

3. G. R. Kirchhoff and R. Bunsen, *Poggendorfs Ann.*, **110**, 161–189 (1860).

4. A. Kekule, *Lehrbuch der organischen Chemie*, Vol. 1, p. 58, F. Enke, Erlangen, 1861.

5. Clara de Milt, *Chymia*, **1**, 153–169 (1948).

6. S. Cannizzaro, *Nuovo cimento*, **7**, 321–366 (1858).

7. H. Sainte-Claire Deville, *Compt. rend.*, **45**, 857–861 (1857).

8. J. W. Döbereiner, *Poggendorfs Ann.*, **15**, 301–307 (1829).

9. Lothar Meyer, *Ann., Supplementband*, **7**, 354–364 (1870).

10. D. I. Mendeleev, *J. Russ. Chem. Soc.*, **1**, 60–77 (1869).

11. D. I. Mendeleev, *Z. Chem.*, **12**, 405 (1869).

12. H. M. Leicester, *Chymia*, **1**, 73 (1948).

13. D. I. Mendeleev, *J. Russ. Chem. Soc.*, **3**, 25–56 (1871); *Ann. Supplementband*, **8**, 133–229 (1872).

14. L. de Boisbaudran, *Compt. rend.*, **81**, 493–495 (1875).

15. D. I. Mendeleev, *ibid.*, **81**, 969–972 (1875).

16. L. F. Nilson, *ibid.*, **88**, 645–648 (1879).

17. P. T. Cleve, *ibid.*, **89**, 419–422 (1879).

18. C. A. Winkler, *J. prakt. Chem.*, **34**, [2], 177–229 (1886).

19. Lord Rayleigh, *Nature*, **46**, 512–513 (1892).

20. Thorpe, *Scientific Papers of the Hon. Henry Cavendish*, Vol. 2, p. 193, The University Press, Cambridge, 1921.

21. Lord Rayleigh and W. Ramsay, *Phil. Trans.*, **186A**, 187–241 (1895).

22. W. Ramsay, *Proc. Roy. Soc.*, **58**, 65–67 (1895).

23. Lord Rutherford, *Phil. Mag.*, **49**, 1–14 (1900).

CHAPTER XXI

Physical Chemistry

IN THE NINETEENTH CENTURY

The three major fields of progress in physical chemistry during the nineteenth century were kinetic theory, thermodynamics, and electrochemistry. In addition, other phases of the subject such as photochemistry and colloid chemistry began to develop, though their major advances did not come until the next century.

The developments in kinetic theory and thermodynamics ran parallel and had their basis in the physics of the early nineteenth century. As has been noted, most chemists of this time were not aware of the new discoveries in physics. Absorbed in the non-quantitative logic of organic chemistry, they disregarded the mathematical laws whose discovery and application were the leading characteristics of the sister science. The physicists, in turn, pursued their own path, using chemical materials, it is true, but attempting to generalize from the specific substances they used to ideal gases, liquids, and solids whose properties and controlling laws should be valid in every case.

Occasionally, a chemist would make an observation that was taken up and used by the physicists, but when this occurred, other chemists paid little attention to the results achieved. Thus, the fact observed by Gay-Lussac in 1807 that a gas expanding into a vacuum and so doing no work shows no change in temperature was utilized by the physicists but not by the chemists. The law relating the volume of a gas to its temperature was formulated by Jacques Alexandre César

Charles (1746–1823) about 1787. Dalton and Gay-Lussac had calculated approximate values for the constant in the expression of this law, but the value of $\frac{1}{273}$, nearly that accepted today, was determined by the physicist Henri Victor Regnault (1810–1878).

An idea of great importance, that of dynamic equilibrium, was suggested by Pierre Prévost (1751–1839) in relation to the absorption and radiation of heat by bodies. It was only gradually that the generalization of this idea to chemical processes occurred, but once it was accepted by chemists the way was opened for many new advances.

The search for an explanation of affinity continued to be a driving force for chemical discovery. It has been seen that the non-mathematical organic chemists, having rejected the idea that the opposite electrical charges of Berzelius accounted for affinity, had given up all attempts to explain its nature and merely used the term "affinity units" for their valence bonds. To a few chemists the newly emerging energetic concepts of the physicist seemed to offer a better approach to an understanding of affinity. In this approach too the ultimate cause of chemical attraction was neglected and was not taken up again until the twentieth century. The new approach proved exceedingly fruitful in other respects, however.

Wenzel in 1777 tried to measure affinity by noting the rate at which metals dissolved in acids. The method did not accomplish what Wenzel hoped, but it was perhaps the first study of reaction rates. The investigations of Berthollet, also made in part in an attempt to study affinities, were essentially studies of the effect of equilibrium conditions on the reacting substances. Neither of these two investigations succeeded in casting much light on affinity. It was not until 1850 that such studies were resumed. In that year Ludwig Wilhelmy (1812–1864) studied the hydrolysis of cane sugar in the presence of acids, using the change in optical rotation of the solution to measure the degree of inversion.[1] He showed that, if Z represented the concentration of sugar, the sugar loss (dZ) in the time interval dT was given by the expression $-dZ/dT = kZ$. This equation for a monomolecular reaction was the first mathematical expression for a chemical process.[2]

Contemporaneously with Wilhelmy, Williamson had seen that when a reaction produces substances at a definite rate, and when these substances in turn react at a definite rate to regenerate the starting materials, a time must come when a balanced equilibrium is reached. This concept of dynamic equilibrium did not at once become popular with chemists, and the work of Wilhelmy was continued by Marcellin

Berthelot and L. Péan de St. Gilles (1832–1863) with the old limitations of thought. They studied the kinetics of esterification of acids and alcohols, again with the idea of measuring the affinity relations of the reactants. Since only the formation of esters was studied, and not their hydrolysis, Berthelot and Péan de St. Gilles failed to recognize the dynamic equilibrium involved in these reactions.

The true significance of the concept was realized by the Norwegian scientists Cato Maximilian Guldberg (1836–1902) and Peter Waage (1833–1900). In a pamphlet published in Norwegian in 1863 they put forward the law of mass action on which so much of modern chemistry is based. The work was virtually ignored even when it was published in French in 1867.[3] A number of special cases of the law were described during this time by van't Hoff and others. Therefore in 1879 Guldberg and Waage published a full statement of their theory in a leading German journal,[4] and since that time they have received credit for their work.

Although they considered affinity forces to be responsible for chemical combination, they introduced such forces into their formulation of the law of mass action only as constants that had little bearing on the significance of their work. The importance of the theory lay in their recognition that the concentration of the reacting substances constituted the "active mass" that determined the equilibrium resulting from the forward and reverse reactions. By their realization of the importance of concentration and of the concept of dynamic equilibrium, they completed the work begun sixty years before by Berthollet.

The remaining fundamental ideas required to prepare chemical kinetics for its modern development appeared at about the same time. In 1877 van't Hoff, who had turned from organic chemistry to the newly recognized field of physical chemistry, classified reactions in terms of the number of molecules taking part. He thus defined the various orders of reaction and so helped to clarify the picture of reaction mechanisms.[5] At about the same time Svante Arrhenius (1859–1927) saw that not every molecular collision, even in a bimolecular reaction, led to reaction. He therefore proposed the concept of "active molecules" and of activation energy.[6] On the basis of these ideas kinetics became a recognized branch of chemistry and contributed greatly to an understanding of the actual course of chemical reactions.

It had been known long before this period that certain reactions proceeded much faster in the presence of small amounts of a foreign substance and that this substance remained apparently unchanged no matter what happened to the other materials involved. Even before such a phenomenon was recognized experimentally, its existence had been assumed by the chemical philosophers. The action of the philosopher's stone in the minds of the alchemists, or the "ferments" by which bodily processes were controlled in the opinion of the iatro-chemists, were certainly typical of phenomena that would today be considered catalytic.

The first purely chemical description of a catalytic process was given by Charles Bernard Désormes (1777–1862) and Nicolas Clément (1779–1841), who in 1806 suggested a theory of the formation of sulfuric acid in the lead chamber process.[7] They recognized that oxygen was carried by the oxides of nitrogen to the sulfur without any loss of nitric acid in the reaction. They thus proposed the theory of intermediate compound formation at the very beginning of the study of catalytic effects.

In the years that followed, many other examples of catalysis were investigated, including the hydrolysis of starch in the presence of acid, studied by Gottlieb Sigismund Kirchhoff (1764–1833), and the oxidation of organic compounds in the presence of metallic surfaces, studied by a number of chemists, including Humphry Davy and his cousin Edmund Davy (1785–1857). This line of work led to the discovery by Döbereiner in 1822 that oxygen and hydrogen combined in the presence of finely divided platinum.[8]

The various observations on the subject of catalysis were scattered through the literature. It remained for the great organizer of chemistry, Berzelius, to draw them together and propose a unifying theory. In 1836 he reviewed all the examples with which he was familiar and suggested that some new force was acting in all these cases. He was not sure what this force was, though he believed it was in some way related to his electrochemical affinities. He suggested that it be called "catalytic force" and the operation of this force "catalysis," from the Greek for decomposition, by analogy with the term analysis.[9]

Theories of the mechanism of this force remained vague, though the idea of intermediate compound formation was never lost. Williamson explained the catalytic formation of ether from alcohol in the presence of sulfuric acid by such a mechanism in 1850.[10] The idea of a mysterious force involving, as the concept of energy entered the minds of chemists, some sort of change in energy state of the molecules concerned remained a very popular theory also.

The modern view of a catalyst as a substance that increases reaction rates without altering the general energy relations of a process was finally stated by the father of physical chemistry, Wilhelm Ostwald

(1853–1932), in 1894.[11] It is interesting that Ostwald presented his theory in the abstract of an article on the heat of combustion of foods. Ostwald prepared the abstract for his own journal. After describing the theory of catalysis proposed by the author of the original article, he criticized it and then gave his own theory. The modern chemist would hardly look in *Chemical Abstracts* for the original presentation of an important new theory. Ostwald's views on catalysis finally related this phenomenon to the field of kinetics. Since his time, catalytic processes have become increasingly important, especially in industry.

None of the nineteenth century pathways to an understanding of affinity that have been discussed so far led to a clear idea of the subject or offered a quantitative approach. The organic chemist merely assumed its existence and made no attempt to explain or measure it. The student of chemical kinetics found too many extraneous factors in his subject to obtain a clear picture. It was through the work of the thermochemists and the application of the principles of thermodynamics as developed by the physicists that a quantitative evaluation of affinity forces was finally obtained.

Following the wide acceptance by chemists of Lavoisier's theory of caloric, they neglected thermochemical studies for nearly fifty years. Meanwhile, the physicists were busy. They became interested in the various manifestations of energy, and their viewpoint was the very opposite of that of the chemists'. They used chemical substances only in order to generalize from their properties to the ideal states of solids, liquids, and gases. The actual variations from the ideal state that were encountered were simply nuisances that made more difficult the proof of the fundamental mathematical laws governing the behavior of bodies. Since it is necessary to know the ideal to which the actual approaches, this phase of physics was a very necessary step in the development of science, but it did not tend to heal the breach between physicists and the chemists who were studying the properties of individual substances.

The kinetic theory of heat, almost universally accepted in the seventeenth century, re-established itself in the physics of the early nineteenth. Benjamin Thompson (1753–1814), one of the earliest American scientists, who did most of his work in Europe and was made Count Rumford by the Elector of Bavaria, cast doubt on the caloric theory when he showed in 1798 that an indefinite amount of heat was produced by the friction of boring a cannon. In 1799 Davy claimed that the heat capacity of the water produced by rubbing pieces of ice together was greater than that of the ice. Clément and Désormes in 1819 showed experimentally that the compressions of air in a sound wave did not follow Boyle's law because the heat produced by the compression did not have a chance to escape. Gradually, physicists realized that heat was a form of energy, and so should behave like the other forms of energy that they studied. The interconvertibility of such forms of energy as electricity, magnetism, heat, and chemical action was demonstrated. Nicolas Léonard Sadi Carnot (1796–1832), a young French military engineer, in his classical study of the steam engine [12] laid the foundations of thermodynamics and introduced the idea of perfectly reversible conditions. After 1840, rapid progress was made in this field.

Benoît Paul Emile Clapeyron (1799–1864) put Carnot's conclusions in analytical form. In 1842 the German physician Robert Mayer (1814–1887), impressed by the red color of venous blood in the tropics, realized that less combustion was needed in hot climates to produce the energy needed by the body.[13] From this observation he was led to derive the law of the conservation of energy, which had been implicitly assumed in much of the previous work in this field. Its implications were fully developed in 1847 by Hermann Helmholtz (1821–1894).[14] The mechanical equivalent of heat was determined in 1845 by James Prescott Joule (1818–1889), an English brewer. In 1850 Rudolf Clausius (1822–1888), and in 1851 William Thomson, later Lord Kelvin (1824–1907), working on the basis of the theories of Carnot and Clapeyron and the law of the conservation of energy, derived the second law of thermodynamics, which showed the impossibility of obtaining an unlimited amount of heat from a Carnot engine. From his work, Thomson had been led to recognize the existence of an absolute zero, implied in Charles' law, and so to set up the absolute or Kelvin scale of temperature. In 1845 Clausius restated the second law in terms of "entropy," [15] which always increases in any but a reversible change. In 1865 he suggested this name and offered his well-known summary of the two laws: "1. The energy of the world is constant. 2. The entropy tends to a maximum." [16] Much of kinetic theory followed from thermodynamics, though it was not until statistical methods were later applied that the full significance of these relationships was realized.

By 1860, then, the physicists had evolved a whole new science of thermodynamics, but it was not yet integrated with the thermochemical studies that had been made about the same time. The physiological investigations of Lavoisier, Laplace, and Séguin had rested implicitly on the concept of the conservation of energy, which was probably carried over by Lavoisier from his demonstration of the conservation of matter. No more work was done along this line until 1840.

In that year, Germain Henri Hess (1802–1850) in St. Petersburg published a study of the heats of various reactions that showed that the same amount of overall heat was evolved no matter how many intermediate steps took place before a final product was obtained.[17] This law of the constant summation of heat was actually a special case of the law of conservation of energy announced by Mayer two years later.

Based on this law, a great number of determinations of the heats of different reactions were made by the Dane Julius Thomsen (1826–1909) and the Frenchman Marcellin Berthelot, another organic chemist who turned to physical chemistry. To Berthelot we owe the terms "endothermic" and "exothermic." Both Thomsen and Berthelot concluded that in the measurement of heats of reaction there had at last been found a quantitative measure of affinity. Berthelot stated this as his "principle of maximum work": "all chemical changes occurring without intervention of outside energy tend toward the production of bodies or of a system of bodies which liberate more heat." [18] This work was criticized almost at once by Helmholtz, and later it was shown by Walther Nernst (1864–1941) in his heat theorem, or third law of thermodynamics,[19] that Berthelot's principle holds true only near absolute zero. After Berthelot announced it, much controversy followed, and important thermochemical work was performed as a result.

The first step in transferring the thermodynamics of the physicist to the work of the chemist was taken in 1869 by August Friedrich Horstmann (1843–1929). He applied the concept of entropy to a study of the sublimation of ammonium chloride [20] and showed that the process followed the same laws as those involved in vaporization of a liquid. Hence the Clausius-Clapeyron equation could be applied.

One of the greatest contributions to chemical thermodynamics was the comprehensive paper of Josiah Willard Gibbs (1839–1903), professor of mathematical physics at Yale University. His study on the equilibrium of heterogeneous substances [21] contains a wealth of ideas. His concept of chemical potential was of the greatest significance. The most famous part of his paper is the phase rule, which relates the number of components (C) or individual substances in a system, and the number of phases (P), such as gas, liquid, or solid, to the number of degrees of freedom (F), such as temperature, pressure, or concentration, at equilibrium, by the equation

$$F = C + 2 - P$$

Unfortunately the obscurity of the *Transactions of the Connecticut Academy of Sciences,* the journal in which he published his paper, and the rigorous mathematical form in which he expressed his ideas prevented a general recognition of their true significance, except by a few specialists such as the physicist James Clerk Maxwell (1831–1879), who in turn explained its importance to J. D. van der Waals (1837–1923). The work was finally translated into German by Ostwald in 1892, and into French by Henri Le Châtelier (1850–1936) in 1899, and it then became known to the scientific world. The importance of the phase rule was pointed out in a series of papers by the Dutch chemist H. W. B. Roozeboom (1854–1907) after van der Waals had told him of the work. Since the beginning of the twentieth century the value of the theories of Gibbs has been appreciated and his work has been continued.

Before this happened, however, van't Hoff had shown chemists how thermodynamics could be applied to their science, especially with reference to ideas of affinity. In his work in 1884 he first drew the distinction between chemical kinetics and chemical thermodynamics and showed that the maximum external work obtained when a chemical reaction was carried out reversibly and isothermally could serve as a measure of chemical affinity.[22] Helmholtz even earlier [23] had called such maximum work "free energy." Gilbert Newton Lewis (1875–1946), of the University of California, proposed that this term be restricted to mean the work available for use. Thus, the maximum useful work obtained when one system passes spontaneously into another represents the decrease in free energy of the system. The influential textbook of G. N. Lewis and Merle Randall (1888–1950) [24] which presents these ideas has led to a replacement of the term "affinity" by the term "free energy" in much of the English-speaking world. The older term has never been entirely replaced in thermodynamic literature, since after 1922 the Belgian school under Théophile De Donder (1872–   ) has made the concept of affinity still more precise.[25]

This thermodynamic concept of affinity, which became dominant at the end of the nineteenth century, represented a change in the thinking of chemists on this subject. They no longer thought of the affinity between atoms, but of the affinity for certain chemical processes. Like all thermodynamics, it was a statistical concept. Thus, there was little relation between the affinity of a follower of thermo-dynamics and that of an organic chemist. Interest in explaining the nature of the affinity between atoms was revived only when interest in the atoms themselves was renewed by the work on atomic structure in the twentieth century. It is significant that some of the leading workers in thermodynamics, such as Ostwald, were not convinced of the existence of atoms.

The thermodynamic laws investigated by van't Hoff were chiefly derived from the behavior of perfect gases and required various cor-rections when applied to actual gaseous individuals. Van't Hoff made another major contribution when he realized that these gas laws ap-plied also to substances in extremely dilute solutions. Infinitely dilute solutions behaved like ideal gases; more concentrated solutions re-quired corrections like actual gases. This work was founded on studies of osmotic pressure.

In 1748 the Abbé Nollet (1700–1770) found that water diffused through an animal membrane into a sugar solution. Attempts to measure the pressures thus built up were made by R. J. H. Dutrochet (1776–1847) in 1826. He concluded that the pressure was proportional to the concentration of the solutions used. Thomas Graham noticed that some substances would not diffuse through such a membrane and laid the foundations of the science of colloid chemistry by distinguish-ing between the colloidal and crystalloidal states of matter on the basis of their diffusion behavior.[26]

The animal membranes used for such studies were of variable pore size. More accurate studies of osmotic effects became possible in 1867 when Moritz Traube (1826–1894) described the preparation of arti-ficial membranes of a colloid deposited in the walls of a porous pot. The botanist William Pfeffer (1845–1920) used such membranes to con-firm that osmotic pressure depends on concentration and increases with the temperature.

The studies of Pfeffer attracted the attention of van't Hoff, who in 1885 showed that the laws of osmotic pressure were the same as the gas laws provided that the solutions used were very dilute. His first pub-lications on this subject were in relatively obscure journals, but after his German publication of 1887 [27] his work became well known.

François Marie Raoult (1830–1901) in 1882 re-investigated the work done in 1788 by Charles Blagden (1748–1820) on the lowering of the freezing point of liquids in which substances were dissolved. Raoult showed that the depression of the freezing point was proportional to the molecular concentration of the solute. In 1887 he showed a simi-

lar effect with relation to the vapor pressure of solutions.[28]   The
results of these observations not only gave a new and important
method for determining molecular weights but they were also shown
to depend on the osmotic properties of solutions, and so fitted into the
theories of van't Hoff.

The laws of osmotic pressure derived by van't Hoff were found to
hold true when the solute was an organic substance such as cane
sugar, but they did not apply to aqueous solutions of acids, bases, and
salts.   These solutions always behaved as if they were more concentrated than they actually were.   The same effects, as might be expected, were noted by Raoult in his work.   It was known that osmotic
effects depended on the number of particles in solution, just as gas
pressures depended on the number of gas molecules in a given space.
Ever since the work of Deville on the thermal dissociation of substances, which he began in 1857,[29] it had been realized that under
proper conditions chemical compounds could dissociate and recom-
bine.   Therefore it seemed probable that some form of dissociation
must be occurring in these anomalous solutions.   They were in all
cases solutions that conducted the electric current, and so it seemed
that there must be some special property of electrolytes that would
account for these results.   Even the genius of van't Hoff did not find
the explanation.   The answer came from the study of the electrical
properties of electrolytes in solution.

In 1805 Theodor von Grotthuss (1785–1822) had suggested that,
when a potential was applied to a solution, chains of molecules were
formed that passed oppositely charged particles along to the electrodes.
Faraday accepted this theory in general and by his formulation of the
terminology of electrolyte and ions gave the suggestion that the application of the current caused the electrolyte to break up into ions.
Here the matter rested, while most chemists were busy with studies
of non-electrolytes, the organic compounds.

Some progress was made in sources of current during this time.
John Frederick Daniell constructed his battery with electrodes of
copper and zinc in copper sulfate solution, separated by a porous
ceramic cylinder.   This gave a constant current for a longer time than
had previously been obtainable.   R. Gaston S. Planté (1834–1889) invented the storage battery in 1859.

In 1839 Daniell showed that salts were not composed of metallic
oxides and acid anhydrides, as Berzelius had believed, but of metallic
ions and acid ions.   This idea was slowly incorporated even into structural organic chemistry.   Daniell used the Faraday concept of ions in

arriving at his explanation. This concept was considerably expanded by Johann Wilhelm Hittorf (1824–1914), who studied the transport of ions in solution. He developed the idea of transport numbers and showed that each ion had a characteristic rate of migration during electrolysis.[30] He came very close to the dissociation theory in his statement, "The ions of an electrolyte cannot be combined in a stable form to whole molecules, and these cannot exist in a definite, regular arrangement." [31] He correctly explained the ionic nature of complex salts. Unfortunately his ideas were so foreign to the minds of most of the chemists of his time that he was forced to engage in numerous controversies and he never made the final step, which was taken by Arrhenius.

Williamson in 1851 [32] and Clausius in 1857 [33] had seen that electrolyte molecules in solution were constantly dissociating and recombining, but the idea that oppositely charged particles could remain separated in the same solution was more than either chemists or physicists could understand.

In 1876 Friedrich Kohlrausch (1840–1910) moved a step nearer to a comprehension of this fact when he showed that the velocity of ions in a solution is not affected by the presence of oppositely charged ions. He developed his method of measuring the conductivities of solutions with an alternating current,[34] a method that proved very helpful in the later studies of Arrhenius.

All the necessary data for the final synthesis were now at hand. The dissociation theory was announced to the Swedish Academy of Sciences by Svante Arrhenius in 1883, and the theory in final form was published in 1887.[35] The essential feature of this theory was that, when an electrolyte was dissolved, it immediately dissociated. Ions were always present in solution, whether or not a current flowed. This at once explained not only the facts of electrolytic conduction developed by Hittorf, Kohlrausch, and others, but also the osmotic anomalies observed by Raoult and van't Hoff. The assumption of Arrhenius that weak electrolytes were only partly dissociated permitted application of the law of mass action to their solutions. Other observations, such as those of Ostwald on the strengths of acids and bases, and the results of studies on the heat of neutralization of acids and alkalies, in which the only essential reaction was the formation of water, were also explained. Nernst developed his theories of solution pressure and electromotive force,[36] as well as his ideas on the common-ion effect,[37] in terms of the dissociation theory.

Although acceptance of the Arrhenius theory was slow at first, since it had to overcome preconceived ideas of the impossibility of the sep- arate existence of oppositely charged ions in solution, the enthusiasm and influence of Ostwald and van't Hoff helped to make it widely known. Its own merits at length made its acceptance almost complete. Few generalizations in chemistry have proved as fruitful as the dis- sociation theory.

The three major branches of physical chemistry that developed dur- ing the nineteenth century were each worked out first in terms of ideal substances under ideal conditions. Subsequent work was neces- sary to make the laws in these branches applicable to actual chemical substances. Much of the later activity in each branch consisted in doing this. In the field of kinetics, van der Waals developed the equation that accounted for the effect of attraction and volume of gas molecules on the pressure-volume relationship. The idea of fugacity has been introduced into thermodynamics. The behavior of solutions of strong electrolytes has been considered by Peter Debye (1884–   ) and Erich Hückel (1896–   ). Many other examples could be cited. Nevertheless, none of these modifications, however important, has changed the basic principles of the various fields.

Even more important than the modifications of these branches, es- pecially in the twentieth century, has been the tendency toward their unification. The ideas and methods of each have enriched and ad- vanced those of the others until they are no longer distinct, but form an accepted and working part of modern physical chemistry which uses all of them in solving its problems.

In addition to those parts that were well established by the end of the nineteenth century, a number of other phases of physical chem- istry began at this time but had to wait until the twentieth before they showed fuller development. One example of such a branch has already been mentioned, the science of colloid chemistry, founded by Graham.

Another was photochemistry, which received its first great impetus from the quantitative work of Robert Bunsen and his English co- worker, Henry Enfield Roscoe (1833–1915). In studying the action of light on the reaction between hydrogen and chlorine, they showed, in the years from 1855 to 1859, that the amount of chemical change was proportional to the intensity of the absorbed radiation multiplied by the time through which it acts.[38]

Hermann Kopp (1817–1892), in addition to being a distinguished historian of chemistry, made fundamental studies on the relation be- tween chemical structure and physical properties such as boiling point or specific volume.[39] This was one of the first attempts to bring together physical and organic chemistry.

By the end of the nineteenth century, the classical branches of chemistry, inorganic, organic, and physical, were well developed, but were more or less independent of one another. Their adherents tended to follow them with a somewhat jealous individuality. It is interesting that Kekule and Clausius were colleagues and friends for a time at Bonn, but neither was influenced in his work or ideas by the other.[40] The greatest overall advance that seems to have been made in the twentieth century lies, as has been said, in bringing these branches into a whole to which each contributes its own particular materials and approach.

REFERENCES

1. L. Wilhelmy, *Poggendorfs Ann. Physik*, **81**, 413–433, 499–526 (1850).
2. W. Ostwald, *Lehrbuch der allgemeinen Chemie*, Vol. 2, part 2, p. 69, 2nd ed., W. Engelmann, Leipzig, 1896–1902.
3. C. M. Guldberg and P. Waage, *Études sur les affinités chimiques*, Impr. de Brøgger & Christie, Christiana, 1867.
4. C. M. Guldberg and P. Waage, *J. prakt. Chem.*, [2] **19**, 69–114 (1879).
5. J. H. van't Hoff, *Ber.*, **10**, 669–678 (1877).
6. S. Arrhenius, *Z. physik. Chem.*, **4**, 226–248 (1889).
7. C. B. Désormes and N. Clément, *Ann. chim. phys.*, **59**, 329–339 (1806); see also P. Lemay, *Chymia*, **2**, 45–49 (1949).
8. J. W. Döbereiner, *Schweigers J. Chem. Phys.*, **38**, 321–325 (1823).
9. J. J. Berzelius, *Ann. chim. phys.*, **61**, 146–151 (1836).
10. A. W. Williamson, *Phil. Mag.*, **37**, 350–356 (1850).
11. W. Ostwald, *Z. physik. Chem.*, **15**, 705–706 (1894).
12. S. Carnot, *Reflexions sur la puissance motrice du feu et sur les machines propres à développer cette puissance*, Bachelier, Paris, 1824.
13. E. Farber, *Isis*, **45**, 3–9 (1954).
14. H. Helmholtz, *Ueber die Erhältung der Kraft*, G. Reimer, Berlin, 1847.
15. R. Clausius, *Poggendorfs Ann. Physik*, **93**, 481–506 (1854).
16. R. Clausius, *ibid.*, **125**, 400 (1865).
17. G. H. Hess, *ibid.*, **50**, 385–404 (1840).
18. M. Berthelot, *Ann. chim. phys.*, [5] **4**, 6 (1875).
19. W. Nernst, *Göttinger Nachrichten*, **1906**, 1–39.
20. A. F. Horstmann, *Ber.*, **2**, 137–140 (1869).
21. J. W. Gibbs, *Trans. Conn. Acad. Sci.*, **3**, 108–248, 353–524 (1875–1878).
22. J. H. van't Hoff, *Études du dynamique chimique*, F. Muller & Co., Amsterdam, 1884.
23. H. Helmholtz, *Sitzber. kgl. preuss. Akad. Wiss., Berlin*, **1882**, 22–39.
24. G. N. Lewis and M. Randall, *Thermodynamics and the Free Energy of Chemical Substances*, McGraw-Hill Book Co., New York, 1923.
25. P. Van Rysselbergh, *Acad. roy. Belg., Bull. classe sci.*, [5] **35**, 209–216 (1949).
26. T. Graham, *Phil. Trans.*, **151**, 183–224 (1861).
27. J. H. van't Hoff, *Z. physik. Chem.*, **1**, 481–508 (1887).

28. F. M. Raoult, *Compt. rend.*, **95**, 1030–1033 (1882) ; **104**, 1430–1433 (1887).

29. H. Ste.-Claire Deville, *ibid.*, **45**, 857–861 (1857).

30. J. W. Hittorf, *Poggendorfs Ann. Physik,* **89**, 177–211 (1853); **98**, 1–33 (1856); **103**, 1–56 (1858); **106**, 337–411, 515–586 (1859).

31. J. W. Hittorf, *ibid.*, **103**, 53 (1858).

32. A. W. Williamson, *Ann.*, **77**, 45–47 (1851).

33. R. Clausius, *Poggendorfs Ann. Physik*, **101**, 338–360 (1857).

34. F. Kohlrausch, *Göttinger Nachrichten*, **1876**, 213–224; *Poggendorfs Ann. Physik*, [n.f.] **6**, 1–51, 145–210 (1879).

35. S. Arrhenius, *Z. physik. Chem.*, **1**, 631–648 (1887).

36. W. Nernst, *ibid.*, **4**, 129–181 (1889).

37. *Ibid.*, **4**, 372–383 (1889).

38. R. Bunsen and H. E. Roscoe, *Poggendorfs Ann. Physik*, **96**, 373–394 (1855); **100**, 43–88, 481–516 (1857); **101**, 235–263 (1857); **108**, 193–273 (1859).

39. H. Kopp, *Compt. rend.*, **41**, 186–190 (1855).

40. R. Anschutz, *August Kekule,* Vol. 1, p. 379, Verlag Chemie, Berlin, 1929.

CHAPTER XXII

The Development of Chemistry as a Profession During the Nineteenth Century

Before taking up the discovery of radioactivity and its striking effects on chemical ideas, it is well to consider the great change in chemistry in the last century not so much in relation to its place as a scientific discipline as in relation to its effects on the individual chemist and on the society in which it flourished.

At the beginning of the century the medical and pharmaceutical influences on chemistry were still strong. Professional chemists were few in number and were considered as individuals, not as members of a distinctive group. At the end of the century chemistry was a profession in its own right, with its own training schools and with assured positions for the graduates of these schools. The organization of chemistry and the dissemination of chemical knowledge had become important activities of chemists. No story of chemistry would be complete without some consideration of how this came about in the course of a single century.

As the eighteenth century closed, France was the world center of chemistry. In part this was due to the overwhelming reputation of Lavoisier, but the brilliant circle of chemists who succeeded him, men such as Berthollet, Gay-Lussac, Chevreul, and Dumas, continued to attract French and foreign students to their laboratories. In spite of their activity, however, these men did not found schools. They were individuals, and their students continued the tradition. They combined industrial and academic work in a stimulating manner, but they did not build up a following large enough to replace themselves either in industrial laboratories or academic positions.

Many important industrial processes, such as the Leblanc method of soda manufacture or the extraction of sugar from beets, began in France, yet as the century advanced all the advantages with which France began did not prevent a shift of chemical leadership to Germany. It is probable that the highly centralized organization of French science was in part responsible for this shift. All important activities in chemistry and the other sciences were supervised by the Academy of Sciences, and only in Paris were there adequate laboratory facilities. The provincial universities had neither funds nor buildings for chemical research. The same men often held several important chairs in different Parisian institutions. When, as occasionally happened, men of genius were banished to the provinces, they had no favorable working conditions, and, impelled by the traditions of their nation, they did not try to develop any. Instead they spent their lives trying to arrange for a transfer back to Paris. Laurent and Gerhardt, who gained the enmity of the powerful Dumas, and through him of the Academy of Sciences, were never able to achieve positions suitable to their abilities. Their greatest accomplishment was to succeed as well as they did under very unfavorable conditions. Centralization of power over the lives of scientists was a vital weakness in French science.

The early years of the century were still the period of great personalities. Berzelius dominated the opening decades; Dumas and Liebig, the latter part of the first half of the century. New journals were founded to take care of the increasing load of manuscripts, and these journals usually bore the names of individual editors. The journals of Poggendorf and Schweigger were well known and respected by chemists and physicists of the day, and the *Annalen der Pharmacie,* founded in 1832, always had Liebig as one of its editors. At his death it was given the name it bears today, *Justus Liebigs Annalen der Chemie.* It became the leading chemical journal of the mid-century. Later it established the policy of publishing only papers on organic chemistry, and it is still a leading journal in that field.

Yet the day of individualism was passing. The accumulation of chemical literature was so great that in 1830 it was necessary to found an abstract journal, the *Pharmaceutisches Central-Blatt,* which became successively the *Chemisch-Pharmaceutisches Centralblatt* in 1850 and the *Chemisches Centralblatt* in 1856. These title changes reflect the relative importance of the two sciences in chemistry, since the journal always abstracted the chemical literature. In 1897 the German Chemical Society assumed responsibility for its publication and thus set the pattern for society control of such expensive necessities as are the abstract publications. The model has been followed and expanded by the American Chemical Society and *Chemical Abstracts*, which began publication in 1907.

During the eighteenth century, Germany was divided politically and almost every small state had its own university. Whereas French scientists were concentrated in Paris, German scientists were scattered throughout their country. The monolithic form of French science favored the activities of the leading chemists, but it did little to foster the growth of a body of chemists who could carry on the less spectacular parts of chemical research upon which chemistry began to rely more and more as the science advanced to more difficult problems.

When Liebig, after studying in Paris with Dumas, returned to Germany as professor of chemistry at Giessen at the age of twenty-one, he established the first truly effective teaching laboratory of chemistry in the world. It was the beginning of the shift in chemical balance from France to Germany. In Liebig's laboratory young men were given an organized training in the methods of chemical research. It was no longer the master-apprentice system that had prevailed for so long. Now the main problem was set by the professor, and a number of students worked in their own way on different phases of it. As these students completed their work and went out into other positions, they carried with them not only an interest in the work of the professor but also a common bond with the other students who had worked with them. The number of students in chemistry was also increased by this system, so that there were many more chemists in Germany than in France, where the system of individualized instruction continued.

The Liebig system soon spread from Giessen. Liebig's students occupied the majority of chairs in Germany and many foreign universities, and the young doctors of chemistry began to seek employment in the newly developing chemical industries. Such industries, founded on chemical research, began to grow throughout Germany. Reflecting the chemistry of the time, these industries were devoted chiefly to organic compounds. The Industrial Revolution had begun in England, and England retained her position as the first industrial power of the world through most of the nineteenth century, but the English industries depended little on chemistry for their advances. It is true that the leading producers of metallurgical goods and textiles used chemical methods, but these were seldom the result of systematic research. Organic chemistry was not prominent in British industry. Though the first synthetic dyestuff, mauve, was discovered in England by William Henry Perkin (1838–1907) when he was only eighteen, the dye industry expanded and remained in German hands until the First World War.

Such growth was largely due to the increasing number of research chemists produced by the German universities. As the laboratories of the great drug and dye industries grew, the professors who had trained the chemists were retained as consultants. They not only guided the development of the plants along scientific lines but they also took back to their own laboratories the problems they encountered in industry. With these, they trained new groups of students. In the industrial laboratories they found increasing numbers of intermediates, substances prepared as part of the syntheses of specific new compounds. These intermediates, studied in the university laboratories, often served as starting points for completely new syntheses. By the end of the century Germany was predominant in both theoretical and industrial chemistry, and the stimulating blend of pure and applied science brought students from all over the world to the German universities.

In spite of the great ability of many of her chemists as individuals, France was not able to keep pace with these developments. Her position in the chemical world steadily declined. In England, with her tradition of the amateur scientist who pursued his own interests regardless of the fashions that prevailed around him, chemistry maintained a more even development. Chemistry was never centralized in England as it was in France. Edinburgh and Manchester were chemical centers as well as London. Moreover, the English did not devote themselves so exclusively to organic chemistry as did the continental chemists. Men like Faraday and Graham followed their own lines of investigation. Often their results were not fully understood for many years.

The English scientist was an individualist in his own right, but he had long been accustomed to meeting his fellow scientists for discussion of problems of mutual interest. It was in England that another major step was taken in the development of chemistry as a profession. The first national chemical society was founded there in 1841. There had been local chemical societies at an earlier date, those in Philadelphia in 1789 and 1792 being among the first.[1] With the founding of the Chemical Society of London and the establishment of its *Journal* in 1847, the pattern of organized chemistry that has since become dominant was determined. The great nations soon followed the British example, and societies and their journals were founded throughout the world. Among the most important were the Société chimique de Paris (founded in 1857) with its *Bulletin* (begun in 1858), the Deutsche chemische Gesellschaft (1867) with its *Berichte* (1867), the Russian Chemical Society (1868) and its *Journal* (1869) (now the *Journal of General Chemistry*), the Italian Chemical Society (1871) and the *Gazzeta* (1871), and the American Chemical Society (1876) and its *Journal* (1879). All these journals are still published. Many of the most important papers of today appear in them.

As chemistry grew more and more complex, various special branches developed so greatly that they began to require journals of their own. Organic chemistry grew up in such close contact with chemistry as a whole that it was hardly realized that it constituted a special branch. The first conscious attempt to set up an autonomous subdivision of chemistry was made by Wilhelm Ostwald on behalf of physical chemistry. He drew together the scattered observations in this field in his great textbook, *Lehrbuch der allgemeinen Chemie* (Leipzig, 1884–1887). More important, he founded one of the first truly specialized journals, the *Zeitschrift für physikalische Chemie,* in 1887. With the enthusiastic support of van't Hoff and Arrhenius, the new science was established. Subsequently the other major branches established journals in organic and inorganic chemistry and in biochemistry. Later still, special topics within the main divisions began to publish journals, and periodicals on colloids, electrochemistry, radiochemistry, and others appeared. This represents the split, psychological as well as scientific, between the practitioners of different phases of chemistry. There is legitimate reason for some of the divisions, but, as has been noted, there is now a tendency to reunite some of the divergent branches.

With the advance of the century, the dominance of Germany, England, and France as the most important chemical centers began to be challenged. The Scandinavian countries and Holland had always been important, but now other countries began to produce first-rank chemists.

Russia in the nineteenth century produced a group of native scientists. In earlier years all scientific activity of that vast country had centered in the Academy of Sciences in St. Petersburg. This situation, reminiscent of France, was even worse because the Academy was under the control of foreign scientists, chiefly Germans who had been appointed because of the lack of Russian scientists. At the start of the century, however, the provincial Russian universities, led by the University of Kazan, began to develop as separate research centers. Russian scientists studied abroad and returned to occupy chairs in their own schools. The result was a flowering of Russian science in the second half of the century, which produced such men as Mendeleev, Butlerov, and Markovnikov.[2]

The United States was too busy expanding into the spaces of the West to develop her chemical activities to any great degree before the middle of the century. Such scientific work as was done was performed in the older settled communities along the Atlantic coast. In Revolutionary times, and for some decades afterwards, Philadelphia was the scientific center of the country. Such men as Benjamin Rush (1746–1813)[3] and Robert Hare (1781–1858), who discovered the oxyhydrogen blowtorch,[4] were among the earliest chemists. Willard Gibbs was one of the greatest American scientists of the century, but he lived and worked in isolation and had little influence on American chemistry. The American universities did not become centers of chemical research until after the opening of the Johns Hopkins University in 1876. It was consciously modeled after the German universities, and from this center the idea of university research spread. The professor of chemistry at Johns Hopkins, Ira Remsen (1846–1927), was most influential in introducing the German system into America.

In almost all countries chemistry remained an academic pursuit. This was because Germany had gained such an advantage in chemical industry and could produce chemical intermediates, dyes, drugs, and perfumes so cheaply that no other nation considered it worth while to compete. The First World War awoke these nations with a shock. Cut off from their sources of supply, they struggled frantically to build their own industries. After 1920 these attempts became more and more successful. Chemical industries are now among the most important manufacturing concerns in all industrialized countries.

There has even been a tendency for the pendulum to swing far in the opposite direction. In the past there was often too much academic research and too little applied. In some countries at present the applied research has taken precedence over the basic studies upon which it depends. This tendency, together with the greatly increased nationalism in science since the Second World War, will undoubtedly influence future developments in chemistry.

REFERENCES

1. W. Miles, *Chymia*, **3**, 95–113 (1950).
2. H. M. Leicester, *J. Chem. Educ.*, **24**, 438–443 (1947).
3. W. Miles, *Chymia*, **4**, 37–77 (1953).
4. E. F. Smith, *The Life of Robert Hare, an American Chemist (1781–1858)*, J. B. Lippincott Company, Philadelphia, 1917.

RADIOACTIVITY AND ATOMIC

STRUCTURE

As the end of the nineteenth century approached, many physicists and chemists had come to believe that the major discoveries of science had been made. Newtonian physics supplied a picture of the world on which the physicist could build a quite satisfactory structure, while the chemist, with his indivisible atoms and fixed elements, had at last abolished all traces of alchemy. He was free to spend his time preparing new compounds and studying their properties and reactions. It was still true, however, that the physicist needed a better understanding of electricity, the last of the old imponderable fluids, and the increasing number of discoveries in the field of spectra lacked a generalized explanation. The chemist did not yet comprehend the nature of the affinity forces that held his molecules together. These problems, it was felt, would probably yield in time to the classic methods of the two sciences. Yet it was the solution of these problems that revolutionized the whole outlook of science and, in a period of about twenty-five years, produced results the consequences of which have changed not only science but also our whole way of life.

As early as 1675, Jean Picard (1620–1682) had noticed that when a column of mercury was shaken in a vacuum it produced a phosphorescent glow. At the beginning of the eighteenth century Francis Hauksbee (?–1713) showed that the glow was due to the production of electricity by friction of the mercury on the walls of the glass tube in which it was contained.[1] In 1785 an English amateur scientist, William Morgan, passed an electric current through an evacuated glass vessel and observed the production of a glow.[2] His observation was extended in 1836 by Faraday, who saw that the light in the tube came from the cathode. The light was produced more easily as the pressure in the tube was lowered. In the years from 1855 to 1860 Heinrich Geissler (1814–1879) invented a mercury pump and used it to produce a very high vacuum in tubes into which he had sealed electrodes. The radiation was studied more intensively by Julius Plücker (1801–1868) in 1859. He showed that the radiation from the cathode caused a fluorescence on the glass near the cathode, and that this fluorescence could be moved by a magnet. In 1869 J. W. Hittorf showed that the "negative discharge," as he called it, could be cut off by obstacles placed in its path. The radiation was finally named "cathode rays" in 1876 by Eugen Goldstein (1850–1930).

Intensive study of the cathode rays was begun by William Crookes (1832–1919), who in 1874 had noticed the turning of a small paddle wheel placed in the path of the rays and concluded that the rays could exert force. This convinced him that the rays were material and, from a study of their deflection in a magnetic field, that they carried a negative charge. He believed, in fact, that he had discovered a "fourth state of matter." [3]

In 1886 Goldstein bored holes in the cathode and discovered an electrical discharge behind it that gave rays opposite in character to the cathode rays, and that varied in the effects they produced, depending on the material used. The cathode rays had the same properties, no matter what the source. These new rays Goldstein called "canal rays." [4]

Still another type of radiation was discovered in 1895 by Wilhelm Konrad Roentgen (1845–1923). He covered with black paper a vacuum tube in which cathode rays were being generated, and observed that crystals of barium platinocyanide placed near it fluoresced. Further study showed that some type of radiation was present that could pass through solid matter, such as flesh, and cast shadows of denser objects, such as bones.[5] The rays were not deflected by electrostatic or magnetic fields. These X-rays, as Roentgen called them, have since become of the greatest importance in the sciences of physics, chemistry, and medicine.

The ionic theory of conductance in solution had existed in various forms from the time of Faraday. At a meeting of the British Association for the Advancement of Science in 1874, George Johnstone Stoney

(1826–1911) suggested that electricity was composed of "atoms" that carried a unit charge. The paper was not published until 1881,[6] and, in the meantime, Helmholtz had made a similar suggestion in his Faraday lecture of 1877. In 1891 Stoney proposed the name "electron" for this unit,[7] which thus represented in his mind a charge, not a particle. The suggestion did not receive much attention at the time.

With the advent of the Arrhenius theory of dissociation, the concept of ions assumed a new importance. It was natural to extend the idea of such electrically charged particles from solutions to gases. If conduction was due to ions, and if cathode and canal rays were composed of particles, then these particles must have an ionic character. The problem became one of calculating their charge, mass, and velocity. Preliminary calculations of the ratio of charge to mass (e/m) by Arthur Schuster (1851–1934) at Manchester in 1890 gave such a large value that his work was not given much credence, since the idea of a very small value for m did not seem reasonable. The work in this direction was continued by Joseph John Thomson (1856–1940) at Cambridge. By using an extremely high vacuum and thus avoiding interference by ionization of residual gases he was able to make accurate comparisons of the deflections of cathode rays in magnetic and electrostatic fields. From this he could make better determinations of e/m and of velocity. His results of 1897 [8] proved that cathode rays consisted of negatively charged particles moving at extremely high velocities and with a mass about $\frac{1}{1000}$ that of the hydrogen atom. Later work corrected this value to $\frac{1}{1845}$. G. F. FitzGerald (1851–1901) proposed that the name electron, which had been coined by Stoney, should be applied to these particles, and this suggestion has since been universally followed.

Further studies of the pathways of ions produced by the various types of radiation were greatly aided by the invention in 1897 of the cloud chamber by Charles Thomson Rees Wilson (1869–   ).[9] In this apparatus, the path of a charged particle could be followed visually by the path of vapor that condensed as it passed through a humid atmosphere. The studies of Robert Andrews Millikan (1868–1953) in Chicago, begun in 1911,[10] employed a suspended oil drop that bore one or more electrons and hung between charged plates. His work finally proved that the electron was the smallest particle of electricity and established the value of its charge.

The investigations of J. J. Thomson showed that electrons could be produced from all the electrodes that he studied, and that no matter how they were prepared they had the same properties. Thus it was evident that they were a fundamental constituent of matter. If electrons, negative particles, were removed from a neutral atom, a positively charged particle had to be left. This must be the explanation for the canal rays. In 1897 Wilhelm Wien (1864–1928) proved this by showing that the positive particles of these rays had the mass of an ion. Thus it was established that gases, like solutions, conducted by ionization. A great advance had been made in understanding the nature of electricity.

Further confirmation of these facts and a much better opportunity to apply them to chemical problems appeared from an entirely unexpected quarter. Early in 1896 Antoine Henri Becquerel (1852–1908), son and grandson of equally distinguished physicists, became interested in the newly discovered X-rays of Roentgen. He knew that the fluorescent spot on the vacuum tube produced by impact of the electrons of the cathode ray was the source of the X-rays. He therefore tested other fluorescent substances to see if they might also give such radiation. The salts of uranium were known to fluoresce when exposed to light, and so he placed such a fluorescent salt, potassium uranium sulfate, on a photographic plate wrapped in dark paper. Subsequent development of the plate showed the outline of the crystals on the film. This seemed to confirm his idea. While preparing to repeat the experiment he was called away and left the salt on another plate in a dark place. Here, of course, the salt did not fluoresce, but when he later developed the plate, he found the same exposed area on it. This accidental discovery showed that the salt was spontaneously emitting rays that resembled X-rays in their ability to pass through non-transparent objects. Further studies showed that this radiation was independent of any treatment given the salt, and always accompanied the uranium when any chemical separations were made.[11] This phenomenon was named "radioactivity" by the Curies. In 1898 Gerhardt Carl Schmidt (1865–1949) discovered radioactivity in thorium.[12]

The major task of investigating the chemistry of these radioactive substances was begun by the young Polish investigator Marie Sklodowska Curie (1867–1934) and her husband, the French physicist, Pierre Curie (1859–1906). They received a large supply of a waste uranium ore, pitchblende, from the Austrian government, which had mines at Joachimsthal in Bohemia, now Czechoslovakia. This is still an important source of uranium. The Curies succeeded in showing that the ore contained two new radioactive elements, polonium [13] and radium.[14] By a long series of laborious fractional crystallizations, a radium salt was finally isolated. Actinium was discovered in pitchblende by André Debierne (1874–1949) in 1900.[15]

While the Curies, working with Debierne and others, were investigating the chemical nature of the radioactive elements, studies were begun on the nature of the rays that they emitted. In 1899, Ernest Rutherford (1871–1937), later Lord Rutherford, working at Montreal, found that two types of radiation were emitted from uranium. He called these α- and β-rays.[16] Later Paul Villard discovered a third type, the γ-rays, whose similarity to X-rays he recognized.[17] By 1900 it was realized that uranium was changing into some other substance. Rutherford noted the presence of a radioactive gas, radon, in thorium about this time. The confusing facts were reduced to order in 1902 by Rutherford and Frederick Soddy (1877–   ) [18] in their theory of atomic disintegration among radioactive substances, resulting in the formation of new elements. The β-rays were identified as electrons, the γ-rays as X-rays. In 1906 Rutherford indicated that α-particles were ions of helium,[19] a fact definitely established by Rutherford and Thomas Royds (1884–1955) in 1909.[20]

It now became possible to speculate on the arrangement of the electrons and positive ions within the atom. The electrons were negatively charged and were found in all atoms that had been studied. Since the atoms were neutral, there must be a positive portion, as studies of canal rays had shown. Early speculations by J. J. Thomson [21] and by Lord Kelvin [22] pictured a uniform mass of positive charge through which the electrons were distributed.

Rutherford devised another arrangement, based largely on studies in the Wilson cloud chamber, which showed that α-particles usually traveled in straight lines, but sometimes showed deflection in their path as if they had struck something. The Rutherford atom was composed of a heavy but relatively small nucleus surrounded by varying numbers of electrons. Most of the atom was empty space.[23] Calculation of the charge on the nucleus gave the number of electrons that must surround it in order to preserve neutrality. This turned out to be about half the atomic weight for each element.

In 1913 a discovery of fundamental importance was made by Henry Gwyn Jeffreys Moseley (1887–1915) working with Rutherford at the University of Manchester, to which Rutherford had gone in 1909. Moseley observed that cathode rays striking targets of different metals produced X-rays of a frequency characteristic of the metal that composed the target. There was a regular shift from one element to the next in the periodic table in accordance with the equation:

$$\nu = A(N - b)^2$$

in which ν is the frequency of a specific spectral line, A and b are constants, and N is an integer characteristic of the metal and shifted with each element. This N Moseley called the "atomic number." He stated that the quantity represented by N could only be the charge on the central positive nucleus.[24] The atomic number gave a more fundamental meaning to the periodic table of Mendeleev. When the elements were arranged in the order of atomic numbers, such discrepancies as the reversal of the atomic weights of iodine and tellurium disappeared. It was clear that atomic numbers were more basic than atomic weights.

The Rutherford picture of the atom as proposed in 1911 was soon greatly amplified by Niels Bohr (1885–   ) of Copenhagen, who had worked for a year with Rutherford at Manchester. Bohr used the quantum theory of Max Planck (1858–1947) to give a picture of the central nucleus surrounded by shells of electrons, of which the outermost was responsible for the chemical properties of the element.[25] It is on the basis of this concept of atomic structure that the more modern ideas have developed.

Atomic structural ideas had now developed sufficiently so that it was possible to explain other puzzling facts that had appeared in the studies of radioactive materials. It had early been recognized that, as uranium, thorium, or actinium disintegrated, a series of new elements was produced. In 1906 Bertram Borden Boltwood (1870–1927) of Yale found that the immediate precursor of radium, and a product of the disintegration of uranium, was an element that he called ionium.[26] In all its chemical reactions, however, ionium was identical with thorium. In 1911 and 1913 Soddy[27] proposed the laws that govern the production of elements in a disintegration series. These laws were expanded by him and by Kasimir Fajans (1887–   )[28] and by Alexander Smith Russell (1888–   )[29] to state that, when an α-particle is lost, the new element formed has moved back two places in the periodic table with loss of atomic weight 4, and that when a β-particle is lost, the new element has moved forward one place without change in atomic weight.

The number of new elements thus produced in the three disintegration series was too great for proper placement in the old periodic table, but, more important, a number of elements were produced that had different atomic weights but the same atomic number and so, in the new sense, were the same element. The case of ionium was by no means unique. This was a totally new idea to chemists, who had by now accepted the constancy of atomic weights as fundamental. Soddy called these new forms of elements "isotopes" from the Greek for "the same place." The crucial test for the correctness of his theory was the varying atomic weight of lead from different sources. By applying the rules of the disintegration series from uranium and thorium it was seen that the final non-radioactive product in each case was lead, but that which came from uranium should have an atomic weight of 206, and that from thorium 208, instead of the value of 207.2 accepted for ordinary lead. These values were experimentally confirmed by T. W. Richards (1868–1928), of Harvard, who had begun the study of variations in atomic weights of lead even before Soddy announced his theory,[30] and by O. Hönigschmidt (1878–1945)[31] of Prague and Munich. Both these men devoted their lives to atomic-weight determinations.

At about this time, J. J. Thomson and Francis William Aston (1877–1945) began to develop the mass spectograph by which, in 1919, Aston demonstrated that the non-radioactive element neon was also a mixture of isotopes.[32] It was quickly shown that practically all elements are composed of such mixtures. Of the many theoretical and applied results of this discovery, the most important at the present time is the use of isotopes as tracers in physical and biological systems.

Most of the work discussed so far in this chapter was done by physicists concerned with the physical structure of the atom. The picture of the atom that was emerging could not fail to be of great interest also to the chemists. Already the periodic table had been placed on a new and firmer basis, and the "modern" idea of the atom had to give way to a view of the transmutation of elements that recalled alchemical theories. The rejected Prout's hypothesis was seen to have a measure of truth. From this time on, chemists began to take an increasing part in developing the implications of atomic structural theory, while physicists, in turn, became more concerned with chemical problems. It is significant that such outstanding physicists as Rutherford and Aston were awarded Nobel Prizes not in physics, but in chemistry.

The Bohr model of the atom was proposed chiefly to explain atomic spectra, but it was the first model that could serve the chemist as well as the physicist. Almost at once chemists began to use it to explain chemical reactions. G. N. Lewis[33] and Walther Kossel (1888–   )[34]

in 1916 developed new theories of chemical affinity whose consequences were further expanded by Irving Langmuir (1881–   ).[35] These theories revived the old Berzelian dualism in a new form, but explained in a different way the affinity bonds of organic chemistry for which Berzelius could offer no satisfactory mechanism. Inorganic ions were formed by gain or loss of electrons in the outer shell to complete a stable octet with an electric charge. The ions of inorganic salts were held together by the electrostatic forces between the ions, forming "polar" compounds. Organic compounds, "non-polar" in character, were held together by sharing a pair of electrons in a "covalent" link that did not have the dualistic character of an ionic bond. Here at last was an explanation of the actual nature of the chemical bond as an individual unit of affinity which chemists had so long sought and which the supporters of some of the thermodynamic theories at the end of the nineteenth century had almost given up hope of discovering.

Still another important development at this time resulted from the discovery by Max von Laue (1879–   ) that crystal lattices could serve as diffraction gratings for X-rays. He at first applied this to determining the wave lengths of X-rays, but the method was equally applicable in determining the structures of crystals. This work was brilliantly carried on by William Henry Bragg (1862–1942) and his son, William Lawrence Bragg (1890–   ).[36]

The years between 1890 and 1915 overthrew completely the conservative views of late nineteenth century scientists and provided the theories and facts upon which almost all the spectacular developments of recent chemistry and physics have grown. Perhaps even more important than the release of atomic energy has been the new relationship established between the various sciences that had been growing apart in pre-atomic days. The old antagonism between physics and chemistry vanished as the physicists and chemists cooperated in applying atomic theory to actual chemical substances. The physical chemist and the organic chemist worked together in developing the electronic theory of organic structure. The mineralogist and geologist united with the chemist and physicist in determining crystal structures and dating rocks by radioactivities. Even the biological sciences, which had been almost disregarded by physical scientists before the twentieth century, have shared in this new cooperation of sciences, using the new techniques of physical chemistry in solving problems on the nature of proteins, or the tool of isotopic tracers in working out the details of metabolism. The individual scientist is perhaps more of a specialist than ever today, but he now realizes the value of working with other specialists as he has never done before. As a result, it is the previously borderline sciences that are advancing most rapidly today.

In the twentieth century, one of these borderline sciences, biochemistry, has attained a rank equal to that of the older branches of chemistry. No history of chemistry would now be complete that did not trace the path by which such a position has been obtained.

REFERENCES

1. A. Wolf, *A History of Science, Technology, and Philosophy in the Eighteenth Century*, The Macmillan Co., New York, 1939, pp. 213–214.

2. W. Morgan, *Phil. Trans.*, **75**, 272–278 (1785).

3. W. Crookes, *ibid.*, **170**, 164 (1879).

4. E. Goldstein, *Sitzber. kgl. preuss. Akad. Wiss. Berlin*, **1886**, 691–699.

5. W. K. Roentgen, *Sitzber. Wurzburger physik.-med. Ges.*, **137**, December 1895; *Nature*, **53**, 274–276 (1896).

6. G. J. Stoney, *Phil. Mag.*, **11**, 381–390 (1881).

7. G. J. Stoney, *Sci. Trans. Roy. Dublin Soc.*, [2] **4**, 583 (1891).

8. J. J. Thomson, *Phil. Mag.*, **44**, 293–316 (1897).

9. C. T. R. Wilson, *Phil. Trans.*, **189A**, 265–307 (1897); **192A**, 403–453 (1899).

10. R. A. Millikan, *Phys. Rev.*, **32**, 349–397 (1911).

11. A. H. Becquerel, *Compt. rend.*, **122**, 420–421, 501–503, 689–694, 1086–1088 (1896).

12. G. C. Schmidt, *Ann. Physik*, **65**, 141–151 (1898).

13. P. Curie and Mme. S. Curie, *Compt. rend.*, **127**, 175–178 (1898).

14. P. Curie, Mme. P. Curie, and G. Bémont, *ibid.*, **127**, 1215–1217 (1898).

15. A. Debierne, *ibid.*, **130**, 906–908 (1900).

16. E. Rutherford, *Phil. Mag.*, **47**, 109–163 (1899).

17. P. Villard, *Compt. rend.*, **130**, 1010–1012, 1178–1179 (1900).

18. E. Rutherford and F. Soddy, *J. Chem. Soc.*, **81**, 837–860 (1902); *Phil. Mag.*, **5**, 576–591 (1903).

19. E. Rutherford, *Phil. Mag.*, **12**, 348–371 (1906).

20. E. Rutherford and T. Royds, *ibid.*, **17**, 281–286 (1909).

21. J. J. Thomson, *ibid.*, **7**, 237–265 (1904).

22. Lord Kelvin, *ibid.*, **8**, 528–534 (1904); **10**, 695–698 (1905).

23. E. Rutherford, *ibid.*, **21**, 669–688 (1911).

24. H. G. J. Moseley, *ibid.*, **26**, 1024–1034 (1913); **27**, 703–713 (1914).

25. N. Bohr, *ibid.*, **26**, 1–25, 476–502, 857–875 (1913); **27**, 506–524 (1914).

26. B. B. Boltwood, *Am. J. Sci.*, **24**, 370–372 (1907); **25**, 365–381 (1907).

27. F. Soddy, *Chemistry of Radioactive Elements*, Longmans, Green and Co., London, 1911, pp. 24–30; *Part II*, London, 1913.

28. K. Fajans, *Physik. Z.*, **14**, 136–142 (1913).

29. A. S. Russell, *Chem. News*, **107**, 49–52 (1913).

30. T. W. Richards and M. E. Lembert, *J. Am. Chem. Soc.*, **36**, 1329–1344 (1914).

31. O. Hönigschmidt and S. Horovitz, *Compt. rend.*, **158**, 1796–1798 (1914); O.

Hönigschmidt, *Z. Elektrochem.*, **23**, 161–164 (1917); see also Maurice Curie, *Compt. rend.*, **158**, 1676–1679 (1914).

32. F. W. Aston, *Phil. Mag.*, **39**, 449–455 (1920).

33. G. N. Lewis, *J. Am. Chem. Soc.*, **38**, 762–785 (1916).

34. W. Kossel, *Ann. Physik*, **49**, 229–362 (1916).

35. I. Langmuir, *J. Am. Chem. Soc.*, **41**, 868–934, 1543–1559 (1919); **42**, 274–292 (1920).

36. W. H. Bragg and W. L. Bragg, *X-rays and Crystal Structure*, G. Bell and Sons, London, 1915.

CHAPTER XXIV

BIOCHEMISTRY

The idea that changes that we now call chemical occur in the human body and can help to explain its behavior is very old. Plato in the *Timaeus* and Aristotle in the fourth book of the *Meteorologica* present as much physiology as they do chemistry and physics. To the alchemists, the phenomena of the microcosm, the human body, merely reflected the events of the macrocosm, the outer world. Paracelsus, the iatrochemist, was more specialized and systematic as he pictured an intelligent being, the Archaeus, presiding over such functions as digestion, but the Archaeus was merely an alchemist in his chemical laboratory. With their increasing search for chemical mechanisms, the later iatrochemists replaced the Archaeus by purely chemical reactions such as the neutralization of acids and bases to explain body functions. The idea of the elixir, the ferment that changed base metals to gold, had its counterpart in the conception of the ferments that Van Helmont believed took part in vital reactions. Nevertheless, ideas of chemicophysiological mechanisms remained vague and disorganized even while Vesalius (1514–1564) was describing in a scientific manner the details of anatomy and the physicomechanical details of physiology were developing toward the discovery of the circulation of the blood by William Harvey (1578–1657).

The medieval and early modern chemists were mostly physicians. They naturally included studies of the more obvious body fluids in their work. Van Helmont, for instance, made many practical discoveries of a biochemical nature. There was little correlation between the studies of different investigators, and almost none of the fundamentals of the subject were discovered because the investigations tended to be sporadic and superficial.

The end of the eighteenth century, when chemistry as a whole was systematized and set on its modern path, was also the period when several basic biochemical discoveries were made. These resulted from the investigation of photosynthetic activity in green plants by Priestley, Ingenhousz, and Senebier, and the studies on animal respiration by Lavoisier with Laplace and Séguin. Even in these studies there was no systematized effort and little conception of their importance to a full understanding of the chemistry of life.

Chemists in the nineteenth century were so busy with their own science that for a long time they did not attempt to systematize the chemistry of biological processes. Most of their biochemical discoveries were incidental to their major chemical work. The most important result of the development of organic chemistry at first, from the viewpoint of biochemistry, was the demonstration that natural organic compounds were responsive to the same laws as inorganic substances. The urea synthesis of Wöhler and the subsequent advances in organic syntheses struck telling blows at the vitalistic hypothesis that a special force controlled living matter. Toward the middle of the century a few chemists, chief among whom was Liebig, really did begin to integrate their work with that of the biological investigators.

Meanwhile physiology was developing as a science in its own right, much as was chemistry. Physiologists were chiefly concerned with the mechanics of bodily organs and with studies of the nervous system. To a lesser extent they investigated chemical processes. Nevertheless, it was from the physiologists that most of the advances in biochemistry came until nearly the end of the century. The approach of these men was usually related to their studies of special systems or organs, and so an overall view of the biochemical functioning of the body was not obtained. Many important discoveries were made in this century, but they were like isolated pieces of a jigsaw puzzle. The science was properly called physiological chemistry at this period, since it was used mostly to help understand specific physiological problems. It was only at the end of the nineteenth century and in the twentieth that the pieces began to fit together so that a unified picture of the chemical changes in the cells and their significance for the body as a whole could be obtained. The borderline between chemistry and physiology then became a science in its own right, and to this the name biochemistry, the chemistry of life, can more properly be applied.

It is because this development occurred so recently that a description of these events has been deferred to the end of this history of chemistry. Actually, most biochemistry is contemporary. Its greatest advances have taken place since 1920, the approximate date at which this historical survey has been terminated. Therefore, the history of biochemistry becomes largely an account of how its various parts were discovered and finally integrated to form the base on which the modern discoveries are founded.

The first important generalization in the nineteenth century came from the pioneer work on photosynthesis. It led to an understanding of some of the complex relations between plants and animals. Priestley and Ingenhousz found that green plants in sunlight gave off oxygen. Senebier showed further that the plants absorbed carbon dioxide during this process. Nicolas Théodore de Saussure (1767–1845) in his classic *Recherches chimiques sur la végétation* (Paris, 1804) showed by quantitative measurements that the carbon in the dry matter of plants came almost entirely from carbon dioxide, and, equally important, that the rest of the dry matter, with the exception of minerals from the soil, came from water. In spite of his recognition of these facts, de Saussure did not break completely away from the idea that the organic matter of the humus, or decayed vegetable matter, in soil was also important for plants. This humus theory was of long standing and dominated the minds of plant physiologists until the middle of the century.

Chlorophyll was isolated and named from the Greek words for "green leaves" by J. Pelletier (1788–1842) and J. B. Caventou (1795–1877) in 1817, though at first its importance was not appreciated.[1] The full significance of the photosynthetic process could not be realized until the concept of energy was better understood. J. R. Mayer, who propounded the law of the conservation of energy, clearly saw the relation of this energy concept to the process. In 1845 he pointed out that plants fixed the energy of sunlight and served later to supply this energy as the source on which humans depended.[2]

In the meantime, steps had already been taken to clarify the mechanisms by which animals released the stored energy of plants. Much of the early work centered upon the values of various sorts of food in nutrition and on the process of digestion.

Ideas on the ideal diet, then as now, varied greatly. Some workers felt that a simple, almost monotonous diet was best for health. That this idea could not be carried too far was shown by William Stark (1740–1770) in a very conclusive way. Following a suggestion of Benjamin Franklin, he lived for two months on a diet of bread and water. This resulted in a severe case of scurvy, from which he recovered by eating a mixed diet. Shortly thereafter he repeated the experiment, this time with fatal results.[3] A similar experiment was performed on animals by the French physiologist François Magendie (1783–1855) in 1816. He fed dogs on diets composed of distilled water and one specific food, such as sugar, olive oil, or butter. Sometimes he added a little gelatine to the diet. The dogs in every case died after about a month. The work indicated that nitrogenous foods (other than gelatine) were needed for life.[4] It is interesting that, during the sugar diet, the dog developed a severe eye infection which Magendie described in detail. This is the first clinical description of the condition of xerophthalmia that results from a deficiency of vitamin A, though Magendie had no conception of deficiency states.

William Prout, the English physician who had proposed the hypothesis of a prime material from which all elements were built, was an acute observer of physiological processes. In 1827 he saw that there were three classes of foodstuffs that had to be included in the diet. These he called the saccharine, the oily, and the albuminous.[5] He attempted to analyze the saccharine constituents (our carbohydrates) but was not very successful, since he did not have a good method of organic analysis. He believed that these saccharine substances were "chiefly derived from the vegetable kingdom" and should be considered to represent "vegetable aliments."

At this time the nature of fats was already fairly well understood from the work of Chevreul. Little advance in knowledge of the nature of carbohydrates or proteins occurred until the work of Emil Fischer at the end of the century.

The studies of Magendie had at least indicated the importance of the nitrogenous part of the diet, and a number of investigations were made on this portion from a nutritional point of view. The name protein was suggested by Gerardus Johannes Mulder (1802–1880). His views on the chemical nature of the proteins were incorrect and led him into a series of violent controversies with Liebig, who, in the latter part of his life, turned his attention to physiological problems. In 1842 Liebig published his famous *Die Thierchemie* (Braunschweig, 1842), in which he applied his theories of chemistry to animal and human physiology. Liebig's influence was very great. His book was translated into many languages and appeared in many editions. Although Liebig himself held a vaguely vitalistic doctrine,[6] his book was bitterly attacked by the vitalists.[7] Nevertheless, in spite of attacks and counterattacks, it did much to convince chemists that chemistry could be applied to physiological problems. It was a major landmark in the development of biochemistry.

Liebig strongly combatted the humus theory of plant nutrition, believing that only minerals were taken from the soil by roots. He was very influential in introducing the use of mineral fertilizers for improving crops, though he overlooked the need for nitrogen in such fertilizers and so was less successful in practical agriculture than were J. B. Lawes (1843–1910) and J. H. Gilbert (1817–1901). In their studies in England they added nitrogen compounds to their fertilizers and showed the importance of such substances for nutrition.

By the middle of the nineteenth century many of the important principles of nutrition had thus been established. At the same time, knowledge of digestive mechanisms was also developing and was leading to the discovery of concepts that had an even wider application than to the digestion of foods.

In 1824 Prout showed that the acid of gastric juice, whose existence had long been known, was actually muriatic acid.[8] This was not accepted at once, since many physiologists believed it to be lactic acid. Even in 1839 an authoritative encyclopedia could state, "Dr. Prout indeed informs us, that a quantity of muriatic acid is always present in the stomach during digestion, but as there does not seem to be any decisive evidence of its appearance previously to the introduction of food into the stomach, we ought probably rather to consider it as developed by the process of digestion, than as entering into the constitution of the gastric juice, nor indeed, if it were so, are we able to explain the mode in which it operates in converting aliment into chyme." [9] Final proof that it was hydrochloric acid came in 1852 from the detailed analyses of Friedrich Bidder (1810–1894) and Carl Schmidt (1822–1894).[10]

It was at first believed that the acid alone caused the breakdown of foodstuffs into simpler components. In 1835 Theodor Schwann (1810–1882) found that gastric juice contained a catalyst which he called pepsin and which was effective in the breakdown of foods. Liebig added a rather skeptical and cautious note to Schwann's paper when he published it in his *Annalen*,[11] showing how little the role of enzymes was appreciated at this time. Others were soon found, however. Ptyalin was obtained from saliva by Louis Mialhe (1807–1886) in 1845.[12] Realization that the gastric juice was not the sole agent responsible for digestion came from the classic work of Claude Bernard (1813–1878) on the pancreatic juice. Beginning in 1846, he extended an earlier observation by Gabriel Gustav Valentin (1810–1883) that this fluid, like saliva, could break down starch. He showed that it also digested fats and proteins.[13] His student Willy Kühne (1837–1900) completed this work by a detailed study of the action of pancreatic juice on proteins [14] and by isolating trypsin in 1876.[15] Kühne and Russell Henry Chittenden (1856–1943) obtained a large number of intermediate products of protein digestion,[16] thus demonstrating something of the nature of the digestive process. Chittenden established at Yale the first laboratory of physiological chemistry in the United States.

The nature of "ferments," as enzymes were called during the first three quarters of the century, was the subject of much discussion. This came to center around the question of fermentation of sugar by yeast to produce alcohol. The non-vitalist chemists, led mostly by Liebig, believed without much experimental evidence that ferments in this process were only incidentally related to life and were actual chemical substances, whereas the vitalists held that alcoholic fermentation was a reaction peculiar to life itself. The careful experiments of Louis Pasteur led him to the belief that the living yeast cell was essential to fermentation.[17] Thus arose the distinction between "unorganized" ferments that occurred outside the cell, and "organized" or "formed" ferments that acted only within the cell. The various digestive ferments were examples of the first class; the alcoholic ferments of yeast were examples of the second. The distinction was more clearly made when Kühne in 1876 introduced the name "enzyme" from the Greek meaning "in yeast" to apply to the organized ferments.[18] The controversy between vitalists and non-vitalists continued until 1897. In that year Eduard Buchner (1860–1917) obtained an extract of yeast that showed fermenting power.[19] It was then realized that the distinction between unorganized ferments and enzymes was artificial and that almost all the reactions of the living organism were carried on with the aid of catalysts, which were thereafter called simply enzymes.

In an attempt to determine the fate of various substances taken into the body, Jean-Baptiste Joseph Dieudonné Boussingault (1802–1887) studied the relative intake and excretion of the various elements found in the foods of domestic animals.[20] Such balance studies became very popular and were applied to humans by many investigators, including Liebig. This method seemed too simple to Bernard, who wished to know what was happening to the various foods in the body cells. In this approach, as in many others, Bernard was a forerunner of modern investigators.[21]

In an attempt to prove that animals could synthesize food materials in their bodies instead of having to obtain all nutriment from plant life, as Dumas and Boussingault had claimed, Bernard discovered that the liver could serve as a source of blood sugar.[22] Numerous studies revealed the details of glycogenic function, and in 1857 he announced the isolation of glycogen from the liver.[23] Glycogen was independently discovered about the same time by Hensen,[24] a medical student who worked under the famous pathologist Rudolf Virchow (1821–1902). The foundations for an understanding of carbohydrate metabolism had been laid, though a real comprehension of the reactions involved had to wait until the structures of the sugars had been worked out.

The basic theory in this field resulted from the investigations of Emil Fischer [25] about 1890. His subsequent studies of the structures of the purines (1882–1901) and the polypeptides (1900–1906) opened the way for an understanding of nitrogen metabolism, which was essential before the biochemistry of these substances could be developed.

The later nineteenth century developments in the field of nutrition were largely influenced by the conceptions of energy that had become dominant in physics and chemistry at this time. The German physiologists under the leadership of Carl Voit (1831–1908) and his student Max Rubner (1854–1932) were especially active in this field.

The first important attempt to determine the fate of foods by analysis of gaseous exchange in animals was made by the physicist Victor Henri Regnault, working with Jules Reiset (1818–1896).[26] They kept animals of many kinds under a bell jar and determined the amount of carbon dioxide breathed out and the amount of oxygen consumed. From this they calculated the ratio that the physiologist E. F. W. Pflüger (1829–1910) later called the respiratory quotient. They showed that it varied with the type of food eaten by the animals. Bidder and Schmidt [10] showed this even more clearly in 1852.

Voit was trained as a physician, but he studied chemistry under Liebig. He began his physiological work by establishing the fact that healthy adult animals are normally in nitrogen equilibrium, excreting as much nitrogen as they take in. Like Liebig and most workers of the time, Voit believed that the energy for muscular work came from the breakdown of proteins, and that carbohydrates and fats were oxidized directly by the oxygen from the lungs. His studies soon showed that both these ideas were false. There was no increase in protein metabolism in a fasting dog when it engaged in muscular work.[27] In 1865 he showed that combination with oxygen was not the first step in energy production, but that a large number of intermediate substances were formed from the original food before the final union with oxygen occurred. Not all these intermediates were necessarily oxidized completely.[28] In 1877 Pflüger proved this by showing that a rabbit breathing quietly or by forced respiration consumed the same amount of oxygen. Hence, oxygen did not cause metabolism.[29] Much of modern biochemistry consists in the search for these products of intermediate metabolism.

Voit, with the assistance of Max Pettenkofer (1818–1901), now began a series of studies of metabolism by analysis of the gaseous exchange of animals and humans. Improving on the method of Regnault and Reiset he published a series of papers between 1866 and 1873 that showed how animal metabolism varied under different conditions.

Rubner continued this work and used more accurate calorimetric methods, both direct and indirect. In 1883–1884 he announced his "isodynamic law" which stated that the three types of food, carbohydrates, fats, and proteins, were equivalent in terms of calorific value.[30] This law was modified by the specific dynamic action of foods, which Rubner also discovered. The accurate quantitative work of Rubner, utilizing the thermochemical data of the chemists, showed that the energetics of living organisms followed the same laws as those of pure chemicals.

The overall requirements of the body for the major energy-producing foods had now been established. It was known from the work of Liebig that small amounts of minerals were essential to life, but it was not yet suspected that any organic substance was required in amounts so small as to have no values as a producer of energy, nor was there any realization of the need for certain individual amino acids. The limitations of the isodynamic law were thus not understood.

Nevertheless, the inadequacy of a highly purified diet of carbohydrates, fats, and proteins began to be recognized as early as 1881, when Nikolai Ivanovich Lunin (1854–1937) showed that a small amount of milk had to be added to these purified diets if experimental animals were to survive on them.[31] Soon afterwards, Christian Eijkman (1858–1930) in Java found that he could induce a disease in birds analogous to beriberi in humans. It resulted from a diet of polished rice, and the addition of rice polishings to the diet relieved the condition.[32]   Eijkman believed that some toxic factor in the rice was neutralized by a factor in the polishings.   Gerrit Grijns (1865–   ) in 1901 [33] first correctly explained beriberi as a deficiency disease.   The older observations that a number of diseases existed that could be relieved by dietary supplements could now be understood.   Scurvy had been cured in the ships of the British East India Company as early as 1601, and James Lind (1716–1794) had proved the value of anti-scorbutic foods experimentally.[34]   In 1804 lemon juice was added to the rations of the British navy, resulting in the name "limey" for British sailors.   In 1882 Kanchiro Takaki (1849–1915), Director General of the Medical Department of the Japanese navy, had prevented beriberi in his navy by adding fresh meat to the diet of the sailors,[35] though he believed the effect was due to the change in proportions of nitrogen and carbon in the diet.   The use of cod-liver oil in preventing rickets had been established for some time on an empirical basis.

The concept of deficiency diseases was extended experimentally from beriberi to scurvy when Axel Holst (1861–1931) and Theodore Frölich (1870–   ) in 1907 established the disease in guinea pigs.[36] In 1912 Casimir Funk (1884–   ) suggested that beriberi, scurvy, and probably pellagra were diseases that required the presence of organic nitrogenous bases in the diet for their prevention.   Since these amines were vital to life, he proposed that they be called "vitamines." [37]

At almost the same time, Frederick Gowland Hopkins (1861–1947), who had been working on dietary supplements, published a classic paper proving the inadequacy of purified diets.[38]   In 1915, E. V. McCollum (1879–   ) showed that rats required at least two substances in the diet,[39] which he subsequently called "fat-soluble A" and "water-soluble B." [40]   By 1920 it was recognized that these substances were not amines, but the name vitamine had become well established, and J. C. Drummond (1891–1952) suggested combining the two systems of nomenclature, dropping the final letter in "vitamine" and referring to vitamin A and vitamin B.[41]   The anti-scorbutic substance was then called vitamin C, and the differentiation of the anti-rachitic substance from vitamin A gave rise to the term vitamin D.[42]   The discovery of vitamin E by Herbert McLean Evans (1882–   ) in 1922 [43] completed the classical list of vitamins.   The discovery of vitamin K and the unraveling of the B complex have occurred in recent times.

During most of the nineteenth century it was assumed that the nervous system exerted almost entire control over the various functions of the body.   Thus, although there were a number of observations that the dysfunction or removal of certain glands resulted in failure in some physiological process, it was not realized that these glands exerted a chemical control.

Probably the first experimental proof of endocrine function was the work of A. A. Berthold (1803–1861) in 1849. He transplanted testicu-lar tissue in fowls and showed that he could thus prevent the effects of caponization.[44] C. E. Brown-Sequard (1817–1894) took up this idea in 1889 and injected testicular extracts into various subjects, including himself. He allowed his enthusiasm to overcome his observational powers and made claims that have not been supported, but he did much to introduce the idea of a chemical mechanism for control of important processes.[45] At about the same time Joseph von Mering (1849–1908) and Oscar Minkowski (1858–1931) showed that removal of the pancreas in a dog caused a sharp rise in blood sugar.[46] Thus, by the end of the century, scientists were ready to believe that certain organs could produce substances that exerted powerful effects on other parts of the body. The possibility of such effects produced by chemi-cals was strengthened by the striking pharmacological discoveries of such men as Paul Ehrlich (1854–1915), who showed the highly specific action of various drugs on living organisms.

In 1895 George Oliver (1841–1915) and Edward Albert Sharpey Schäfer (1850–1935) obtained an extract from the adrenal gland that had a powerful action in raising the blood pressure.[47] They pointed out that "the supra renal capsules are to be regarded, although duct less, as strictly secreting glands." The active principle of these glands, adrenaline or epinephrine, was isolated in 1901 by Jokichi Takamine (1854–1922) [48] and independently by Thomas Bell Aldrich.[49] This was the first isolation of a hormone.

The concept of hormones was clarified and placed on a firm basis by the studies of William Maddock Bayliss (1860–1924) and Ernest Henry Starling (1866–1927), who in 1902 discovered secretin, the hor-mone that stimulates the flow of pancreatic juice.[50] They demon-strated that secretin caused flow of this juice even when all nerves to the pancreas had been cut. They thus put beyond doubt the fact of chemical control. Bayliss then generalized the whole concept in his Croonian lectures of 1905.[51] Here he first suggested the name "hor-mone," from the Greek for "I excite, or arouse," for these "chemical messengers." He showed further how the other endocrine glands such as the thyroid or gonads also secreted hormones. From this time on, the idea of the hormones was clearly established, and it was only a question of isolating the secretions of the various glands in a state of purity and determining their physiological effects (not always an easy task). Thyroxine was isolated by Edward Calvin Kendall (1886–   ) on Christmas Day, 1914,[52] and insulin by Frederick Grant Banting (1891–1941) and Charles Herbert Best (1899–   ) in 1921.[53] Many hormones have since been obtained, and the work still goes on.

It can be seen that by about 1920 biochemistry possessed the basic principles upon which it is still developing. The chemical nature of the body constituents was fairly well understood, the nutritional requirements could be seen, and the enzymatic and hormonal mechanisms by which metabolic processes occurred were at least known to exist. Without these fundamental discoveries, which began to fit together in the twenties, biochemistry could not have made the tremendous progress of recent decades.

REFERENCES

1. J. Pelletier and J. B. Caventou, *J. pharmacie,* **3,** 486–491 (1817); *Ann. chim. phys.,* [2] **9,** 194–196 (1818).

2. J. R. Mayer, *Die organische Bewegung in ihrem Zusammenhang mit dem Stoffwechsel,* Heilbronn, 1845.

3. G. Lusk, *Nutrition,* Clio Medica Series, Hoeber, New York, 1933, pp. 66–67.

4. F. Magendie, *Ann. chim. phys.,* [2] **3,** 66–77 (1816).

5. W. Prout, *Phil. Trans.,* **117,** 355–388 (1827).

6. J. Jacques, *Rev. hist. sci. et leur applications,* **3,** 32–66 (1950).

7. H. S. Klickstein, *Chymia,* **4,** 129–157 (1953).

8. W. Prout, *Phil. Trans.,* **114,** 45–49 (1824).

9. J. Bostock, article on *Digestion* in *The Encyclopedia of Anatomy and Physiology,* edited by Robert B. Todd, Vol. II, p. 17, Longman, Brown, Green, Longmans and Roberts, London, 1839.

10. F. Bidder and C. Schmidt, *Die Verdauungssafte und der Stoffwechsel,* G. A. Reyher, Mitau und Leipzig, 1852.

11. T. Schwann, *Ann.,* **20,** 28–34 (1836).

12. L. Mialhe, *Compt. rend.,* **20,** 954–959, 1485–1488 (1845).

13. C. Bernard, *Mem. soc. de biol.,* **1,** 99–115 (1849); *Mémoire sur le pancréas,* J.-B. Baillière, Paris, 1856.

14. W. Kühne, *Virchows Arch. path. Anat. Physiol.,* **39,** 130–174 (1867).

15. W. Kühne, *Verhandl. naturhist.-med. Verein zu Heidelberg,* **1,** 194–198, 233–235 (1876).

16. W. Kühne and R. H. Chittenden, *Z. Biol.,* **19,** 159–208 (1883); **20,** 11–51 (1884); **22,** 409–422, 423–458 (1886); **25,** 358–367 (1889).

17. L. Pasteur, *Ann. chim. phys.,* **58,** 323–426 (1860); cf. also H. Finegold, *J. Chem. Educ.,* **31,** 403–406 (1954).

18. W. Kühne, *Verhandl. naturhist.-med. Verein zu Heidelberg,* **1,** 190 (1876).

19. E. Buchner, *Ber.,* **30,** 117–124 (1897).

20. J. B. Boussingault, *Ann. chim. phys.,* **71,** 113–136 (1839).

21. J. M. P. Olmsted and E. Harris Olmsted, *Claude Bernard and the Experimental Method in Medicine,* Henry Schuman, New York, 1952, p. 63.

22. C. Bernard and C. Barreswil, *Compt. rend.*, **27**, 514–515 (1848).

23. C. Bernard, *ibid.*, **41**, 461–469 (1855); **44**, 578–586, 1325–1331 (1857).

24. V. Hensen, *Virchows Arch. path. Anat. Physiol.*, **11**, 395–398 (1857).

25. E. Fischer, *Ber.*, **24**, 1836–1845, 2683–2687 (1891).

26. V. H. Regnault and J. Reiset, *Ann. chim. phys.*, **26**, 299–519 (1849).

27. C. Voit, *Ann.*, **119**, 193–199 (1861).

28. C. Voit, *Z. Biol.*, **1**, 69–107, 109–168, 283–314 (1865).

29. E. F. W. Pflüger, *Pflügers Arch. ges. Physiol.*, **14**, 1–37 (1877).

30. M. Rubner, *Z. Biol.*, **19**, 313–396 (1883).

31. N. Lunin, *Hoppe-Seylers Z. physiol. Chem.*, **5**, 31–39 (1881).

32. C. Eijkman, *Geneesk. Tijdschr. Ned. Indië*, **30**, 295 (1890); German translation of his work in *Arch. path. Anat. Physiol.*, **148**, 523–532 (1897).

33. G. Grijns, *Geneesk. Tijdschr. Ned. Indië*, **41**, 3–110 (1901).

34. J. Lind, *A Treatise of the Scurvy*, Sands, Murray and Cochran, Edinburgh, 1753.

35. K. Takaki, *Trans. Sei-I-Kwei*, No. **39**, Suppl. **4**, 29–37 (1885).

36. A. Holst and T. Fröhlich, *J. Hyg.*, **7**, 634–671 (1907).

37. C. Funk, *J. State Med.*, **20**, 341–368 (1912).

38. F. G. Hopkins, *J. Physiol.*, **44**, 425–460 (1912).

39. E. V. McCollum and M. Davis, *J. Biol. Chem.*, **23**, 181–230, 231–246 (1915).

40. E. V. McCollum and C. Kennedy, *ibid.*, **24**, 493 (1916).

41. J. C. Drummond, *Biochem. J.*, **14**, 660 (1920).

42. E. V. McCollum, N. Simmonds, J. E. Becker, and P. G. Shipley, *J. Biol. Chem.*, **53**, 293–312 (1922).

43. H. M. Evans and K. S. Bishop, *Science*, **56**, 650–651 (1922).

44. A. A. Berthold, *Mullers Arch. Anat. Physiol.*, **1849**, 42–46.

45. C. E. Brown-Sequard, *Arch. physiol. norm. Pathol.*, [5] **1**, 651–658, 739–746 (1889).

46. J. von Mering and O. Minkowski, *Arch. exptl. Pathol. Pharmakol.*, **26**, 371–387 (1890).

47. G. Oliver and E. A. Sharpey Schäfer, *J. Physiol.*, **18**, 230–276 (1895).

48. J. Takamine, *Am. J. Pharm.*, **73**, 523 531 (1901).

49. T. B. Aldrich, *Am. J. Physiol.*, **5**, 457–461 (1901).

50. W. M. Bayliss and E. H. Starling, *J. Physiol.*, **28**, 325–353 (1902).

51. W. M. Bayliss, *Lancet*, **1905**, II, 339–341, 423–425, 501–503, 579–583.

52. E. C. Kendall, *J. Am. Med. Assoc.*, **64**, 2042–2043 (1915).

53. F. G. Banting and C. H. Best, *J. Lab. Clin. Med.*, **7**, 251–266 (1922).

NAME INDEX

243

SUBJECT INDEX

cellulose acetate electrophoresis

techniques and applications

cellulose acetate electrophoresis

techniques and applications

H. P. Chin

University of
Southern California

ANN ARBOR ■ LONDON

a h
s p ann arbor-humphrey science publishers

© 1970 by Ann Arbor — Humphrey Science Publishers, Inc.
Drawer No. 1425, 600 S. Wagner Road, Ann Arbor, Michigan 48106

Library of Congress Catalog Card No. 71-99222
SBN 250-39972-5
Printed in the United States of America

Ann Arbor — Humphrey Science Publishers, Ltd.
5 Great Russell Street, London, W. C. 1, England

Preface

Cellulose acetate, used for years in membrane filters, has recently attained popularity as a supporting medium for electrophoresis. While many volumes have been written concerning the use of various stabilizing materials for zone electrophoresis, none has dealt to any extent with cellulose acetate. This book is devoted exclusively to a discussion of procedures which employ cellulose acetate as the supporting medium, although some similarities between it and other media obviously occur. It is hoped that this volume will fill a need for a source book which describes established techniques and helps to define the importance of electrophoretic analysis in a number of related disciplines.

I thank Dr. E. Bulba, Department of Environmental Health Sciences, Harvard University School of Public Health, for Figure 4; the Gelman Instrument Company, Ann Arbor (Figures 7 and 12); the Editors, *Clinica Chimica Acta*, Amsterdam: Elsevier Publishing Company (Figure 18); and New York: Interscience Publishers, Inc. (Figures 20 and 21).

My sincere thanks to Mr. Everett Moore, Manager of Educational Programs, Gelman Instrument Company, for his fancy footwork in catalyzing the compilation of this volume. Special thanks are due my colleagues at the University of Southern California School of Medicine, Mrs. Barbara Dewar, Mrs. Franziska Schmidt, Miss Barbara Layton, and Dr. Violetta Ries, for their help in performing many of the procedures described in the text. I am grateful to Dr. David Blankenhorn for reading the manuscript and making valuable suggestions; to my wife, Trucilla, who helped uncover and correct many flaws in the text; and to my secretary, Mrs. Diane Marvin, for typing the manuscript.

H. P. CHIN

Los Angeles
December, 1969

Contents

CHAPTER 1

Introduction

Particles carrying a charge when placed in a conducting medium will migrate under the influence of an electrical field. This behavior is based on principles of electrolysis by which Cruikshank[1] demonstrated that copper and silver metals could be recovered from their respective salt solutions. Electrokinetic movement of colloidal particles was first described in 1809 by Reuss[2], a Russian physicist. He positioned two glass tubes vertically in a bed of wet clay, filled them with water, and placed some sand at the bottom of each tube. Upon connecting the tubes to the terminals of a battery which he had constructed, water at the positive electrode which was originally clear became turbid, while that at the negative electrode remained clear but increased in volume. This experiment demonstrated two important principles. First, the turbidity of the solution at the positive electrode was caused by the migration toward it of charged colloidal particles; migration of charged particles is now known as electrophoresis. Second, the increase in volume of liquid at the negative electrode was due to movement of liquid along the stationary conducting medium in response to a charge induced on the medium by the flow of electrical current; this movement of liquid is called electro-osmosis or electro-endosmosis.

In 1892, Picton and Linder[3] employed V-shaped and U-shaped glass tubes to observe the migration of inorganic compounds and hemoglobin in solution. A U-tube design was used by Michaelis[4] to determine the isoelectric points of several enzyme preparations. By adjusting the pH of the buffer solution, a value at which no electromigration would occur was determined for each enzyme. In the 1930s, Theorell[5, 6] described the separation of a number of enzymes ("respiratory ferments")

1

based on their electrophoretic behavior. These were among the original applications of free or moving boundary electrophoresis reported in detail by Tiselius in 1937.[7]

Moving boundary electrophoresis can be extremely valuable for determination of isoelectric points and measurement of exact mobilities of pure compounds. It is a precise technique which requires elaborate equipment and stringently controlled conditions for proper execution. However, boundaries between separated fractions are usually difficult to maintain and observe with accuracy.[8] Due to this considerable interest was generated, early in the evolution of electrophoresis, in stabilizing the zone of migration so that solute particles, having undergone electromigration, could be examined or isolated. This led to the development of zonal or zone electrophoresis which today is the most commonly practiced means for electrophoretic separation of compounds. The difference between moving boundary electrophoresis and zonal electrophoresis is that the latter makes use of a rigid or semirigid supporting medium to hold the separated components in discrete zones for examination or for further study. In addition, zonal electrophoresis possesses greater sensitivity than moving boundary electrophoresis and generally requires much smaller quantities of sample for analysis.

Some of the early experiments in zone electrophoresis were conducted during the period when techniques of moving boundary electrophoresis were being developed. In 1886, Lodge[9] measured the migration velocities of inorganic ions in a tube containing a medium stabilized with gelatin. Field and Teague[10] studied the electrophoretic behavior of diphtheria toxin and antitoxin in agar jelly. Shortly thereafter, Kendall and Crittenden[11] and Kendall and White[12] carried out electrophoretic separation of metals in a conducting medium employing agar gel as the supporting matrix. These experiments demonstrated some basic concepts of zone electrophoresis and offered evidence for the potential uses of electrophoretic analysis in a wide variety of scientific endeavors.

The work of Tiselius and his colleagues on moving boundary electrophoresis was followed by rapid developments in zone electrophoresis. It was found that a variety of rigid and semirigid materials remained stable even when saturated with buffer and could therefore form efficient supporting structures for the separation of charged particles. In the same year that Tiselius' article appeared, König[13] successfully used filter paper as a supporting medium for the electrophoretic separation of snake venom.

Consden *et al.*[14] derived mathematical expressions to describe factors which affect the electrophoretic mobility of colloidal substances in silica gel. Their studies, and those of Crémer and Tiselius,[15] Durrum,[16] Flynn and de Mayo,[17] and Grassmann and colleagues,[18, 19] using paper electrophoretic strips, have led to the popular use of electrical current to separate substances of biological importance.

Various terms have been used to designate the migration of particles in an electrical field. The process was called "cataphoresis" by Theorell[5] to describe the migration of ions of positive charge. Martin and Synge[20] felt that "electrophoresis" should be reserved for migration of colloidal particles and that the movement of ionic species was best described as "ionophoresis." Other terms such as "ionography"[21] and "electrochromatography"[22] have been proposed. Tiselius and Flodin[23] suggested that "zone electrophoresis" should be used to describe all electrical separations in which discrete solute zones are formed, regardless of the method used for stabilization of the zones. This term in recent years has come to represent all types of migration of solute particles in stabilized conducting media.

Zone electrophoresis has attained a position of importance in analytical biochemistry, and many books and monographs have been written on the principles and applications of this technique. The practical application of zone electrophoresis in recent years has involved the use of various media in a number of shapes and forms, including strips or sheets of paper or cellulose acetate, and columns, plates, blocks, or slabs of starch, acrylamide, or agar gels. Many components have been discovered as the direct result of the use of these media. With the introduction of purified media, particularly cellulose acetate, many procedures which formerly required the better part of a 24-hour day to complete can now be accomplished in 1 hour or less. A number of these have been adopted for routine use in the laboratory. The aim of this book is to supplement the existing literature on electrophoresis with a discussion centering on the evolution and development of cellulose acetate electrophoresis and to describe the uses of cellulose acetate membranes for the separation of some substances of current scientific interest.

It is clear that the development of purified supporting media has broadened the scope of electrophoretic procedures. Undoubtedly, continual development of electrophoretic equipment and techniques and additional refinement and improvement in the purification and manufacture of supporting media will result in improved separation and identification of biologically important substances. The underlying principles governing separation of electrically charged substances are unchanged but may undergo modification as a result of variations in methodology. Improved electrophoretic media have been developed as the need arose for detailed information in areas where knowledge was limited by a lack of adequate technology. One needs only to read the recent literature on such topics as hemoglobins, isoenzymes, proteins, and lipoproteins to realize the tremendous expansion of information which has occurred largely as the result of improvements in the design and application of electrophoretic procedures. It appears that we are just now embarking on an era in which significant achievements in science will be derived directly from appropriate use of these procedures.

Cellulose acetate membranes have been employed for many years for filtration purposes and have demonstrated their usefulness in a variety of procedures ranging from ultrafiltration of bacteriological materials and recovery of particulate matter from aerosols to concentration of solutes from liquid media. They are also in common use as a supporting medium for electrophoretic analysis. Two primary considerations in the choice of a procedure are simplicity of use and reproducibility of results. Because cellulose acetate membranes are notable in these respects, their use for a number of electrophoretic procedures has attained importance in recent years.

As a supporting medium for electrophoresis, cellulose acetate is probably unsurpassed in its convenience to the analyst. No special preparation is required before cellulose acetate strips are ready to accept the sample to be analyzed; on the other hand, some media require extensive preparation prior to sample application. The wet strength of cellulose acetate is greater than that of filter paper strips; therefore, cellulose acetate membranes are easier to handle than paper strips or other supporting media. As a rule, electrophoretic procedures with cellulose acetate require only a short time for completion, often as little as 20–30 minutes. This is a distinct advantage, as those who have labored with various time-consuming electrophoretic procedures can certainly appreciate. Because mild conditions and short running times are employed for cellulose acetate electrophoresis, special provisions for cooling the electrophoretic chamber need not be employed; in contrast, media which call for high voltages and/or long running times require rigorous control of experimental conditions to prevent production of artifacts. Furthermore, cellulose acetate strips can be cleared after staining, and transparent strips can be evaluated by means of straightforward densitometric procedures. This feature is of great importance to scientists who need quantitative measurements of changes under experimental conditions.

This book will consider briefly the principles and the fundamental operations of cellulose acetate electrophoresis which are applicable to all types of electrophoretic procedures. These will form the background for a discussion of applications of cellulose acetate membranes for the electrophoretic separation of specific substances of biological importance.

REFERENCES

1. Cruikshank, W.   Ann. Physik. **7**, 105 (1801).
2. Reuss, F. F.   Mém. Soc. Impér. Nat. Moscou **2**, 327 (1809).
3. Picton, H., and S. E. Linder.   J. Chem. Soc. **61**, 148 (1892).
4. Michaelis, L.   Biochem. Z. **16**, 81 (1909).
5. Theorell, H.   Biochem. Z. **223**, 93 (1930).
6. Theorell, H.   Naturwiss. **22**, 289 (1934).
7. Tiselius, A.   Trans. Faraday Soc. **33**, 524 (1937).
8. Martin, N. H., and G. T. Franglen.   J. Clin. Pathol. **7**, 87 (1954).
9. Lodge, O.   Brit. Assoc. Adv. Sci. Rept. 56th Meeting, 1886, p. 389.
10. Field, C. W., and O. Teague.   J. Exp. Med. **9**, 6 (1907).
11. Kendall, J., and E. D. Crittenden.   Proc. Nat. Acad. Sci. U.S. **9**, 75 (1923).
12. Kendall, J., and J. F. White.   Proc. Nat. Acad. Sci. U.S. **10**, 458 (1924).
13. König, P.   Actas e trabalbos Congr. Sul-Amer. Chim. 3rd Congr., Rio de Janeiro **2**, 334 (1937).
14. Consden, R., A. H. Gordon, and A. J. P. Martin.   Biochem. J. **40**, 33 (1946).
15. Crémer, H. D., and A. Tiselius.   Biochem. Z. **320**, 273 (1950).
16. Durrum, E. L.   J. Am. Chem. Soc. **72**, 2943 (1950).
17. Flynn, F. V., and P. de Mayo.   Lancet **2**, 235 (1951).
18. Grassmann, W., K. Hannig, and M. Knedel.   Deut. Med. Wochschr. **76**, 333 (1951).
19. Grassmann, W., and K. Hannig.   Z. Physiol. Chem. **290**, 1 (1952).
20. Martin, A. J. P., and R. L. Synge.   Advan. Protein Chem. **2**, 32 (1945).
21. McDonald, H. J., M. C. Urbin, and M. B. Williamson.   J. Colloid Sci. **6**, 236 (1951).
22. Lecoq, H.   Bull. Soc. Roy. Sci. Liége **13**, 20 (1944).
23. Tiselius, A., and P. Flodin.   Advan. Protein Chem. **8**, 461 (1953).

CHAPTER 2

Basic Principles of Electrophoresis

Molecules held together by chemical bonds contain groups which dissociate into ionic species under appropriate conditions. When an electrical field is imposed, these ionic species, if suspended in an appropriate conducting medium, will migrate toward the pole of opposite charge. A given solute molecule undergoes separation in aqueous solution to an extent which is governed by the pH of the solution and by the dissociation constant of the solute. The equilibrium condition for a weak acid is described by the well-known Henderson-Hasselbalch equation

$$pH = pK_a + log \frac{A}{HA} \qquad (1)$$

where pH is the negative logarithm of the hydrogen ion concentration, pK_a the negative logarithm of the dissociation constant for the weak acid, A the concentration of the ionized salt, and HA the concentration of the acid. This expression states that when the pH of the solution equals the pK_a, the molecule is 50% ionized. It can be seen that at a pH value one unit greater than the pK_a, the molecule is 90% ionized, and when the pH is two units greater than pK_a, it is 99% ionized. Conversely, when pH is one unit less than pK_a, the molecule is only 10% ionized, and when pH is two units less than pK_a, it is only 1% ionized. The degree of dissociation of a given molecule, which is determined by its chemical structure and expressed as a constant (K_a), has an important effect on the net charge of the molecule in solution and hence its mobility in an electrical field.

Amino acids, which make up proteins, contain both carboxyl (COOH) and amino (NH$_2$) groups. For example, the glycine mole-

7

cule, NH_2CH_2COOH, possesses both positive and negative charges in solution. It has two dissociation constants, $pK_{a1} = 2.4$ and $pK_{a2} = 9.6$. At its isoelectric pH of 6.0, the number of positive charges exactly balances the number of negative charges, and the molecule is electrically neutral.

$$NH_2CH_2COO^- \xleftarrow{\quad OH^- \quad} {}^+NH_3CH_2COO^- \xrightarrow{\quad H^+ \quad} {}^+NH_3CH_2COOH$$

In alkaline solution the acid group of the molecule is neutralized, forming $NH_2CH_2COO^-$ with a net negative charge. In mild acid solution, the glycine molecule possesses a net positive charge: ${}^+NH_3CH_2COOH$. It is obvious that selection of the appropriate buffer pH is essential to successful application of any electrophoretic procedure because buffer pH governs the charge and magnitude of charge on a given substance and hence its electrophoretic mobility.

As a further example, serum albumin has an isoelectric point of 4.7 and hence is strongly ionized with a negative charge in buffer solution of pH 8.6. It exhibits a high rate of electrophoretic mobility in the anodic direction. In comparison, the isoelectric point of gamma globulin is 7.2. At pH 8.6, it also is negatively charged and moves toward the anode. But albumin, being more strongly charged, has a higher rate of anodic mobility than gamma globulin at any given voltage; by means of electrophoresis, the two proteins are readily distinguishable.

Migration of charged particles in solution depends not only on the charge which the particles possess, but also on a number of other factors. Surface charge and hydrated density of the solute particle are determined by molecular size, structure, shape, and density. The concentration of solute, assuming it is soluble in the buffer solution, and interaction between solute and the electrophoretic medium affect electrophoretic mobility. Buffer viscosity, ionic strength, and concentration of electrolytes are important factors, and interrelationships of potential drop, current flow, temperature, and evaporation have significant effects on mobility. Physical and chemical properties of the medium employed govern such phenomena as molecular sieving, adsorption, and electro-osmosis; these are important considerations in all electrophoretic procedures. Some of these effects will be considered briefly.

When a particle with a charge q is subjected to an electrical field of strength H in a liquid medium, a force of magnitude qH results which causes acceleration of the particle to take place. When the accelerative force is balanced by frictional resistance exerted by the liquid medium in which it moves, the particle attains a constant velocity of migration which reflects the difference between frictional re-

sistance and electrical driving forces. The movement of the particle
with charge q can be described by the expression

$$qH = \frac{RTv}{D} \tag{2}$$

where H is the field strength, D the diffusion constant under the experimental conditions selected, R the Boltzmann (gas) constant, T the absolute temperature, and v the migration velocity. If the particle has a valency Z, $q = Ze$ where e is the electrostatic charge (4.8×10^{-10} electrostatic units), and H is the potential gradient in V/cm across the migration channel.

The electrophoretic velocity which a particle attains, from Equation 2, is

$$\frac{v}{H} = \frac{qD}{RT} = \frac{ZeD}{RT} \tag{3}$$

The frictional resistance, f, which the particle encounters in moving through the medium is given by Stokes' law

$$f = 6\pi\eta rv \tag{4}$$

where η is the viscosity of the medium and r represents the radius of the spherical molecule. Under steady state conditions, accelerative forces driving the particle forward and the frictional forces retarding movement of the particle are equal:

$$qH = f$$

Electrophoretic mobility, M, is defined as the velocity of a particle under standard conditions, *i.e.*, in an electric field of unit strength ($H = 1$ V/cm):

$$M = \frac{v}{H}$$

By combining Equations 2 and 4,

$$M = \frac{q}{6\pi\eta r} \tag{5}$$

Thus it can be seen that the mobility of a particle is governed by its size, net charge, and by the properties of the medium as well.

Equation 5 describes the mobility of a charged particle or ion at infinite dilution, that is, if the particle is not exposed to electrostatic interactions with other ions; presence of other ions will result in a decrease in the mobility of the particle under study. When buffer salts or other electrolytes are used, ionic interaction becomes important. The charge which the central particle possesses causes an aggregation of ions of opposite charge (counterions) in its neighborhood into a diffuse double layer.[1] The resulting phenomenon has been described by Debye and Hückel as the "electrical double layer."[2] Introduction of the Debye-Hückel parameter modifies Equation 5 describing movement of the particle in the following manner:

$$M = \frac{q}{6\pi\eta r} \cdot \frac{1}{1 + Kr} \qquad (6)$$

K is the Debye-Hückel parameter which is defined as

$$K = \left(\frac{4\pi e^2}{ERT} \sum n_i Z_i^2 \right)^{\frac{1}{2}} \qquad (7)$$

where Z_i is the valence, n_i the number of ions, and E the dielectric constant of the medium. If the ionic concentration is given in C moles per liter,

$$K = \left(\frac{4N^2 e^2}{1000\ ERT} \sum C_i Z_i^2 \right)^{\frac{1}{2}} \qquad (8)$$

where N is Avogadro's number. It can be seen, therefore, that the presence of the surrounding atmosphere of ions opposite in charge to that of the central particle produces a tendency for the particle and its atmosphere to move in the opposite direction. Knowing the degree of ionization and hence the magnitude of charge on the solute particle, a general expression of ionic mobility can be derived. Consden *et al.*[3] calculated the differences in theoretical mobility through slabs of silica gel for two or more weak electrolytes and amphoteric substances in solution at various pH values.

In free electrophoresis, mobility of the ionic species follows the expression

$$M = \frac{v}{H} = \frac{dl}{tV} \qquad (9)$$

where l is the path length, V the voltage, H the field strength, v is the velocity, d distance, and t time. At unit field strength,

$$d = \frac{vt}{l} \qquad (10)$$

In paper or other supportive matrix, however, the charged particle migrates along a tortuous channel (Figure 1),

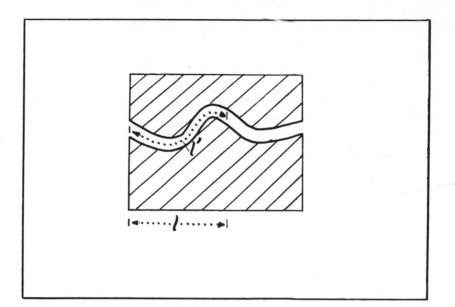

Figure 1. The effect of tortuous channels in the supporting medium on electrophoretic migration.

and the distance which the particle moves is increased by the factor

$$l' = l\left(\frac{l'}{l}\right);$$

hence

$$d' = \frac{vt}{l'} \tag{11}$$

The ionic strength (U) of the buffer solution is given by the expression

$$U = \frac{1}{2} \sum_{i=1}^{i=n} C_i Z_i^2 \tag{12}$$

where C is the molarity of each ionic species in solution from 1 to n, and Z is the ionic charge of each.[4] The Debye-Hückel treatment of the double layer of electrical charge on colloidal particles indicates that electrophoretic mobility is highly dependent upon the ionic strength of the buffer solution used. Buffers of low ionic strength permit fast migration rates with low heat production. High ionic strength buffers afford sharpening of electrophoretic zones, accompanied with slower migration rates. However, the use of high ionic strength buffers usually requires application of a higher potential gradient between the anode and cathode to enhance migration velocity. Under these conditions, problems may arise because heat production and evaporation may introduce artifacts. In practice, solutions of ionic strength 0.025–0.075 for barbital buffers and 0.03–0.12 for Tris buffers are the most commonly used.

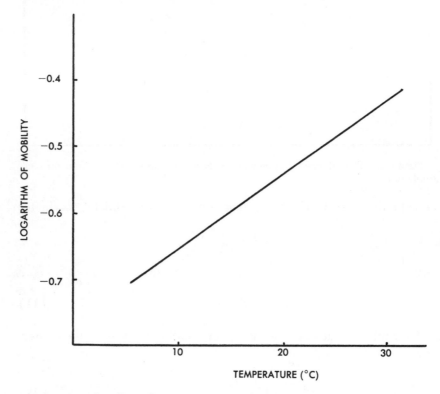

Figure 2. The effect of temperature on electrophoretic mobility. Reconstructed from McDonald and Spitzer.[5]

The mobility of an ionic species generally increases with temperature. McDonald and Spitzer[5] determined the influence of temperature on the mobility of polyvinylpyrrolidone and found a linear relationship between the logarithm of the mobility and the absolute temperature (Figure 2). They derived the following equation to express the relationship between mobility and temperature for various substances studied, including Bromphenol Blue, bovine serum albumin, and human serum lipoproteins:[6]

$$log\ M = m\frac{1}{T} + B \tag{13}$$

where M is the electrophoretic mobility, m the slope of the curve, T is the absolute temperature, and B is a constant.

While it tends to enhance electrophoretic mobility, excessive temperature often exerts an adverse influence directly by denaturation of substances being analyzed or indirectly through evaporation of volatile substances leading to solute and buffer concentration, denaturation, and artifact formation. Heat and voltage drop or current are related by the following equation:

$$\text{heat} = \text{electric energy (joules)} = R'I^2t \tag{14}$$

where I is the current, R' the resistance, and t is time. Since $V = IR'$ and the product of current and time equals coulombs, the expression can also be written as

$$\text{heat} = \text{Volts} \times \text{coulombs},$$

or

$$\text{heat} = \text{Volts} \times \text{current} \times \text{time} \tag{15}$$

At higher voltages or current, heat must be dissipated; proper cooling must be provided in order to achieve satisfactory and reproducible results. In some cases, heat production during electrophoresis is so intense, especially when high voltages and long running times are employed, that the substance being analyzed is denatured and the support may actually become charred. In summary, the adverse effects of elevated temperature include dehydration of volatile components, changes in pH and ionic strength of the buffer, and creation of local areas of discontinuity within the buffer system and the electrophoretic support. It is apparent that at any given ionic strength of buffer solution under constant conditions of voltage or current, reduction of time allotted for the electrophoretic run results in a reduction of heat production. More rapid rates of migration can be achieved by increasing the voltage or current flow between the electrodes, with the potential danger of producing artifacts due to increased heat production.

Most supporting media acquire a negative charge relative to the buffer. Since the support remains stationary, this causes the buffer to move electro-osmotically toward the negative electrode (cathode). Electro-osmosis is most pronounced in alkaline solution. It varies with the make-up of the support. Electro-osmosis is strong in agar which contains sulfate and carboxyl groups, weak in agarose which is poor in polysaccharides of agar and weak in acrylamide gel. Movement of the electrolyte has been shown to obey the expression derived by Mac Innes[7]

$$M_e = \frac{\zeta E}{4\pi\eta} \tag{16}$$

where M_e is the electro-osmotic mobility, ζ the zeta potential, and E the dielectric constant of the medium. The zeta potential or electro-kinetic potential represents the charge on the colloidal particle and is defined as the work required to bring a unit of charge from infinity to the outer surface of the solvated layer surrounding the particle (surface of shear). Helmholtz[8] first developed the concept of the electrical double layer at the solid-liquid interface. The electrical interface between solid and liquid can be regarded as a condenser with parallel plates separated by a finite distance, d, each carrying a surface charge, q:

$$\zeta = \frac{4\pi q d}{E} \tag{17}$$

The similarity between Helmholtz' equation and Equation 16 should be noted.

Paper contains COOH groups (from cellulose) which are largely ionized with a negative charge in aqueous solution. The ionized carboxyl groups induce on nearby solvent molecules a positive charge which causes electro-osmotic flow of buffer toward the cathode. The phenomenon is enhanced in the presence of alkaline buffers. Kunkel and Tiselius[9] used the neutral polysaccharide, dextran, to measure electro-osmotic movement of the buffer electrolyte arising from the negative charge of paper strips. N-dinitrophenylethanolamine does not become ionized and can also be used to measure electro-osmotic flow. Other substances such as xylose[10] and creatinine[11] have also been used. The electro-osmotic flow as determined by dextran can be expressed as

$$M_e = \frac{d_{dex}}{Ht} \tag{18}$$

where d_{dex} represents the distance which dextran moves. Since

$$-M_{alb} = \frac{d_{alb} + d_{dex}}{Ht} \tag{19}$$

where $-M_{alb}$ is the mobility of albumin, combining Equations 18 and 19 results in

$$\frac{d_{dex}}{d_{alb} + d_{dex}} = \frac{M_e}{-M_{alb}} \qquad (20)$$

In practice, electro-osmosis is frequently disregarded in considering the electrophoretic migration of proteins and charged particles. The relative mobility (M_r), or the apparent separation of substances being analyzed, is the parameter of practical importance in most cases. M_r is calculated as a ratio of the mobility of the unknown to that of a reference substance, and it includes actual electromigration as well as electro-osmosis.

It is worth noting that under some conditions electro-osmotic effects can materially aid in the separation of substances. For example, substances whose isoelectric points are in close proximity to the pH of the buffer solution can sometimes be differentiated more clearly when electro-osmotic flow is employed to enhance the electrophoretic separation of those substances.

Adsorptive, chromatographic, and molecular sieving effects are occasionally encountered in electrophoresis in various media. Adsorptive effects are especially important when filter paper is employed as the supporting medium,[9, 12] and adsorption of cationic particles to paper often causes streaking and tailing during electrophoresis.[13] Paper fibers act as a barrier in the path of migrating particles. The effect varies with the molecular volume of the substance; therefore, paper and other porous media may in fact exhibit a sieving effect which governs the migration of particles by their molecular size. In certain cases, ion exchange effects occur when charged groups are present in the supporting medium. A possible advantage which adsorption and ion exchange effects offer is in retarding the migration of one of two or more substances which would otherwise move equally in the same direction; these effects render separations which often prove useful. Molecular sieving effects are more apparent when starch gel or polyacrylamide gel are used as the supporting media. In these cases, displacement of macromolecules may be a function of electrophoretic migration, modified by filtration which is determined by the molecular dimensions of the substances being separated.

When a solute is present in high concentration, distortion of the zone of migration may occur if the support becomes overloaded. Overloading the support causes distortion of the zone of migration so that the edges of the zone may move faster than the middle of the zone of higher concentration (Figure 3). This phenomenon is called "self-

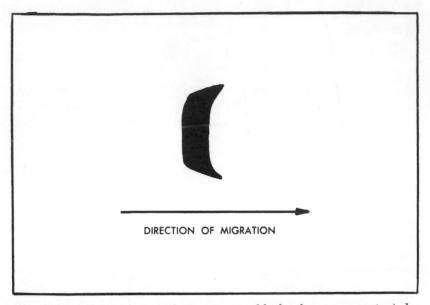

DIRECTION OF MIGRATION

Figure 3. Self-slowing (retardation at areas of high solute concentration) due to sample overload.

slowing" and can frequently be observed when a large sample load is applied to the electrophoretic support.[14, 15]

In summary, conditions for electrophoresis must be selected for each type of supporting medium in such a manner that optimum results are obtained. The selection of conditions is empirical and must be determined for each laboratory and tailored to specific procedures. The type of buffer, the pH and ionic strength of the buffer, voltage and duration of the electrophoretic run, and other factors such as effects of temperature and electro-osmotic flow on the desired separation must be determined by experimentation so that satisfactory separation is accomplished in a convenient time interval while avoiding circumstances that would denature the solute particles or produce artifacts. Electroosmosis and adsorption may both be used to advantage at times to separate two or more substances which would otherwise migrate equally under the conditions selected for electrophoresis.

The relative mobility, M_r, is usually taken as the criterion of prime practical significance in electrophoretic separations; however, when measures of relative mobility are stated, it is imperative to define exactly all operating conditions employed. For example, when the relative mobility of beta globulin is given as 0.50, it must be accompanied by the requisite accessory data, including the identity of the reference substance having unit mobility (*e.g.*, M_r of beta globulin = 0.50 when M_r of albumin = 1.00). In addition, buffer composition, pH and ionic strength, the temperature at which the electrophoretic run was conducted, the type and composition and size (length and width) of the supporting medium, voltage and/or current applied across the electrodes, and size or concentration of the sample being analyzed are necessary. Statements and data given for relative mobilities and electrophoretic separations are meaningful only when all conditions of the electrophoretic procedure are clearly defined.

REFERENCES

1. Gouy, G.   J. Phys. Radium **9**, 457 (1910).
2. Debye, P., and E. Hückel.   Phys. Z. **24**, 185, 305 (1923).
3. Consden, R., A. H. Gordon, and A. J. P. Martin.   Biochem. J. **38**, 224 (1946).
4. Lewis, G. N. E., and M. Randall.   J. Am. Chem. Soc. **43**, 1112 (1921).
5. McDonald, H. J., and R. H. Spitzer.   Circulation Res. **1**, 396 (1953).
6. McDonald, H. J., J. L. Foresman, and E. W. Bermes, Jr.   Proc. Soc. Exp. Biol. Med. **94**, 493 (1957).
7. Mac Innes, D. A.   *The Principles of Electrochemistry* (New York: Reinhold Publishing Corp., 1939).
8. Helmholtz, H.   Wied. Ann. **7**, 337 (1879).
9. Kunkel, H. G., and A. Tiselius.   J. Gen. Physiol. **35**, 89 (1951).
10. Schwimmer, S.   Arch. Biochem. Biophys. **43**, 108 (1958).
11. Consden, R., and W. M. Stanier.   Nature **170**, 1069 (1952).
12. Kunkel, H. G.   In *Methods of Biochemical Analysis*, ed. D. Glick (New York: Interscience, 1954), p 141.
13. Monty, K. J., M. Morrison, E. Alling, and E. Stotz.   J. Biol. Chem. **220**, 295 (1956).
14. Uriel, J., and P. Grabar.   Bull. Soc. Chim. Biol. **38**, 1253 (1956).
15. Wieme, R. J.   *Agar Gel Electrophoresis* (Amsterdam: Elsevier Publishing Co., 1965).

CHAPTER 3

Cellulose Acetate Properties and Electrophoresis Equipment

Cellulose acetate is the acetylated product obtained by the action of acetic anhydride on cellulose. Membranes made from this material consist of a three-dimensional structure of interlocking pores which make up approximately 80% of the total volume (Figure 4). In addition, they have a refractive index of 1.47 and can be rendered transparent by the use of a liquid of comparable refractive index. Cellulose acetate membranes which vary in the degree to which cellulose is acetylated are commercially available; some of those most commonly used for electrophoresis are made of cellulose triacetate (*e.g.*, Sepraphore III, Gelman Instrument Company). In their dry state the membranes are rather brittle but exhibit a high tensile strength. After saturation with buffer, they acquire a gel-like appearance and lose their brittleness, so that handling of wet strips is relatively easy.

An important consideration in performing and evaluating results of electrophoretic studies is the reproducibility of electrophoretic behavior. This is highly dependent upon the structure and composition of the supporting medium. Cellulose acetate membranes used for electrophoresis generally exhibit only minor variations in pore size, density, thickness, and other physical properties. Their uniform properties and their versatility as a supporting medium for various procedures are desirable features which frequently make cellulose acetate the medium of choice in performing electrophoretic analysis of a number of substances of biological importance.

Membranes produced for use in electrophoresis are available in various dimensions. A commonly used size is 2.5×17 cm ($1 \times 6\frac{3}{4}$ inches). Other sizes are available, and sheets of cellulose acetate mea-

19

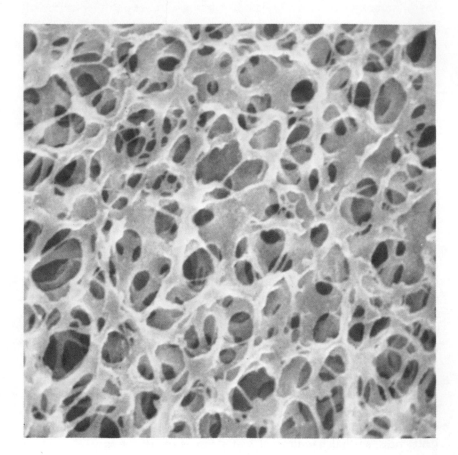

Figure 4. Electron micrograph of cellulose acetate membrane, showing microporous structure. (Courtesy of Dr. E. Bulba, Department of Environmental Health Sciences, Harvard University School of Public Health.)

suring 17 cm square can also be obtained. Each membrane has a thickness of approximately 120μ consisting of pores approximately 0.4μ in diameter. These characteristics have empirically been found to be suitable for membranes used for electrophoresis, although thickness and pore diameter can be regulated during production. For example, when used as bacteriological filters, the pore size of cellulose acetate is tailored to meet the needs of specific applications. It is also possible that membranes can be fabricated which would have graded pore size and density. Such membranes would allow substances to be separated on cellulose acetate by both electrophoretic behavior and molecular size.

Cellulose acetate membranes are completely stable in aqueous solvents and are resistant to dilute acid and alkali. They are stable in alcohols and phenolic solvents but can be dissolved with ketonic solvents or with concentrated acetic acid (Table I).

Table I

Solvent Resistance of Cellulose Acetate Membranes

Not affected by alcohols	Not affected by hydrocarbons	Dissolved by
methanol	benzene	acetone
ethanol	xylene	acetic acid (glacial)
propanol	toluene	chloroform
butanol	petroleum ether	dioxane
		ethyl acetate
		methylene chloride

Some impurities and trace elements are present in cellulose acetate; these are tabulated in Table II. It is possible that the presence of trace metals may affect the electrophoretic separation of certain substances, although this has not been determined.

Cellulose acetate electrophoretic strips are produced by a number of manufacturers and come packaged and ready for use, requiring only equilibration with buffer. Some of the major manufacturers are listed at the end of this chapter. Membranes produced by these firms may differ somewhat in density, thickness, pore size, and degree of acetylation of cellulose. Cellulose acetate is also available with a mylar backing, or in the form of a prepared gel. Some of the cellulose acetate membranes are provided with perforations near the ends to accommodate different chamber configurations equipped with guide notches for holding them in a horizontal position.

The basic design of the electrophoresis chamber used for cellulose acetate membranes resembles that used for horizontal paper electrophoresis. This consists of a rigid plastic case with wells for anode and cathode compartments separated by glass or plastic. The basic design is illustrated in Figure 5. Various modifications of this design are available, and some are equipped with adjustable feet used to maintain horizontal alignment of buffer fluid within the chamber. Most chambers used for paper electrophoresis can readily be adapted for cellulose

Table II

Impurities and Trace Elements in Cellulose Acetate

Element	Concentration (mg/100 g)				
	Sartorius	Schleicher & Schuell	Sepraphore III	Millipore	Oxoid*
Aluminum	1.4	1.3	2.8	1.0	NA
Barium	0.03	0.05	0.01	0.05	NA
Cadmium	ND	ND	ND	ND	NA
Calcium	1.0	3.5	3.5	0.50	21.0
Chromium	0.08	0.06	0.13	0.25	< 0.05
Cobalt	ND	ND	0.04	0.01	< 0.05
Copper	ND	ND	0.04	0.01	< 0.05
Iron	ND	ND	0.39	ND	1.6
Lead	ND	0.01	0.01	0.01	< 0.05
Lithium	0.02	0.01	0.03	0.04	NA
Magnesium	1.0	0.80	1.2	2.0	NA
Manganese	ND	0.01	0.02	0.03	< 0.05
Molybdenum	ND	ND	Tr	ND	< 0.05
Nickel	0.02	ND	ND	ND	< 0.05
Phosphorus	10.0	8.5	10.0	8.5	NA
Potassium	NA	NA	NA	NA	1.9
Silver	ND	ND	ND	ND	< 0.05
Sodium	12.5	12.5	NA	20.8	26.6
Strontium	ND	0.02	Tr	ND	NA
Tin	NA	NA	NA	NA	< 0.05
Vanadium	ND	ND	ND	ND	NA
Zinc	0.10	0.11	0.02	0.03	< 0.05

Tr = trace;   ND = not detected;   NA = not analyzed

*Values for Oxoid adapted from J. Kohn, in *Chromatographic and Electrophoretic Techniques, Vol. II, Zone Electrophoresis*, I. Smith, ed., New York: Interscience, 1960, p. 56

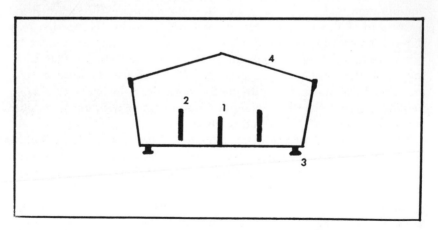

Figure 5.   Section illustrating an electrophoresis chamber which can be used for cellulose acetate membranes or other supporting media. (1) Center divider; (2) bridge for cellulose acetate membrane supporting rack; (3) adjustable leveling feet; (4) gabled cover for collection of condensate.

Figure 6. Electrophoretic equipment (A. H. Thomas Company) used in the author's laboratory, including cabinet, power supply, and supporting rack (right foreground) for cellulose acetate membranes.

acetate electrophoresis, using the same electrical power supplies for both (Figure 6).

Most designs in use require sequential, one-by-one application of samples to cellulose acetate membranes. A recently introduced model

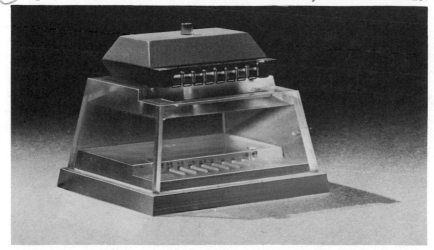

Figure 7. Multisample applicator which allows simultaneous application of up to eight samples. (Courtesy of the Gelman Instrument Company, Ann Arbor, Michigan.)

uses an applicator which is capable of simultaneous application of up to eight samples on a 5.6×12.7 cm membrane (Figure 7). This offers the advantage of increased convenience and speed and may help to reduce irregularities in mobility among samples such as are occasionally observed with serial application.

Covered staining trays, used for the various staining and rinsing procedures, are generally constructed from plastic; they are available from manufacturers of electrophoresis equipment. These same trays can be employed as moisture-retaining incubation chambers. When used for the isoenzyme procedures, for example, water is placed in the bottom of the closed chamber to keep cellulose acetate membranes moist during incubation of the isoenzyme strips with mixtures of substrate and dye.

Dye substances employed for detection of a variety of compounds separated electrophoretically are available from distributors of chemical supplies and from manufacturers of electrophoresis materials. Buffer salts can be purchased as ready-made solutions or in packages which need only to be dissolved in the appropriate volume of water before use. Some staining chemicals and mixtures of chemical reactants are available in capsules which contain premeasured quantities of each required component. These afford an additional convenience for the laboratory worker since the contents of the capsules need only be dissolved before use. Furthermore, use of these capsules avoids problems associated with storage and limited shelf life of certain chemicals and dyes.

Several brands of cellulose acetate are listed below with the names of manufacturing firms. Some of these firms also supply equipment and accessories for electrophoresis, including densitometers, recorders, or spectrophotometers used for quantitative evaluation of results.

Brand Names of Cellulose Acetate	*Manufacturing Firms*
Sepraphore III	Gelman Instrument Co., Ann Arbor, Michigan
S & S 2500 Cellulose Acetate Membrane	Carl Schleicher and Schuell Co., Keene, New Hampshire
Celotate, Phoroslide	Millipore Corp., Bedford, Massachusetts
Titan	Helena Laboratories, Allen Park, Michigan
Celagram	Shandon Scientific Co., Inc. (England)
Oxoid	Oxo, Ltd. (England)

Brand Names of Cellulose Acetate	*Manufacturing Firms*
Sartorius Membrane Filters	Sartorius (Germany)
Cellogel	Chemetron (Italy)
Separax	Fuji Photo Film Co. (Japan)

Suppliers of Electrophoresis Equipment and Accessories

Arthur H. Thomas Co., Philadelphia, Pennsylvania
Carl Schleicher and Schuell Co., Keene, New Hampshire
Gelman Instrument Co., Ann Arbor, Michigan
Beckman Instrument Co., Fullerton, California
Brinkmann Instruments Inc., Westbury, New York
Millipore Corp., Bedford, Massachusetts
Shandon Scientific Co., Inc., Sewickley, Pennsylvania

CHAPTER 4

General Procedures

Procedures employed for the electrophoretic separation of a number of substances are similar in many respects, and a discussion of basic techniques employed in performing electrophoresis on cellulose acetate membranes is generally applicable to the procedures described in greater detail in the appropriate sections to follow.

To ensure proper handling of the membranes, essential for good results, it is advisable to use clean forceps with smooth, flat tips. Before the membrane is prepared for electrophoresis, each strip should be marked so that the sample being analyzed can readily be identified. A marking pencil or pen with indelible ink should be used so that the mark will not wash off in the buffer solutions used for electrophoresis or be eluted by solvents used during the staining and clearing procedures. If the mark is used to designate the origin or the point of sample application, it must also be made of a substance that will not migrate in either direction when current is passed through the membrane. Electrophoresis markers are available from some firms which manufacture and distribute electrophoresis supplies and equipment. Certain commonly used ball-point pens (*e.g.*, Bic) can also be used. It is generally preferable to mark the strips when dry—once saturated with buffer, they become soft and pliable, and pressure generated in marking may produce distortions on the strip.

Special care should be exercised in wetting the strip in preparation for receiving the sample. The cellulose acetate membrane should be allowed to float on the surface of the buffer solution for several seconds in order to absorb the solution into its porous structure. The initially opaque, white strip will then take on a gel-like appearance. It can then be immersed completely in the buffer. This procedure must be followed; improper wetting of the strip will result in formation of discontinuous areas within the membrane. For example, if a strip were directly plunged into the buffer, pockets of air would be trapped within the membrane and appear as opaque areas against the translucent, gel-like background where buffer has penetrated into the matrix. The air pockets would constitute areas of discontinuity and interfere with electrophoresis. Application of the correct procedure for preparing the membrane should therefore be emphasized as the first requisite for good electrophoretic results. Some workers prefer to leave the cellulose acetate strips in buffer solution for several hours, or even overnight. Prolonged soaking does not adversely affect the membranes although saturation with buffer should be complete within a few minutes.

Membranes saturated with buffer should be placed on an electrophoresis blotter fashioned from filter paper so that excess buffer can be removed by absorption. When droplets of liquid are no longer visible on the surface, the membranes should promptly be mounted in the electrophoresis chamber. It is important to avoid delay at this juncture, because dehydration of the strips will produce irregularities in electromigration. Some workers prefer to facilitate removal of excess buffer from the membranes by blotting them between two layers of filter paper. Only gentle pressure should be used when doing this in order to avoid creating distortions within the membranes.

Positioning of the strips is accomplished either with or without the use of retainers. Small magnetic bars to hold the strips in a horizontal position are supplied with some chambers. The membranes can also be fixed in a horizontal position without the use of retaining bars by lightly pressing the moist ends of the membranes against the edges of the supporting rack. The membranes are held in the desired position by means of liquid capillary action. This is a convenient and rapid method for positioning the strips. The important point is to maintain a horizontal alignment of the cellulose acetate strips so that catenary effects can be avoided. Care should be taken to ensure that only the ends of the strips are handled in all steps. Forceps should be employed for all but the final step of positioning the membrane within the chamber since fingerprints transfer readily to cellulose acetate and may cause electrophoretograms to stain abnormally. In addition, accidental folding or bending may permanently crease the membranes and result in production of artifacts.

It is also important to be certain that the buffer level is equal in both the anodal and cathodal sections of the electrophoresis chamber, and that the chamber itself is level on the working surface. Differences in fluid level between the ends of the electrophoresis chamber may give rise to gradients in hydrostatic pressure and cause buffer to be siphoned from the higher to the lower end of the chamber, resulting in irregularities in electrophoretic migration.

Samples can be applied by means of transferance from parallel wires or by use of transfer strips. For best results, sample application should be carried out after the membranes have been mounted in the electrophoresis chamber. The use of wire applicators on cellulose acetate membranes should be undertaken with care. Again, it is advisable to use gentle pressure when applying·samples, since excess pressure will produce distortions in the supple membranes which may then take up dye abnormally. This problem can frequently be avoided by use of transfer strips (available from A. H. Thomas Company, Philadelphia, Pennsylvania); 1–2 mm × 15 mm strips can also be fabricated from filter paper (Whatman #1, Schleicher and Schuell #595, Munktell #1F, or the equivalent of these) or cellulose acetate. Transfer strips allow the sample to be applied to the supporting medium by means of absorption. Generally, 60–70% of the sample is transferred to the supporting membrane in this manner. When desired, application of precise volumes may be accomplished by direct delivery from calibrated micropipets to the starting point on the membrane. However, distribution patterns are of primary importance in the great majority of electrophoretic separations, and quantitative transfer of sample is not normally of vital concern. The use of transfer strips offers an additional advantage because they can restrict diffusion of sample and hence provide a more uniform distribution of clearly separated bands.

Sample size or volume will depend upon the concentration in solution of substance or substances being separated. As a general rule, it is advisable to use only as much sample as is required to give distinctly stained fractions. When sample size is large, the membrane may become overloaded and resolution of fractions impaired. In general, when human serum or plasma samples are being analyzed, 1–3 μl are sufficient for protein, 5–10 μl for lipoprotein, and 10–20 μl for lactate dehydrogenase electrophoresis. The lateral edges of cellulose acetate membranes should be kept free of sample in order to avoid distortions in electrophoretic patterns. Evaporation of liquid, accelerated at the edges because of larger exposed areas, may produce alterations in buffer ionic strength and sample concentration.

Samples are usually applied near the anodal or cathodal bridge, depending upon the charge of the substance or substances being separated and the pH of the buffer solution. For example, proteins which have a negative charge at pH 8.6 will migrate toward the anode, and samples containing proteins should be applied near the cathodal bridge. On the other hand, substances with a net positive charge at the pH of the buffer should be applied near the anodal bridge since they will exhibit cathodal migration. This may be the case when mixtures of certain amino acids are being analyzed.

Occasionally, electro-osmotic effects may be employed to enhance electrophoretic separation of unknown substances. Hence, a substance whose isoelectric point is close to the pH of the buffer solution can be made to move as the result of electro-osmotic flow. In such a case, the sample may be applied at some intermediate location on the membrane away from the direction of electro-osmotic flow. When voltage is applied along the electrophoretic strip, the substance will be carried along by electro-osmotic buffer flow and be separated from those which are charged at the pH of that buffer.

The time required for completion of electrophoresis is dependent upon factors such as potential gradient across the electrodes and heat build-up as well as electrical charge of the substance. Relatively short running times can be used for cellulose acetate electrophoresis. Satisfactory separations have occurred in as little as 20–30 minutes. Intervals in excess of 1½–2 hours are seldom necessary when the appropriate buffer solution and operating conditions are employed.

Reference dyes are sometimes used to monitor the rate of migration. Such dyes may contain mixtures of several indicator substances with different rates of migration. The RBY reference dye (Gelman Instrument Company, Ann Arbor, Michigan), for example, consists of a mixture of Apalon Yellow, Amaranth Red, and Brilliant Blue which will separate electrophoretically into the three colored products. Albumin can be stained with Bromphenol Blue prior to electrophoresis, and this complex is frequently used to determine the rate of migration of albumin and indicate when sufficient separation of serum proteins has been achieved. Dyed reference substances can serve as internal controls to follow the progress of individual electrophoretic runs. In addition, markers can be used to locate and isolate bands of intermediate mobility prior to staining; this would be of particular value for the recovery and subsequent characterization or analysis of separated fractions.

In routine use, once standard conditions for electrophoresis of a particular substance or group of substances have been established, indicator dyes are not normally needed except in special cases because the rates of migration under standardized conditions will not vary appreciably.

Staining and detection of specific substances on cellulose acetate membranes will be discussed in later sections of this book along with descriptions of specific electrophoretic procedures. In general, three types of procedures are used to detect the presence of substances separated by electrophoresis. The most commonly used is that employed for the staining of proteins and lipids. This consists of absorption of the dye by means of mutual solubility of dye and reactant in a common solvent, as in the staining of lipids with Oil Red O or Sudan Black B in alcoholic solutions, or of chemical reaction of anionic dyes (*e.g.*, Amido Black 10B, Ponceau S) with basic groups such as the amino groups of proteins in acid solution. A second type of detection system makes use of the ability of separated molecules to catalyze the oxidation or reduction of a dye to its colored derivative which can then be visualized and measured photometrically. Such systems have been devised for use in the detection, for example, of isoenzymes and of hemoglobin and haptoglobin. Detection by measurement of fluorescence has also been employed for some substances which, under defined conditions or upon reaction with certain chemicals, will fluoresce at given wavelengths of light.

Stained electrophoretic strips can be preserved and filed with permanent records. A commonly used method of preservation consists of immersing the stained electrophoretograms in a solution of approximately 10–12% glacial acetic acid in methanol. This procedure causes dehydration of the strips. They become transparent upon drying and can be stored permanently. It should be noted that methanolic solutions containing greater than 15% glacial acetic acid may dissolve the membranes. In some cases, dimethylformamide may be substituted for glacial acetic acid. Aqueous solutions of 30% dimethylformamide or dimethylsulfoxide have also been used successfully to clear and make transparent stained electrophoretograms. When the stain used in a particular procedure is not water soluble, electrophoretic strips can be preserved by impregnation with glycerol. This consists of placing the stained electrophoretic strips which have been rinsed in aqueous solution in a vessel containing glycerol and allowing the glycerol to penetrate the structure of the cellulose acetate membranes. This method of preservation avoids the possibility of eluting dye from stained strips as is occasionally encountered when strips stained with lipophilic agents are cleared with acetic acid and methanol. In addition, strips impregnated with glycerol can be mounted on glass slides for photometric scanning, after which they can be placed in polyethylene bags, sealed, and retained for permanent records.

Quantitation of substances separated by electrophoresis and stained with the appropriate reagent solutions is accomplished most conveniently and rapidly by densitometry or fluorometry. These methods of measurement require no further preparation of the strip after color development. Response of the photometer or fluorometer can be displayed and recorded on permanent charts. When these recorders are equipped with electronic integrators, estimates of relative distributions are obtained by simple calculation of areas enclosed by individual peaks.

An alternate method for quantitation consists of identifying individual stained bands and cutting them from the electrophoretogram. The stained substances are eluted with appropriate solvents, or segments of cellulose acetate together with the stained fractions are completely dissolved in organic solvents. An estimate of the concentration of a given substance is obtained by spectrophotometric or fluorometric measurement of the eluted dye or the dissolved membrane containing stained material.

Some of the commonly used buffer solutions can be prepared in accordance with the following schedule which gives the amount of each substance required to make one liter of solution.

Barbital, pH 8.6, ionic strength 0.1
   diethyl barbituric acid 2.80 g
   sodium diethyl barbiturate 20.60 g

Barbital, pH 8.6, ionic strength 0.075
   diethyl barbituric acid 2.76 g
   sodium diethyl barbiturate 15.45 g

Barbital, pH 8.6, ionic strength 0.05
   diethyl barbituric acid 1.84 g
   sodium diethyl barbiturate 10.30 g

Acetate, pH 4, ionic strength 0.1
   glacial acetic acid 25.60 ml
   sodium acetate $3H_2O$, 13.61 g

Phosphate, pH 7.5, ionic strength 0.028
   $NaH_2PO_4 \cdot 2H_2O$, 0.156 g
   $NaH PO_4 \cdot 2H_2O$, 1.596 g

Tris-citrate, pH 8.6, ionic strength 0.075
   Tris-(hydroxymethyl)-aminomethane, 9.10 g
   citric acid 1.05 g

Tris-HCl, pH 8.3, 0.2M
   Tris-(hydroxymethyl)-aminomethane 24.2 g dissolved in 700
      ml H_2O, add conc. HCl to pH 8.3, dilute to 1 liter

Tris-EDTA-borate, pH 8.4
   Tris-(hydroxymethyl)-aminomethane, 10.8 g
   Na_2-EDTA, 0.9 g
   boric acid, 5.5 g

Tris-EDTA-borate, pH 8.9
   Tris-(hydroxymethyl)-aminomethane, 10 g
   Na_2-EDTA, 1.3 g
   boric acid, 0.8 g

Tris-EDTA-borate, pH 9.6
   Tris-(hydroxymethyl)-aminomethane, 9.6 g
   Na_2-EDTA, 1.0 g
   boric acid, 0.45 g

Tris-glycine, pH 9.3
   Tris-(hydroxymethyl)-aminomethane, 34.5 g
   glycine, 5.2 g

CHAPTER 5

Evaluation of Electrophoretic Patterns

A particularly attractive feature of cellulose acetate membranes is that their index of refraction is close to those of immersion oil and glycerol; therefore electrophoretic strips can be stained and rendered transparent for subsequent evaluation. In contrast with paper electrophoretograms, often plagued with adverse effects of diffusion and adsorption which combine to create areas of unclear differentiation, cellulose acetate electrophoretograms usually present clearly differentiated fractions which can readily be stained with the common histological stains.

Evaluation of electrophoretic patterns is carried out in several ways. Visual inspection of electrophoretic strips is the most convenient means and is frequently practiced. Patterns of electrophoretic behavior often can be discerned by noting the appearance of the stained electrophoretogram, and grossly abnormal patterns are easily distinguishable without resorting to quantitative estimations of fractional composition which require more extensive procedures. Although it has been claimed that the experienced eye can detect variations of as little as 10% on electrophoretic strips, visual evaluation is often subjective. It introduces the additional variable of differences among individual observers and is therefore not the method of choice except when perception of gross changes in electrophoretic behavior is of primary interest, or for inspection of immunoelectrophoretic strips. In nearly all other cases, quantitative determination of separated substances is preferred because objective interpretation of data depends upon careful, precise acquisition of data, whether the information obtained is to be used for screening purposes, for clinical diagnosis, or for investigative research. Proper use of quantitative measurements can make data meaningful to many individuals in a number of fields of related interest.

Most of the methods for estimating or quantitating fractions of substances separated by electrophoresis on cellulose acetate are easily accomplished by means of several basic procedures which depend upon optical measurement of the intensity of dye or colored complex

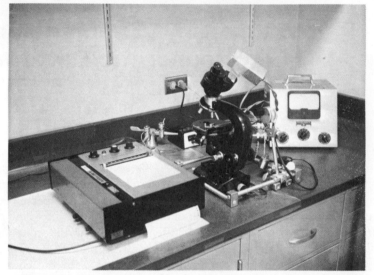

Figure 8.   Equipment employed in the author's laboratory for transmission densitometry. Center: microscope with motor-driven stage; right: Photovolt photometer; left: Bausch and Lomb V.O.M.–5 recorder. Note phototube positioned atop ocular of the microscope.

formed by chemical reaction of the unknown substance with indicator dye. Densitometric scanning is the simplest and most direct method because all measurements are made on the electrophoretic strip. By this means, the intensity of a light beam passing through a transparent or translucent membrane containing the fractionated stained substances is measured. Light transmitted through the strip is detected by means of a phototube, and the signal is amplified and registered electronically on a photometer or displayed on a strip chart recorder (Figure 8). With the development of improved instruments for electronic scanning, either cleared or uncleared membranes can be scanned and results quickly calculated.

Densitometric scanning usually produces a recording on a strip chart. Since the magnitude of the photometric response is proportional to the intensity of the stain, which in turn is proportional to the amount of material present on the electrophoretic strip, the densitometric tracing gives a visual record of individual fractions in the form of a peak or a series of peaks. These peaks are usually of Gaussian configuration[1] unless tailing or skewing of peaks occurs due to sample overloading or to the nonhomogeneous nature of substances separated. Peaks of Gaussian shape can be calculated either manually or by automatic integrators.

Planimetry is a convenient and precise method for manually calculating areas enclosed by individual peaks on densitometric tracings. This is accomplished by tracing the outlines of individual peaks with the moving arm of the compensating polar planimeter; the area within the peak is obtained directly by reading the value recorded on the scale of the planimeter (Figure 9).

Figure 9. Planimeter used for calculating peak areas from densitometric tracings.

Triangulation may be employed as a means for calculating peak areas; isosceles triangles are drawn using tangents to the sides of the sloping peaks (Figure 10) and the area approximated by applying the formula for computing the area of a triangle (height × width of base ÷ 2). As expected, the precision and accuracy of this method depend upon the manner of construction of the triangles.

It is also possible to cut out and weigh individual peaks from the strip chart recording. Since the density of the paper is quite uniform, an estimate of the relative size of each peak can be obtained by this method.

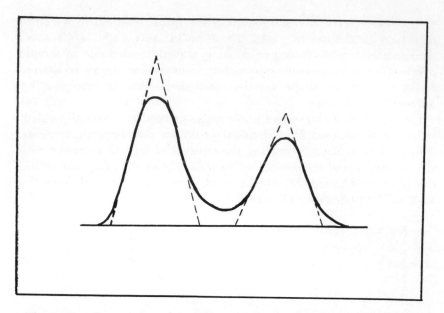

Figure 10.   Construction of isosceles triangles by drawing tangents to sides of peaks.

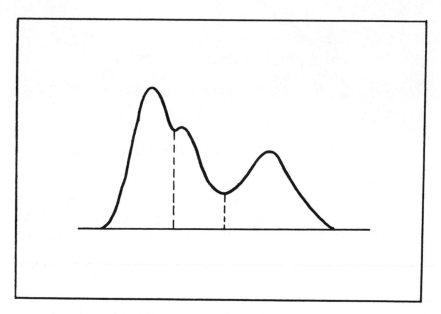

Figure 11.   Separation of adjacent peaks with perpendicular lines drawn to the base.

Some densitometers are equipped with electronic integrating circuits which will automatically integrate the areas under individual peaks as the tracings are being recorded. To calculate the relative area in each peak, one needs only to add the individual counts registered for each peak and obtain the relative proportion of each. This method requires dropping a perpendicular line from the lowest point between two curves to the baseline of the tracing (Figure 11), and may be subject to error when overlapping peaks are encountered. Nevertheless, electronic integration of peak areas offers a considerable saving in time and effort, especially when a large number of densitometric tracings need to be performed routinely. The incorporation of computer circuitry into scanning densitometers has further increased the convenience of densitometric measurement and reduced the possibility of human error in calculation of peak areas. This type of instrument will scan electrophoretograms, integrate peak areas, store the raw data, compute and present the results in printed form with the relative percentage composition of each fraction; it will also calculate the concentration of each component if the overall concentration is known (Figure 12).

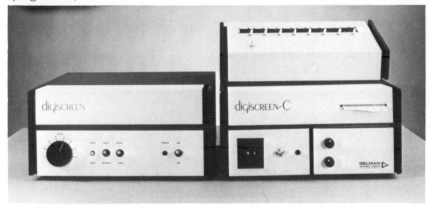

Figure 12. Computerized scanning densitometer. (Courtesy of the Gelman Instrument Company, Ann Arbor, Michigan.)

Occasionally, densitometric tracings will show the presence of overlapping peaks. These may arise when bands are not completely resolved by electrophoresis or do not appear completely separated on the densitometric tracing because of optical limitations in the scanning apparatus. Overlapping peaks may present a problem to the analyst because it is frequently difficult to decide how the peaks can be set apart from one another and whether the unresolved peaks are in fact harboring

minor components which are not immediately apparent to the eye or
to the electronic integrator. Such tracings are difficult to examine and
evaluate by electronic integrating scanners in general use. Planimetry,
which is based on visualization of separate peaks, may offer a slight
advantage in this regard because overlapping curves can at times be
segregated by extrapolating to the baseline the sides of what appear
to be separate peaks. However, doubts may arise regarding the accuracy of this method since the mind may influence the eye in deciding
the configuration of overlapping peaks. The problem can be partially
solved by use of an instrument which is designed to perform this
function electronically. The Du Pont 310 Curve Resolver incorporates
an analog computer which electronically synthesizes component peaks
to fit the original data; it is designed to resolve and quantitate con-
tiguous, poorly-separated peaks on densitometric tracings as well as,
of course, to calculate the areas of distinctly separated peaks (Figure
13). This instrument may not lend itself so readily to routine or screen-

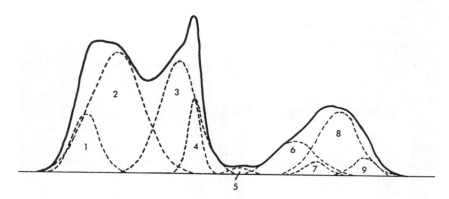

Figure 13. Densitometric tracing showing overlapping peaks (solid line) and
component peaks (broken lines) obtained with Du Pont 310 Curve Resolver.

ing procedures as scanning densitometers with electronic integrators.
When properly used, the Du Pont 310 Curve Resolver yields results
which cannot be attained by other means. Electronic synthesis and
resolution can be particularly valuable when exhaustive analysis of
densitometric tracings is desired, for example when the nature and
composition of minor components are under investigation, or when
calculation of relative electrophoretic mobility is of importance to an
experimental design.

When performing densitometry, it is important to know the specificity of the stain for the substance being analyzed and to determine the

linearity of the photometric detection system; that is, whether the staining reaction occurs in reproducible fashion for compounds being measured, and whether the intensity in color of stained substances is proportional to their concentrations. Both of these are important factors in ascertaining whether quantitative determinations of individual electrophoretic fractions are required or whether qualitative evaluation is sufficient.

Some of the more commonly used stains, for example, Amido Black 10B, Sudan Black B, Ponceau S, Oil Red O, and the tetrazolium salts, exhibit specificity for certain substances, and do this in a reproducible fashion. Several examples of these are discussed below.

Bartlett[2] observed that the optical density of proteins stained with Amido Black 10B increases linearly with increasing concentration of dye and that albumin and globulins have equivalent affinity for Amido Black 10B on a percentage basis. Therefore, photometric measurements (densitometry or spectrophotometry) of serum protein fractions stained with this agent can be used for quantitative determination of protein distributions without correction for differences in dye affinity.

Ponceau S is also frequently used to stain proteins separated on cellulose acetate. Briere and Mull[3] showed that the color intensity of serum protein fractions stained with Ponceau S is proportional to the concentration of each fraction. Similarly, Lissamine Green has been used for quantitative electrophoretic analyses of serum proteins.[4] Nigrosine possesses great sensitivity for proteins. This dye is less frequently used for routine protein staining because dye uptake declines with increasing protein concentration[5,6] but may be employed to advantage in immunoelectrophoretic and immunodiffusion procedures which will be discussed in a later chapter.

Two stains commonly used to stain lipids and lipoproteins are Sudan Black B and Oil Red O. Lansink[7] demonstrated that the Sudan dyes and Oil Red O consist of several fractions which are revealed by thin-layer chromatography. Since blood and tissues contain various lipids of different chemical structure, a question frequently asked is whether all lipids and lipoproteins are stained with equal intensity on electrophoretic strips. The affinity of various lipid classes and subclasses for lipophilic stains has not been established. However, Swahn[8] showed that the coloration of different types of lipids (cholesterol, cholesterol stearate, triglycerides and corn oil) by Sudan Black occurred with equal affinity and that staining intensity was proportional to the concentration of each lipid. Hence serum lipoproteins fractionated by electrophoresis can be compared quantitatively.

Tetrazolium salts are the most commonly used compounds for the detection of enzymatic activity of lactate dehydrogenase and other enzymes. The transfer of hydrogen from reduced coenzyme ($NADH_2$) to the tetrazolium salt through the mediation of phenazine methosulfate produces a colored formazan. Whitaker's studies[9] show that the optical density of the colored product formed by the reaction of LDH isoenzymes with 2-*p*-iodophenyl-3-*p*-nitrophenyl-5-phenyltetrazolium chloride (INT) is linear with increasing concentrations of coenzyme. Therefore, individual isoenzymes separated electrophoretically on cellulose acetate membranes and stained with INT can be evaluated by densitometric scanning and results calculated according to the area enclosed by the peak representing each isoenzyme.

Elution of stained fractions from cellulose acetate is frequently practiced. In this case, dye is removed from the supporting medium with the appropriate solvent and its intensity measured spectrophotometrically at an appropriate wavelength. A solution of 0.1N sodium hydroxide can be used for this purpose.[3, 10, 11] This is a very reliable method for quantitation but is more time-consuming than densitometric scanning.

Another method is to cut separated fractions from stained electrophoretic strips, after which the cellulose acetate segments along with the stained fractions can be dissolved completely in mixtures of organic solvents. Varying proportions of chloroform–methanol, chloroform–ethanol, acetone–acetic acid, and other mixtures incorporating methylene chloride, dioxane, and ethyl acetate may be used. In addition, cellulose acetate membranes containing protein fractions stained with Ponceau S can be dissolved in a nonvolatile solvent made up of 10% formic acid in dimethylsulfoxide. The stable solution of stained proteins is measured by spectrophotometry at 525 mμ.[12] Dimethylsulfoxide has also been used alone to dissolve segments of electrophoretograms containing stained proteins; dissolved mixtures are measured at 630 mμ against the appropriate blank.[13]

Of the methods outlined, elution of dye from the strips followed by spectrophotometric measurement is perhaps the most accurate and the most reliable because possible interference due to background dye absorbance and other effects can be eliminated. However, in most cases densitometric evaluation gives comparable results,[3] and densitometric scanning followed by quantitation of peak areas is the most convenient quantitative procedure. Reproducible results are obtained with normal care in the use of properly-designed equipment.

It should be noted that under normal circumstances calculation of peak areas from densitometric tracings gives relative percentage distributions of fractions separated electrophoretically. In most cases relative distribution is of primary interest, and overall concentrations of solutions of unfractionated sample are usually obtained by routine chemical procedures. If desired, these values can be used in conjunction with electrophoretic distributions to derive levels of individual fractions. Direct estimation of fractional composition can also be obtained by applying precisely known volumes of sample to the membrane prior to electrophoresis; densitometric or spectrophotometric analysis will then yield fractional distributions which can also be expressed in terms (mg/100 ml, m moles/1, etc.) of their concentrations in solution.

REFERENCES

1. Svedberg, T., and K. O. Pederson. *The Ultracentrifuge* (London and Oxford: The Clarendon Press, 1940).
2. Bartlett, R. C. Clin. Chem. **9**, 317 (1963).
3. Briere, R. O., and J. D. Mull. Am. J. Clin. Pathol. **42**, 547 (1964).
4. Brackenridge, C. J. Anal. Chem. **32**, 1353 (1960).
5. Kohn, J. In *Chromatographic and Electrophoretic Techniques*, Vol. II, ed. I. Smith (New York: Interscience, 1960) p 56.
6. Rice, J. D., Jr., and B. Bleakney. Clin. Chim. Acta **12**, 343 (1965).
7. Lansink, A. G. W. Histochemie **16**, 68 (1968).
8. Swahn, B. Scand. J. Clin. Lab. Invest. **5**, Suppl. 9 (1953).
9. Whitaker, J. F. Clin. Chim. Acta **24**, 23 (1969).
10. Kohn, J. Clin. Chim. Acta **2**, 297 (1957).
11. Cherrey, H., C. Cherrey, and G. Siest. Pharm. Biol. **5**, 163 (1967).
12. Rice, E. W., and P. A. Hammer. Am. J. Clin. Pathol. **51**, 293 (1969).
13. Gadd, K. G. Nature **212**, 628 (1966).

CHAPTER 6

Proteins

The plasma proteins have been characterized very well and their physical and chemical properties have undergone exhaustive study. Detailed information concerning them can be found in the very extensive literature and textbooks describing their chemistry and physiology.[1,2,3] First isolated by differential precipitation in aqueous salt solutions, proteins and their amino acid subunits have been characterized by a wide variety of procedures. The discussion here will deal primarily with application of cellulose acetate membranes for the electrophoretic analysis of proteins and include a brief discussion of some conditions which give rise to abnormal distributions of serum proteins.

Electrophoretic analysis of serum and plasma proteins has become a widely employed analytic technique since Tiselius[4] first separated serum proteins into four main fractions (albumin and alpha, beta, and gamma globulins) by means of free boundary electrophoresis. Since that time, numerous supporting media have been employed for the separation of serum proteins. Some semisolid gels have shown an ability to resolve serum proteins into many fractions, and agar, acrylamide, and starch media have been used successfully. The relative convenience and low cost of filter paper strips have been instrumental in establishing electrophoresis of proteins as a useful technique for many research and diagnostic applications. However, long recognized adsorptive effects of filter paper can sometimes present problems in resolution and identification of the various fractions. Protein electrophoresis employing cellulose acetate membranes offers much better resolution and can be performed in a very short time.

PROCEDURE FOR PROTEIN ELECTROPHORESIS

Electrophoresis of serum and plasma proteins is commonly carried out in barbital buffer of pH 8.6 and ionic strength 0.05 or 0.075. Small sample volumes of 1–3 μl, applied with wire applicators or by means of transfer strips, are sufficient to define electrophoretically the composition of serum or plasma proteins. Use of large sample volumes may overload the cellulose acetate membranes and produce distortions in the pattern which interfere with interpretation. The electrophoretic run is carried out in a horizontal chamber at voltages ranging from 150–350 volts, depending upon the configuration of the chamber. Voltage drop between the electrodes is adjusted to provide approximately 1.5 mA of current per strip measuring 2.5 cm (1 inch) in width for 30–90 minutes. Upon completion of the electrophoretic run the strips are stained, after which they can be made transparent by clearing or by preservation in glycerol. Quantitation is carried out by densitometric scanning of transparent membranes. Alternatively, spectrophotometric evaluation is conducted by measuring at a selected wavelength the intensity of dye eluted with 0.1N sodium hydroxide solutions from individual protein fractions.

Several stains are widely employed for staining protein fractions. Amido Black 10B (Amido Schwarz 10B, Naphthalene Black 12B, Buffalo Black) was used initially by Grassmann and Hannig,[5] Flynn and de Mayo,[6] and Loeffler and Wunderly[7] for staining paper electro-

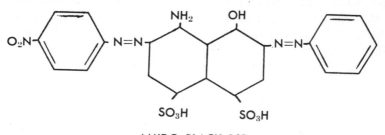

AMIDO BLACK 10B

phoretic strips, and is equally effective for staining proteins on cellulose acetate strips. The stain is prepared by dissolving 0.5 g of Amido Black 10B in 100 ml of a mixture of 10% glacial acetic acid in methanol. Protein fractions are completely stained in this solution within 5 minutes at which time the electrophoretic strips can be rinsed in several baths of 10% glacial acetic acid in methanol to remove background staining.

After removal from the rinsing fluid, the background will become transparent as the membranes dry, and proteins will show up as dark blue bands. For preservation in glycerol, the final glacial acetic acid–methanol rinse should contain 5–10% water to facilitate the penetration of glycerol. The membranes are then transferred directly to a glycerol bath containing 5–10% glacial acetic acid and sealed in polyethylene bags following impregnation.

Quantitation of separated fractions is readily accomplished by densitometric scanning of transparent strips. If desired, spectrophotometric measurements can be carried out at 600 mμ on individual stained fractions eluted with an alcoholic solution of 0.1–0.5N sodium hydroxide.

Ponceau S is used extensively for staining protein fractions on cellulose acetate.[8] The staining solution contains 0.2% Ponceau S dissolved in a 3–5% aqueous solution of trichloroacetic acid. Membranes are stained in this solution for 15 minutes followed by rinsing with

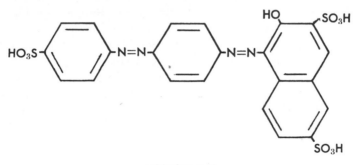

PONCEAU S

5% glacial acetic acid in water. Stained strips are preserved by drying or by impregnation with glycerol containing 5–10% glacial acetic acid.

As with strips stained with Amido Black 10B, Ponceau S-stained electrophoretograms are frequently scanned densitometrically, or the intensity of dye in each protein fraction is measured spectrophotometrically at 515–525 mμ after prior elution from stained membranes. Elution of dye is effected with 0.1N sodium hydroxide followed by acidification with a small volume of glacial acetic acid to restore the red color.

Other protein stains may be used effectively. For example, Azocarmine B dissolved in acetic acid–methanol is used in the same manner as Amido Black 10B. Bromphenol Blue, Lissamine Green (Light Green),[9, 10] Bromcresol Green,[11] and Nigrosine have also been used. The latter is a very sensitive protein stain. Protein bands are easily detected with a 0.001–0.002% solution of Nigrosine in 2–5% aqueous acetic acid.[12, 13] Staining with Nigrosine, however, requires a longer period of time, and strips are usually left overnight in the staining solution. Excess dye can be removed by rinsing in distilled water.

Selection of a stain for detection and evaluation of protein fractions separated by electrophoresis is usually made empirically. Since most of the stains described in this section have been demonstrated to yield satisfactory results, the final choice would depend upon personal preference as much as efficiency of the staining procedure and affinity of individual proteins for the dyes.

PHYSIOLOGY AND PATHOLOGY OF PLASMA PROTEINS

The approximate percentage distribution of plasma proteins in normal adults is shown in Table III. Abnormal protein patterns may occur in a variety of physiological disturbances, but, except for a few conditions, strict correlations between abnormal proteins and specific diseases have not been established. Some of the aberrations have been revealed by electrophoretic analysis. A decrease in plasma proteins usually reflects a loss of protein into the alimentary tract, or reduced synthesis or malabsorption of protein from the alimentary tract due to various diseases. Conversely, protein content is increased after dehydration due to vomiting or diarrhea, in some infectious diseases, and in the paraproteinemias. Factors governing the metabolism of proteins have been discussed by Munro.[14]

Hemorrhage, traumatic shock, burns, surgical procedures, or liver and kidney diseases may bring about a reduction in protein concentration and hence a reduction in osmotic pressure of the blood. As a consequence, water passes from plasma into the tissue spaces to give rise to edema. Albumin, especially because of its high concentration, is important for the maintenance of plasma osmotic pressure.

Table III

Approximate Percentage Distribution of Plasma Proteins

albumin	50
alpha$_1$ globulin	4
alpha$_2$ globulin	12
beta globulin	13
fibrinogen	8
gamma globulin	13

Changes in serum or plasma albumin are relatively nonspecific. Decreased albumin concentrations have been observed during pregnancy,[15,16,17] after surgery,[18] and in some acute infections of the liver[19] and kidneys.[20]

Polymorphisms of serum albumin have been reported in various animals[21,22,23] but rarely occur in human populations. Bisalbuminemia, or double albumin, first reported by Knedel,[24] appears to be an inherited condition of low incidence[25,26] characterized by the presence of two electrophoretically distinct albumin bands roughly equal in magnitude. Both of the albumins are immunochemically identical,[27] although Gitlin *et al.*[28] showed that a faster-moving variant albumin contained one additional peptide (lysine) residue in its structure when compared with the normal albumin. No obvious clinical disorder or congenital anomaly has been found to be associated with bisalbuminemia. More recently, several slow-moving albumin variants have been found.[29,30,31,32,33] These also seem to occur independently of manifestations of physiological abnormality.

The globulins consist of a heterogeneous population of proteins whose concentrations may fluctuate in various diseases. Gamma globulins of fetal serum appear to be of maternal origin; their concentration declines in the newborn from the time of birth, reaches its lowest level at three months, and gradually rises to adult levels.[34] Gamma globulins are increased in many inflammatory and infectious diseases because antibodies (immunoglobulins) are present in this fraction. Agammaglobulinemia, an inherited absence of gamma globulin from the serum or plasma, may result in loss of the ability to form antibodies.[35,36]

The alpha and beta globulins carry a number of substances, among them lipids, enzymes, polysaccharides, hormones, and certain metal ions. Elevations in alpha globulin, especially the alpha$_2$ globulin fraction, occur in acute inflammatory processes and are usually accompanied by an increase in the glycoprotein associated with alpha$_2$ globulin; on the other hand, hyperbetaglobulinemia occurs more frequently in chronic diseases such as myxedema and Waldenström's macroglobulinemia. Alpha$_2$ and beta globulins are increased in pregnancy.[15,16,17] In liver diseases, alpha globulins are increased and may be accompanied by a rise in beta globulin along with a fall in serum albumin.[19,37,38] Similar changes have been observed in renal diseases.[20] Following surgery, alpha globulins may be elevated for several days while albumin content is reduced.[18]

A rise in serum lipoproteins frequently occurs in atherosclerotic heart disease. It is possible that elevations in alpha and beta globulins which have been reported in diseases of the heart and arteries[39,40,41,42] may be related to disturbances in lipid metabolism because lipids traverse the circulation as lipid-protein complexes.

Fibrinogen is present in plasma and absent from serum. The concentration of fibrinogen appears in many cases to reflect changes in physiologic state. For example, increased levels are observed after bacterial and virus infections and in various pathological conditions which have been summarized by Munro.[14] Fibrinogen has an electrophoretic mobility intermediate between gamma globulin and beta globulin; afibrinogenemia, the absence of fibrinogen in affected individuals,[43,44] can be determined by eletrophoretic analysis of plasma.

The diagnostic applicability of serum or plasma protein electrophoresis is most amply demonstrated in the gammapathies of monoclonal or polyclonal nature. In multiple myeloma (a monoclonal gammopathy) the globulin component is elevated in blood and urine. The presence of Bence-Jones proteins in the urine (proteins which characteristically precipitate at 50°C and dissolve at 100°C) is diagnostic, and the electrophoretic pattern is distinguished by marked elevation of a single globulin component, usually in the gamma globulin region, which may comprise 70% of the total plasma protein. Densitometric tracings or patterns of multiple myeloma serum show characteristic spiked or "church spire" peaks. Macroglobulinemia (a polyclonal gammopathy) was first described by Waldenström.[45] Serum in patients with this disease contains 1–10 g% of immunoglobulin M. The electrophoretic pattern is characterized by an intense broad band in the gamma or beta globulin region which may give rise to a "saw tooth" type of pattern.

Gamma-1 macroglobulin with a sedimentation constant of 19S comprises 5–10% of the total gamma globulin and is separated from the major gamma globulin component (7S) by means of ultracentrifugation. Franklin and Kunkel[46] and Korngold and van Leeuwen[47] showed that normal gamma-1 macroglobulin and the pathological Waldenström's macroglobulins have similar immunological features. Both possess up to 10% carbohydrate, compared with normal 7S gamma globulin which contains approximately 2.5% carbohydrate and myeloma proteins which contain approximately 4% carbohydrate.[48,49]

Immunoglobulins are proteins which function as antibodies or are chemically related to antibodies. They are composed of two identical short-chain polypeptides (molecular weight approximately 30,000) and two identical long-chain polypeptides (molecular weight approximately 50,000). The four chains are linked by disulfide groups. Immunoglobulins are divided into several major groups, γA-globulin

(IgA), γG-globulin (IgG), γM-globulin (IgM), and the recently characterized γD-globulin (IgD)[50] and γE-globulin (IgE).[51] IgA, IgD, and IgG are 7S proteins with a molecular weight of approximately 150,000, and are produced by plasma cells in multiple myeloma, while IgE has a sedimentation constant of approximately 8S and exhibits reaginic activity. IgM is a 19S protein with a molecular weight of approximately one million and is produced excessively in Waldenström's macroglobulinemia due to a proliferation of lymphocytoid cells.

Waldenström's macroglobulinemia is primarily a disease of older age, usually associated with enlargement of lymphoid tissue and enlargement of the spleen or liver. Patients with this condition may not experience appreciable symptoms. Myeloma, on the other hand, is a progressive and generally fatal neoplastic disease characterized by proliferation of plasma cells and infiltration of the bone marrow by myeloma cells. Abnormal (Bence-Jones) globulins may be present in plasma or urine or both. Differentiation between the two can be accomplished by examination of electrophoretic patterns. In contrast with the spiked appearance of the myeloma proteins, macroglobulinemia presents a broad, diffuse enhancement of gamma globulin.

An explanation of the mechanism underlying macroglobulinemia and myeloma, proposed by Waldenström,[52] is based on Burnet's[53] clonal theory (one clone of plasma cells produces one protein) and assumes the presence of an inhibitor of gamma globulin synthesis which is normally present, possibly in the form of antibodies directed against an individual's particular single clone of cells. Removal of this inhibitor results in the synthesis of an excess of gamma globulin, as in essential hypergammaglobulinemia. If, on the other hand, removal of this inhibitor is accompanied by a mutation or stimulus to unlimited production of gamma globulin, myeloma or macroglobulinemia results.

Although all of the serum protein fractions are also present in cerebrospinal fluid, their concentrations are much less (0.02–0.04%) than those encountered in serum (6.5–7.5%); therefore, samples may need to be concentrated for electrophoresis. Concentration of cerebrospinal fluid may be accomplished by dialysis, by ultrafiltration on cellulose acetate membrane filters alone or in combination with centrifugation (centrifuge ultrafiltration), or by absorption of aqueous fluid with beads of acrylamide gel, a hydrophilic polymer. By means of centrifuge ultrafiltration, large volumes of fluid can quickly be reduced to yield solutions of proteins in the desired concentration for electrophoresis. A variety of membrane filters and accessory equipment is available which will perform this function efficiently. Proteins of other tissue fluids including urine, synovial fluid, edema fluid, aqueous humor, and vitreous humor may also be studied with similar methods for sample concentration.

Unconcentrated cerebrospinal fluid can be examined by electrophoresis on cellulose acetate. The method of Rice and Bleakney[54] utilizes 20 μl of unconcentrated sample. After electrophoresis, membranes are stained with a 0.0025% solution of Nigrosine in 2% aqueous acetic acid.

Proteins from a wide variety of sources have been examined electrophoretically, including serum proteins from a number of domestic and experimental animals, proteins and enzymes from various tissues, as well as venoms of the snake and the bee. In addition to its application for the detection of genetic variations in human proteins, electrophoretic analysis has been employed commercially to distinguish various species of fish. The need to identify the fish used is a matter of considerable concern to packers of fish products for human consumption since the species used governs the price of the finished product. Fish proteins from various species have been characterized by means of cellulose acetate electrophoresis, and periodic checks can therefore be performed on products being distributed for retail marketing.[55]

REFERENCES

1. Putnam, F. W., ed. *The Plasma Proteins*, Vol. I, Vol. II (New York: Academic Press, 1960).
2. Haurowitz, F. *The Chemistry and Function of Proteins*, 2nd ed. (New York: Academic Press, 1963).
3. Hitzig, W. H. *Die Plasmaproteine in der Klinischen Medizin* (Berlin: Springer-Verlag, 1963).
4. Tiselius, A.   Trans. Faraday Soc. **33**, 524 (1937).
5. Grassmann, W., and K. Hannig.   Naturwiss. **37**, 496 (1950).
6. Flynn, F. V., and P. de Mayo.   Lancet **2**, 235 (1951).
7. Loeffler, W., and C. Wunderly.   J. Clin. Pathol. **6**, 282 (1953).
8. Briere, R. O., and J. D. Mull.   Am. J. Clin. Pathol. **42**, 547 (1964).
9. Brackenridge, C. J.   Anal. Chem. **32**, 1353 (1960).
10. Laurent, B.   Scand. J. Clin. Lab. Invest. **14**, 563 (1962).
11. Clark, A.   Clin. Chim. Acta **7**, 299 (1962).
12. Ortega, M.   Nature **179**, 1086 (1957).
13. Kohn, J.   Nature **181**, 839 (1958).
14. Munro, H. N.   In *Mammalian Protein Metabolism*, Vol. II, eds. H. N. Munro and J. B. Allison (New York: Academic Press, 1964) p 267.
15. Brown. T.   J. Obstet. Gynaecol. Brit. Emp. 41, 781 (1954).

16. Kuhns, W. J., and P. J. Hyland. Proc. Soc. Exp. Biol. Med. **92,** 1 (1956).
17. Sternberg, J., P. Dagenais-Perusse, and M. Dreyfuss. Can. Med. Assoc. J. **74,** 49 (1956).
18. Hoch-Ligeti, C., K. Irvine, and E. P. Sprinkle. Proc. Soc. Exp. Biol. Med. **84,** 707 (1953).
19. Bogoch, A., W. G. B. Casselman, M. P. Margolies, and H. L. Bockus. Am. J. Med. **19,** 583 (1955).
20. Jayle, M. F., G. Lagrue, and G. Boussier. Presse Méd. **62,** 1246 (1954).
21. Ashton, G. C. Nature **181,** 849 (1958).
22. McIndoe, W. M. Nature **195,** 353 (1962).
23. Quinteros, I. R., R. C. Stevens, C. Stormont, and V. S. Asmundson. Genetics **50,** 579 (1964).
24. Knedel, M. Clin. Chim. Acta 3, 72 (1958).
25. Cooke, K. B., T. E. Cleghorn, and E. Lockey. Biochem. J. **81,** 39P (1961).
26. Efremov, G., and M. Braend. Science **146,** 1679 (1964).
27. Wieme, R. J. Clin. Chim. Acta **5,** 443 (1960).
28. Gitlin, D., K. Schmid, D. P. Earle, and H. Givelber. J. Clin. Invest. **40,** 820 (1961).
29. Robbins, J. L., G. A. Hill, S. Marcus, and J. H. Carlquist. J. Lab. Clin. Med. **62,** 753 (1963).
30. Sandor, G., L. Martin, M. Porsin, A. Rousseau, and R. Martin. Nature **208,** 1222 (1965).
31. Melartin, L., B. S. Blumberg, and R. Lisker. Nature **215,** 1288 (1967).
32. Weitkamp, L. R., D. C. Shreffler, J. L. Robbins, O. Drachmann, P. L. Adner, R. J. Wieme, N. M. Simon, K. B. Cooke, G. Sandor, F. Wurhmann, M. Braend, and A. L. Tarnoky. Acta Genet. (Basel) **17,** 399 (1967).
33. Lau, T., F. W. Sunderman, Jr., S. S. Agarwal, A. I. Sutnick, and B. S. Blumberg. Nature **221,** 66 (1969).
34. Kekwick, R. A. Advan. Protein Chem. **14,** 231 (1959).
35. Hayles, A. B., G. B. Strickler, and B. F. McKenzie. Pediatrics **14,** 449 (1954).
36. Martin, N. H. Lancet **2,** 1094 (1954).
37. Brante, G. Scand. J. Clin. Lab. Invest. **4,** 293 (1952).
38. Cooper, G. R. Am. J. Med. **19,** 646 (1955).
39. Zsótér, T., and I. Pintér. Cardiologia **26,** 182 (1955).
40. Sonnet, J., and A. Sibille. Acta Cardiol. **8,** 479 (1953).
41. Halasz, N. A., and W. A. Krehl. Yale J. Biol. Med. **27,** 119 (1954).
42. Oliver, M. F., and G. S. Boyd. Minn. Med. **38,** 794 (1955).
43. Prichard, R. W., and R. L. Vann. Am. J. Dis. Child. **88,** 703 (1954).
44. Hardisty, R. M., and J. L. Pinninger. Brit. J. Haematol. **2,** 139 (1956).

45. Waldenström, J.   Acta Med. Scand. **117**, 216 (1944).
46. Franklin, E. C., and H. G. Kunkel.   J. Immunol. **78**, 11 (1957).
47. Korngold, L., and G. van Leeuwen.   J. Exp. Med. **106**, 467 (1957).
48. Laurell, C. B., H. Laurell, and J. Waldenström.   Am. J. Med. **22**, 24 (1957).
49. Müller-Eberhard, H. J., and H. G. Kunkel.   Clin. Chim. Acta **4**, 252 (1959).
50. Rowe, D. S., and J. L. Fahey.   J. Exp. Med. **121**, 171, 185 (1965).
51. Ishizaka, K., T. Ishizaka, and M. M. Hornbrook.   J. Immunol. **97**, 75, 840 (1966).
52. Waldenström, J.   In *Progress in Hematology*, Vol. III, ed. L. M. Tocantins (New York: Grune and Stratton, 1962), p 266.
53. Burnet, M.   *The Clonal Selection Theory of Antibody Production* (London: Cambridge University Press, 1959).
54. Rice, J. D., Jr., and B. Bleakney.   Clin. Chim. Acta **12**, 343 (1965).
55. Lane, J. P., W. S. Hill, and R. J. Learson.   Comm. Fish. Rev. **28**, 10 (1966).

CHAPTER 7

Lipoproteins

Blood and tissue lipids have been studied extensively in recent years. It is believed that elevated levels of lipids in the circulation are not consistent with normal physiology. For example, the presence of large amounts of cholesterol in the blood plasma or serum is presumed to be related to a higher incidence of heart disease,[1,2,3,4] and a similar correlation is believed to exist between serum triglyceride concentration and risk of atherosclerotic heart disease.[5,6] Since lipids in the circulation are bound in varying proportions to plasma proteins and are transported as lipoprotein complexes, many studies of lipid metabolism in health and disease include examinations of lipoprotein changes with analyses of lipid classes.

Lipoproteins can be separated into groups which differ in density, electrophoretic mobility, and antigenic activity. Separation of lipoprotein classes has been achieved by various means, including precipitation with ammonium sulfate[7] or cold ethanol,[8] polyanion precipitation,[9] and flocculation in polyvinylpyrrolidone gradients.[10,11] Detailed separation of plasma lipoproteins according to their molecular size and flotation properties has been achieved by ultracentrifugation in salt solutions of known density,[12,13,14,15] and variations in composition of lipoproteins as a function of small variations in density have been examined by means of density gradient ultracentrifugation.[16,17]

Much of the current information regarding properties of serum lipoproteins has been obtained by ultracentrifugal flotation of lipoproteins in salt solutions of known density combined with chemical analysis of separated fractions. However, ultracentrifugal analysis requires elaborate and expensive instrumentation and time-consuming procedures and therefore is not widely used in clinical medicine where rapid diagnosis is required.

Electrophoresis is a convenient and inexpensive means of separating lipoproteins for diagnostic studies and epidemiologic surveys and can also be employed for basic research on problems of lipoprotein metabolism. In addition, since electrophoretic separation of lipoprotein fractions takes place under mild conditions of pH and electrical current, it appears to reflect differences in chemical and physical properties of the native lipoproteins. The ease with which electrophoresis can be carried out has made it an important biochemical tool, and much significant information concerning lipoprotein metabolism in health and disease is being derived by use of this technique.

Electrophoretic studies have been carried out on starch granules,[18, 19, 20] and paper electrophoresis has been widely employed for the separation of plasma lipoproteins since Swahn[21, 22] and Durrum *et al.*[23] introduced the use of Sudan Black and Oil Red O, respectively, as lipophilic stains. Recently, several newer types of electrophoretic media have been developed. Some of these can provide better resolution of the lipoprotein fractions than paper and are more convenient to use than starch gel. In particular, cellulose acetate and agarose and polyacrylamide gels are coming into general use for lipoprotein studies. A procedure which offers excellent resolution and makes possible quantitation of serum and plasma lipoproteins will be described at the end of this chapter; this procedure utilizes cellulose acetate membranes as the supporting medium.

CHEMISTRY OF LIPOPROTEINS

Chylomicrons are large spherical particles which function primarily to transport plasma glycerides of dietary origin. These particles have an average diameter of 5,000 Å, a density of 0.94, and a flotation rate of approximately 10,000 Svedberg (S_f) units. They migrate to the region of alpha$_2$ globulin on starch gel but remain at the origin on filter paper electrophoretograms. Their electrophoretic behavior on cellulose acetate resembles that on filter paper.[24] They are composed of 81% glyceride, 7% phospholipid, 8% esterified cholesterol, 2% free cholesterol, and 2% protein.[25] By observing their behavior in a polyvinylpyrrolidone gradient, Bierman *et al.*[26] have separated "secondary particles," containing endogenous glyceride, from the chylomicra containing exogenous glyceride ("primary particles").

Despite the numerous studies which have been conducted, the origin and nature of chylomicron protein are unclear. Evidence indicates that chylomicron protein is synthetized in mucosal cells of the intestine[27, 28] or derived from the serum protein pool.[29] Part of the uncertainty exists because chylomicron particles isolated by ultracentrifugation in different laboratories under varying conditions exhibit differences in size, flotation rate, and chemical composition.[30]

Beta lipoproteins are so named because their electrophoretic mobility is equivalent to that of beta globulin on paper,[22, 31, 32] starch,[19, 20] agarose,[33, 34] and cellulose acetate.[24, 35] They have a flotation rate of S_f 0–20 and are also called low-density lipoproteins (LDL). In normal serum or plasma, beta lipoproteins comprise 50–60% of the circulating lipid. The beta lipoprotein fraction is the major cholesterol-bearing lipoprotein class; it has a mean density of 1.032 and a mean S_f of 6. This fraction consists of 37% esterified cholesterol, 11% glyceride, 22% phospholipid, 21% protein, and 8% free cholesterol.[25] The average molecular weight of beta lipoprotein is 2.3 million. A beta lipoprotein, with a density between 1.020 and 1.060 and a mean molecular weight of 3.2 million, has been reported by Heide and Haupt.[127]

Alpha$_2$ or pre-beta lipoproteins, also called very low-density lipoproteins (VLDL; S_f 20–400), float in salt solutions of density less than 1.006. This fraction is especially rich in glyceride and is perhaps the primary endogenous glyceride-transporting fraction in normal human plasma. It contains 55% glyceride, 22% phospholipid, 10% protein, 5% esterified cholesterol, and 8% free cholesterol. The molecular weight of VLDL ranges from 5–10 million. Kunkel and Trautman[19] isolated a lipoprotein with density less than 1.019 which had the electrophoretic mobility of an alpha$_2$ globulin in starch gel, and determined its molecular weight to be between 5 and 20 million. On cellulose acetate membranes, alpha$_2$ lipoprotein migrates to the alpha$_2$ globulin region,[24] while this fraction is only poorly separated from beta lipoprotein on filter paper strips.[31, 32] Very low-density lipoproteins appear to be produced in the liver.[36, 37] VLDL (alpha$_2$ or pre-beta lipoprotein) and LDL (beta lipoprotein) have identical amino acid compositions[38] and are immunochemically indistinguishable by presently available means.[39, 40] All of the lipoproteins contain a small amount of bound carbohydrate, 1.5–1.8%.[41] Gustafson[42] has demonstrated that very low-density lipoproteins may be further subdivided and examined for chemical composition and molecular structure. Systematic study of this lipoprotein class may yield significant information regarding atherosclerosis in man.

Alpha$_1$ or alpha lipoproteins (high-density lipoproteins, HDL) float in salt solutions of density 1.063–1.21. They have an average molecular weight of 200,000 and exhibit a sedimentation constant of 5S. Their

Table IV

Some Properties of the Major Lipoprotein Classes

Lipoprotein class	Electrophoretic mobility on cellulose acetate	Other designations	Flotation rate (S_f)	Density	Average molecular weight ($\times 10^6$)	Major lipid class bound by lipoprotein
chylomicrons	—	—	10,000	1.002	10^3–10^4	exogenous glyceride
β lipoproteins	β globulin	β lipoproteins, LDL	0–20	1.006–1.063	2–3	cholesterol
α_2 lipoproteins	α_2 globulin	pre-β lipoproteins, VLDL	20–400	1.006	5–20	endogenous glyceride
α_1 lipoproteins	α_1 globulin	α lipoproteins, HDL	—	1.063–1.21	0.2	phospholipid

Table V

Chemical Composition and Distribution of Lipoproteins in Normal Serum and Plasma

Fraction	Chemical composition (%)					Approximate range in normal serum or plasma
	Protein	Esterified cholesterol	Free cholesterol	Triglyceride	Phospholipid	
chylomicron	2	8	2	81	7	—
β lipoprotein	21	37	8	11	22	50–60
α_2 lipoprotein	10	5	8	55	22	0–20
α_1 lipoprotein	50	15	3	6	26	10–40

electrophoretic mobility is equivalent to that of alpha₁ globulin. Approximately one-third of the alpha₁ lipoprotein molecule is made up of lipids. The high phospholipid and protein content of HDL may contribute to its solubility in distilled water.[41] HDL is recovered in fractions IV, V, and VI isolated by the Cohn procedure and contain approximately one-third of the serum lipids. They contain an average of 26% phospholipid, 15% esterified cholesterol, 3% free cholesterol, 6% glyceride, and 50% protein.[15]

The physical and chemical properties and electrophoretic behavior of the major lipoprotein classes are summarized in Tables IV and V.

An additional fraction which precipitates in solutions of density 1.21 can occasionally be isolated in normal and hyperlipemic individuals.[43] Phillips[44] demonstrated that this fraction contained about 8% of the total serum phospholipid, of which lysolecithin was the principal constituent. Cholesterol was absent from this fraction, as it was from the lipoprotein studied by Turner *et al.*[45] The nature and the physiological role of this component are as yet undetermined. It may include the protein-phospholipid complex and the albumin-free fatty acid complex.[14,43] The latter appears sometimes to be observed as the so-called "lipalbumin" band;[46] however, the concentration of free fatty acid in plasma is very low (approximately 10 mg/100 ml plasma), and it is doubtful whether such a low concentration of the complex is detectable under normal circumstances.

Biosynthesis of plasma lipoproteins may occur in cells of the intestine[28,47] and aortic tissue.[48] Incorporation of ¹⁴C-labeled amino acids into high- and low-density lipoproteins of rat liver slices was demonstrated by Radding *et al.*,[49] but specific sites of lipoprotein synthesis and detailed mechanisms by which lipid and protein are combined are, by and large, unknown. Although transport of lipids is perhaps the most important function of lipoproteins, other functions are known to occur. For example, lipoproteins may bind and transport carbohydrates[50] and exhibit several types of enzyme activity.[51] In addition, lipoprotein polymorphism has been demonstrated to occur.[52,53,54,55]

EFFECTS OF NUTRITIONAL FACTORS

The influence of nutritional factors on serum lipid classes (cholesterol, triglycerides, phospholipids, free fatty acids) has been studied extensively. However, proportions of the lipid classes may vary in the lipoproteins, and changes can be correlated only roughly with alterations in lipoproteins. In general, restriction of fat and carbohydrate intake causes a reduction of the very low-density (alpha$_2$ or pre-beta) lipoprotein class.[56,57] Chronic ingestion of saturated fats increases the level of beta lipoprotein, while use of unsaturated fats or diets high in carbohydrate content promotes a reduction of this fraction.[56,57,58] Herbst and Hurley[59] observed that the serum of normal persons acquired a lactescent appearance shortly after ingesting a meal rich in fat. Upon electrophoresis on filter paper, the lactescent serum was found to contain chylomicrons which formed a trail originating at the point of sample application. Similar observations have been reported by others.[32,60,61] Diets high in carbohydrate and low in fat content increase alpha$_2$ (pre-beta, S$_f$ 20–400, or VLDL) lipoproteins.[56,62,63]

EFFECTS OF HORMONES AND DRUGS

Steroid hormones may affect the distribution of plasma lipoproteins. The effects of estrogens on lipids and lipoproteins have been examined by several groups of investigators.[64,65,66] Androgens increase beta lipoprotein levels in plasma.[67,68] Hellman *et al.*[69,70] reported that androsterone, given intramuscularly, lowered serum cholesterol, phospholipids, and triglycerides and reduced beta lipoproteins, but oral administration[71] did not affect plasma lipids. The administration of androsterone in combination with ethyl-α-p-chlorophenoxyisobutyrate resulted in significant hypolipemic activity.[72] These results were corroborated by other investigators. The combination was reported to specifically lower plasma lipoproteins of S$_f$ 20–400 (alpha$_2$ or pre-beta) with only a moderate effect on lipoproteins of S$_f$ 0–20 (beta lipoproteins)[73,74] and was used in certain hyperlipidemias characterized by increased levels of pre-beta or very low-density lipoproteins. More recent studies have shown that chlorophenoxyisobutyrate alone is the active ingredient in this combination;[75,76] however, it should be noted that reduction of alpha$_2$ lipoprotein is usually accompanied by a rise in beta lipoprotein.[77]

Intravenous administration of heparin decreases the lactescence of alimentary hyperlipemia within 15 minutes.[59] Clearing of lipemic plasma occurs through the activation of lipoprotein lipase by heparin; the enzyme catalyzes the hydrolysis of chylomicron and low-density lipoprotein triglycerides.[78] Free fatty acids liberated by this mechanism may be transported by albumin[79] to adipose tissue sites for absorption. Moreover, lipoprotein lipase, through its hydrolytic action on triglycerides, may promote the degradation of pre-beta to beta lipoprotein.[80] In some pathological conditions, plasma lipoprotein lipase activity is reduced or inhibited, resulting in elevation of pre-beta lipoprotein, and occasionally in chylomicronemia. Among cases which have been studied are nephrosis,[81] pancreatitis,[82, 83] hyperlipidemia,[84, 85, 86] and chronic alcoholism.[87]

LIPOPROTEIN METABOLISM IN DISEASE

Liver Disease

Beta lipoprotein is increased in liver disease.[18, 31] This has been confirmed by studies showing that beta lipoprotein is increased and alpha$_1$ lipoprotein reduced in obstructive jaundice or biliary cirrhosis; plasma cholesterol is elevated, chiefly in the unesterified fraction.[88, 89]

Nephrotic Syndrome

Deranged lipid and protein metabolism occurs secondarily to the primary renal lesion in the nephrotic syndrome. Proteinuria, lipiduria, and hyperlipemia occur, and in advanced cases pre-beta lipoprotein is markedly increased. Since conversion of pre-beta to beta lipoprotein is believed to be associated with uptake by adipose tissue of triglycerides released from pre-beta lipoprotein through the action of lipoprotein lipase,[90, 91] it has been suggested that a partial metabolic block occurs in this important step in patients with the nephrotic syndrome.[92] Lipoprotein lipase activity is reduced in nephrotic subjects;[93] this may account for the abnormal distribution of lipoproteins observed.[18, 94, 95]

Myxedema

Myxedema is frequently accompanied by the presence of hypercholesterolemia along with an increase in beta lipoprotein content.[96, 97, 98] The lipoprotein pattern at times resembles that seen in patients with coronary involvement.[64] Olson and Vester[99] reported that low-density lipoproteins are increased in hypothyroid subjects. Treatment of myxedematous patients with thyroid extract or synthetic L-thyroxin may restore normal lipoprotein distributions[97, 100] through a readjustment of endocrine activity.

Diabetes Mellitus

Diabetes mellitus is usually associated with hyperlipemia. Triglyceride transport is abnormal;[101] the lipoprotein pattern is characterized by an elevation in chylomicrons and alpha$_2$ or pre-beta lipoproteins and by diminished levels of beta and alpha$_1$ lipoproteins.[102] The distribution of the low-density lipoprotein fractions has been reported to resemble that seen in essential hyperlipemia.[98, 103] An elevated beta: alpha lipoprotein ratio is found in diabetics who demonstrate clinical evidence of atheroma.[104]

Arterial Disease

In 1950, Gofman *et al.*[105] presented evidence that individuals with proven coronary artery disease had significantly higher levels of serum lipoproteins than normal. These investigators suggested measurement of serum lipoprotein levels to indicate subclinical arterial disease. Although the relative importance of lipoprotein distributions versus serum cholesterol or triglyceride determinations as accurate and reliable predictors of coronary artery disease is unsettled,[5, 106] there is strong evidence that serum lipoprotein distributions are abnormal in patients with heart disease; therefore, reliable diagnosis must depend upon a combination of chemical and clinical data. The studies of Russ *et al.*[107] showed that patients with clinical evidence of arteriosclerosis exhibited an increased content of beta lipoprotein. Nikkilä[81] noted that the percentage of cholesterol and phospholipid bound to alpha$_1$ lipoprotein was much lower, and the percentage bound to beta lipoprotein was correspondingly higher than normal in individuals with a tendency toward arteriosclerosis (survivors of myocardial infarction and patients with proven coronary insufficiency). It has also been demonstrated that patients of both sexes between 40 and 70 years of age with arteriosclerosis exhibit significantly higher beta:alpha lipoprotein ratios than normal.[108] The transfer of fatty acids between lecithin and cholesterol in plasma is catalyzed by the enzyme lecithin–cholesterol acyl transferase.[109] It is possible that the activity of this enzyme, through its effect on the metabolism of cholesterol and phospholipid, is involved in regulating the distribution of lipids among the lipoprotein fractions.

Dangerfield and Smith[31] were the first to report the presence of a "pre-beta" lipid on paper electrophoretograms of patients with coronary artery disease. This lipid-protein complex showed a mobility slightly greater than that of beta lipoprotein in barbital buffer of pH 8.6. Their results were confirmed by Besterman,[110] who found a significant elevation of pre-beta lipid in patients with ischemic heart disease. Recent studies of lipoprotein changes have led to the development of several schemes for classifying lipoprotein disorders.[111, 112, 113, 114, 115] These represent significant attempts to bring about a better understanding of the causes underlying various lipoproteinemias.

INFLUENCE OF GENETICS ON LIPOPROTEIN METABOLISM

Hyperlipoproteinemias

A classification of hyperlipoproteinemias based on qualitative evaluation of paper electrophoretic strips combined with data from preparative ultracentrifugation has evolved from the studies of Fredrickson and his colleagues.[111,112]

Type I hyperlipoproteinemia is frequently called idiopathic or essential familial hyperlipoproteinemia, fat-induced hyperlipoproteinemia, or familial hyperchylomicronemia. Patients complain of acute abdominal pain and frequently have a distended abdomen and enlarged liver and spleen. Retinal vessels appear white (lipemia retinalis), and yellow papules are seen on the skin and oral mucosa. Glucose tolerance is normal. Serum or plasma from the Type I patient is lactescent and contains a high concentration of chylomicrons 14 or more hours following a normal meal. Chylomicrons, which separate as a creamy layer when the sample is allowed to stand overnight, disappear when the patient is placed on a fat-free diet. Plasma free cholesterol is elevated and may make up as much as 50% of total cholesterol content, compared with the normal free cholesterol: total cholesterol ratio of approximately 0.3. Triglyceride content is high in all Type I patients and falls rapidly on a fat-free diet. It is believed that patients with this syndrome are deficient in the enzyme lipoprotein lipase and are homozygous for a mutant gene governing activity of the clearing enzyme.

Type II hyperlipoproteinemia is characterized by the absence of chylomicronemia; the serum or plasma is clear. Xanthelasma, tendon and tuberous xanthomas are often seen along with early cardiovascular involvement. Patients exhibit grossly elevated levels of beta lipoprotein, with serum cholesterol levels usually much greater than 250 mg %. A modest elevation of pre-beta lipid is found on electrophoresis, along with the presence of a heavy beta lipoprotein band. It is believed that this condition is inherited as an autosomal dominant trait.

Type III hyperlipoproteinemia is distinguished by the presence of planar xanthomas, usually occurring on the backs of the hands and in creases on palmar surfaces. Eruptive xanthomas appear on the extremities. Patients frequently suffer from occlusive arterial disease, both coronary and peripheral. Chemically, a fraction of beta lipoprotein is present which is characterized by an abnormally low density and may appear as a "broad beta" lipoprotein on electrophoresis. Cholesterol and triglyceride levels may both exceed 1,000 mg %. Type III individuals are intolerant of carbohydrates. Some relatives of Type

III indivduals have exhibited lipoprotein patterns characteristic of Type IV hyperlipoproteinemia, giving rise to the suggestion that these two states are genetically related.

Type IV hyperlipoproteinemia (hyperpre-beta lipoproteinemia) is also known as carbohydrate-induced hyperlipidemia. Patients frequently exhibit eruptive xanthomas, lipemia retinalis, and complain of abdominal pain. They are often obese and exhibit abnormal glucose tolerance. The serum lipoprotein pattern is characterized by markedly elevated levels of $alpha_2$ or pre-beta lipoprotein. Triglyceride levels are high and may be accompanied by moderate elevation of cholesterol. The Type IV pattern often appears secondary to diabetes mellitus, pancreatitis, and alcoholism.

Type V hyperlipoproteinemia is characterized by the presence of chylomicrons and increased pre-beta lipid in the post-absorptive state. Recurrent abdominal pain appears to be the most common complaint. Patients are frequently obese; many are diabetic and show eruptive xanthomas, lipemia retinalis, and hepatosplenomegaly. Type V patients are also characterized by an abnormal glucose tolerance curve. They exhibit normal post-heparin lipase activity in contrast to Type I patients in whom post-heparin lipase activity is low. Plasma triglyceride in both types of hyperlipoproteinemia is highly elevated. Both Type I and Type V respond to a fat-free diet; however, patients with Type V hyperlipoproteinemia do not exhibit the rapid and profound decline in triglyceride level seen in Type I patients when placed on low-fat, high-carbohydrate diets. This distinction aids in differentiating between the two types; it is possible that Type V represents a combination of Types I and IV.

The arrangement of hyperlipoproteinemias into these five classes has proved helpful in diagnosing expressions of inherited lipid disorders. However, it is possible that these phenotypes represent points along a spectrum of gradual change. $alpha_2$ or very low-density lipoproteins, in particular, exhibit a progressive rise in Types II, III, IV, and V. A continuous and progressive rise in lipoproteins of very low density or high flotation rate could achieve its greatest expression in the Type I phenotype which consists of a severe hyperchylomicronemia arising from inheritance of the homozygous genetic condition for lipoprotein lipase deficiency.

Lipoprotein Deficiency States

Among the disorders classified as essential hypolipoproteinemias are the congenital deficiencies of beta lipoproteins and $alpha_1$ lipo-

proteins. In 1960, Salt *et al.*[116] reported that certain individuals possessed no beta lipoprotein and had no ability to form chylomicrons
after a fat meal. This condition was named "abetalipoproteinemia."
The first patient with this syndrome was an eighteen-year-old girl who
had steatorrhea and retinitis pigmentosa, and whose red blood cells
exhibited a thorny appearance.[117] Since that time, several other cases
have been reported in which acanthocytosis was accompanied by a
low or absent beta lipoprotein (LDL) as determined by ultracentrifugal and electrophoretic techniques. Characteristic clinical findings
in abetalipoproteinemia are retarded growth, steatorrhea, and abdominal distention. Neurologic effects become apparent in late childhood and are expressed as muscle weakness, nystagmus, and retinal
degeneration. Serum cholesterol, phospholipid and glyceride levels
are all low in persons who have inherited a double dose of the mutant
allele which is probably transmitted as an autosomal recessive gene.
Low levels of plasma high-density lipoprotein have been reported to
accompany the absence of low-density lipoprotein, and patients
heterozygous for the mutant gene show a reduced ability to form
chylomicrons. These observations are consistent with current views
regarding the role of apoproteins from both high- and low-density
lipoproteins in the formation of chylomicrons.[47] Serum phospholipids
of patients with abetalipoproteinemia show a reduced lecithin-sphin-
gomyelin ratio[118] which may be specific for this abnormality.[119]

Congenital deficiency in high-density lipoprotein (Tangier disease)
was first observed in 1961 by Fredrickson and colleagues[120] in two
siblings, living on the island of Tangier on Chesapeake Bay, whose
blood was nearly devoid of high-density (alpha₁) lipoprotein. Low-
density lipoprotein content was approximately one-half of that seen
in normal individuals, while very low-density lipoprotein was elevated.
The serum lipids were characterized by increased triglyceride and
decreased cholesterol and phospholipid. This disease is characterized
by the deposition of cholesteryl esters in reticulo-endothelial tissues,
giving rise to enlarged tonsils of orange-red coloration. Hepatosplenomegaly and lymphadenopathy are also present. There is evidence that
Tangier disease is governed by the inheritance of a single autosomal
gene.

It is evident that the large amount of information accumulated on
lipoproteins has been made possible through a number of technological
improvements. One of these is the application of electrophoretic
analysis to the study of lipoprotein abnormalities. Electrophoretic fractionation of lipoproteins is becoming a standard procedure in the
lipid research laboratory, and recent development of various types of

supporting media for electrophoresis has made application of this technique even more convenient, with more reproducible results. Tailing of the beta lipoprotein fraction and incomplete resolution of pre-beta from beta lipoprotein, commonly seen on filter paper strips even with the addition of albumin to the buffer solution, have been largely eliminated by the use of such supporting media as agarose and cellulose acetate.

In addition to providing improved separation of the lipoprotein fractions, cellulose acetate electrophoresis offers simplicity of operation, speed of separation, reproducibility of results, and ease of quantitation. Figures 14 and 15 show typical electrophoretic separations of plasma lipoproteins performed on cellulose acetate membranes. The

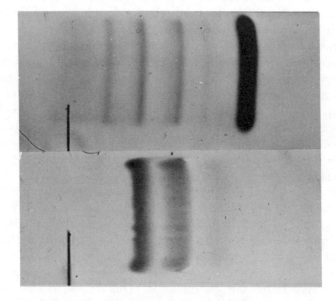

Figure 14. Plasma proteins (upper strip, stained with Amido Black 10B) and lipoproteins (lower strip, stained with Oil Red O). Note that mobilities of alpha$_1$-, alpha$_2$-, and beta-lipoproteins correspond with alpha$_1$-, alpha$_2$-, and beta-globulins. (Electrophoresis conducted in barbital buffer, pH 8.6, ionic strength 0.075.)

use of cellulose acetate membranes makes possible further separation of individual lipoproteins into subfractions. Antigenic polymorphism of human alpha and beta lipoproteins has been reported.[52, 53, 121, 122] Cohen and Djordevich[54] suggested that genetic variations give rise to alpha$_1$ lipoproteins with varying electrophoretic mobilities. Seegers

A B

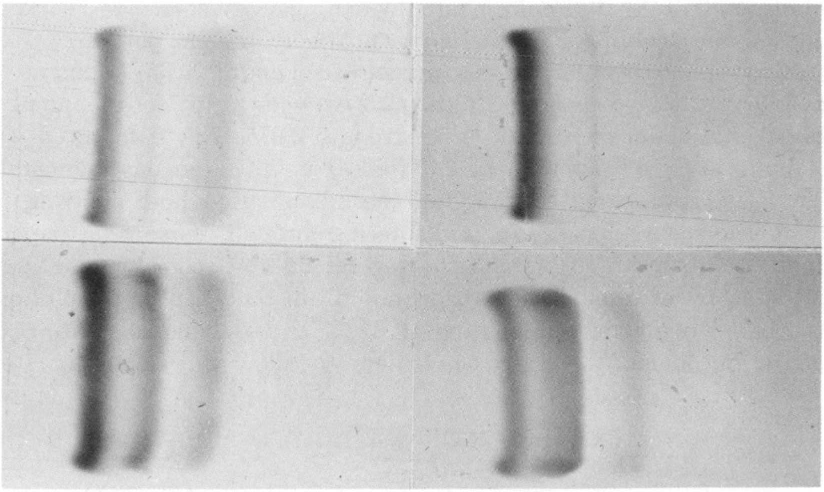

C D

Figure 15. Typical lipoprotein separations on cellulose acetate, stained with Oil Red O. Compare the lipid and lipoprotein distributions in a normal patient (A) with patients showing abnormal metabolism (B, C, D).

Lipoprotein Distribution (%)				*Lipid Composition* (mg/100 ml)*		
Strip	α_1	α_2	β	*C*	*TG*	*PL*
A	48	10	42	139	62	185
B	16	5	79	427	164	340
C	20	29	51	307	307	305
D	13	50	27	192	564	316

*C = total cholesterol, TG = triglyceride, PL = phospholipid

et al.[55] found an additional beta lipoprotein in one family studied; this appeared to be absent in the general population. The existence of multiple components of alpha$_1$ and alpha$_2$ lipoprotein fractions observed on cellulose acetate[63, 123] suggests that genetic influences regulate the distribution and metabolism of human lipoproteins, and hence their response to diet or therapy. This view appears to be supported by recent data.[124]

PROCEDURE FOR ELECTROPHORESIS OF LIPOPROTEINS

Either serum or plasma can be used for lipoprotein electrophoresis. Freshly collected samples should be used whenever possible, although storage for 3–4 days at 4°C appears not to produce significant alterations in distributions of the lipoprotein fractions. Freezing of speci-

mens should be avoided because of possible disruption and/or rearrangement of lipid-protein bonds which may give rise to marked
changes in electrophoretic mobility and in lipoprotein patterns.

Electrophoresis is carried out at room temperature using a potential
of 150 volts (approximately 1.5 mA/2.5 cm wide strip) for 90 minutes
in barbital buffer of pH 8.6, ionic strength 0.075. This is followed by
staining in a 0.4% solution of Oil Red O in 70% aqueous methanol.
The stain is prepared by bringing the mixture to a boil, allowing it
to cool to room temperature, and filtering through coarse filter paper.
If the solution is left to stand for several days at room temperature,
filtration is not usually necessary. Staining in the Oil Red O solution
is carried out at a temperature of 37°C and is complete within 6
hours, but it may be more convenient to allow the electrophoretic

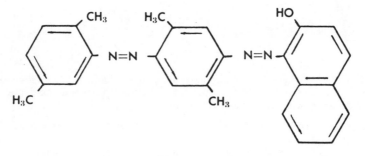

OIL RED O

strips to remain in the staining solution overnight.[24] Stained membranes can be rendered transparent by impregnation with glycerol or
by treatment with a clearing solution of 12% glacial acetic acid in
methanol. Aqueous mixtures of 30% dimethylformamide or dimethylsulfoxide may be used when elution of stain from lipoprotein fractions
is encountered with the acetic acid–methanol solution.

An alternate method for staining separated lipoproteins entails
the ozonation of lipids in a closed chamber with barium sulfate and
sulfuric acid, followed by immersion in Schiff's reagent.[125, 126] Staining
of lipoproteins by this method can be accomplished within 2 hours.
However, the mechanism of the reaction is not fully understood, and
occasional bands may be seen which appear not to be classified with
the commonly recognized lipoprotein fractions. On the other hand,
Oil Red O has been used successfully for some time as a lipid stain
and is known to exhibit specificity for serum and plasma lipids. Reproducible results can be obtained with either staining procedure.

REFERENCES

1. Keys, A., O. Mickelsen, E. V. O. Miller, E. R. Hays, and R. L. Todd. J. Clin. Invest. **29**, 1347 (1950).
2. Dawber, T. R., F. E. Moore, and G. V. Mann. Am. J. Publ. Health **47** Suppl., 4 (1957).
3. Carlson, L. A. Acta Med. Scand. **167**, 399 (1960).
4. Keys, A., J. T. Anderson, and F. Grande. Metabolism **14**, 759 (1965).
5. Albrink, M. J. J. Clin. Invest. **40**, 536 (1961).
6. Kuo, P. T., and D. R. Bassett. Ann. Intern. Med. **59**, 495 (1963).
7. Macheboeuf, M. Bull. Soc. Chem. Biol. **11**, 268 (1929).
8. Cohn, E. J., F. R. N. Gurd, D. M. Surgenor, B. A. Barnes, R. K. Brown, G. Derouaux, J. M. Gillespie, F. W. Kahnt, W. F. Lever, C. H. Liu, D. Mittleman, R. F. Mouton, K. Schmid, and E. Uroma. J. Am. Chem. Soc. **72**, 465 (1950).
9. Cornwell, D. G., and F. A. Kruger. J. Lipid Res. **2**, 110 (1961).
10. Burstein, M., and A. Prawerman. Rev. Hémat. **13**, 329 (1958).
11. Gordis, E. Proc. Soc. Exp. Biol. Med. **110**, 657 (1962).
12. Gofman, J. W., F. T. Lindgren, and H. Elliott. J. Biol. Chem. **179**, 973 (1949).
13. DeLalla, O. F., and J. W. Gofman. In *Methods of Biochemical Analysis*, Vol. I, ed. D. Glick (New York: Interscience, 1954) p 459.
14. Havel, R. J., H. A. Eder, and J. H. Bragdon. J. Clin. Invest. **34**, 1345 (1955).
15. Lindgren, F. T., and A. V. Nichols. In *The Plasma Proteins*, Vol. II, ed. F. W. Putnam (New York: Academic Press, 1960) p 1.
16. Oncley, J. L., K. W. Walton, and D. G. Cornwell. J. Am. Chem. Soc. **79**, 4666 (1957).
17. Gurd, F. R. N. in *Lipide Chemistry* (New York: John Wiley, 1960) p 260.
18. Kunkel, H. G., and R. J. Slater. J. Clin. Invest. **31**, 677 (1952).
19. Kunkel, H. G., and R. Trautman. J. Clin. Invest. **35**, 641 (1956).
20. Bierman, E. L., E. Gordis, and J. T. Hamlin, III. J. Clin. Invest. **41**, 2254, (1962).
21. Swahn, B. Scand. J. Clin. Lab. Invest. **4**, 98 (1952).
22. Swahn, B. Scand. J. Clin. Lab. Invest. **5**, Suppl. 9 (1953).
23. Durrum, E. L., M. H. Paul, and E. R. B. Smith. Science **116**, 428 (1952).
24. Chin, H. P., and D. H. Blankenhorn. Clin. Chim. Acta **20**, 305 (1968).
25. Oncley, J. L. In *Brain Lipids and Lipoproteins, and the Leucodystrophies*, eds. J. Folch-Pi and H. Bauer (Amsterdam: Elsevier Publishing Co., 1963) p 1.
26. Bierman, E. L., D. Porte, Jr., D. D. O'Hara, M. Schwartz, and F. C. Wood, Jr. J. Clin. Invest. **44**, 201 (1965).

27. Rodbell, M., D. S. Fredrickson, and K. Ono.   J. Biol. Chem. **234**, 567 (1959).
28. Hatch, F. T., L. M. Hagopian, J. J. Rubenstein, and G. P. Canellos. Circulation **28**, 659 (1963).
29. Furman, R. H., S. S. Sanbar, P. Alaupovic, R. Bradford, and R. P. Howard.   J. Lab. Clin. Med. **63**, 193 (1964).
30. Scanu, A. M.   Advan. Lipid Res. **3**, 63 (1965).
31. Dangerfield, W. G., and E. B. Smith.   J. Clin. Pathol. **8**, 132 (1955).
32. Lees, R. S., and F. T. Hatch.   J. Lab. Clin. Med. **61**, 518 (1963).
33. Rapp, W., and W. Kahlke.   Clin. Chim. Acta **19**, 493 (1968).
34. Kalab, M., and W. G. Martin.   Anal. Biochem. **24**, 218 (1968).
35. Charman, R. C., and R. A. Landowne.   Anal. Biochem. **19**, 177 (1967).
36. Cornwell, D. G., F. A. Kruger, G. J. Hamwi, and J. Brown.   Am. J. Clin. Nutrition **9**, 24 (1961).
37. Havel, R. J., J. M. Felts, and C. M. van Duyne.   J. Lipid Res. **3**, 297 (1962).
38. Shore, B., and V. Shore.   Plasma **2**, 621 (1954).
39. Levine, L., D. L. Kauffman, and R. K. Brown.   J. Exp. Med. **102**, 105 (1955).
40. Reiner, W. W., J. W. Riddle, and D. G. Cornwell.   J. Exp. Med. **110**, 113 (1959).
41. Heide, K., and H. Haupt.   Behringwerk-Mitt. **33**, 11 (1957).
42. Gustafson, A.   Acta Med. Scand. **179**, Suppl. No. 446 (1966).
43. Hillyard, L. A., C. Entenman, H. Feinberg, and I. L. Chaikoff.   J. Biol. Chem. **214**, 79 (1955).
44. Phillips, G. B.   Proc. Soc. Exp. Biol. Med. **100**, 19 (1959).
45. Turner, R. H., J. R. Snavely, W. H. Goldwater, and M. L. Randolph. Yale J. Biol. Med. **24**, 450 (1952).
46. Straus, R., and M. Wurm.   In *Lipids and the Steroid Hormones in Clinical Medicine*, eds. F. W. Sunderman and F. W. Sunderman, Jr. (Philadelphia: J. B. Lippincott, 1960) p 47.
47. Rodbell, M., and D. S. Fredrickson.   J. Biol. Chem. **234**, 562 (1959).
48. Hollander, W.   Circulation **28**, 660 (1963).
49. Radding, C. M., J. H. Bragdon, and D. Steinberg.   Biochim. Biophys. Acta **30**, 443 (1958).
50. Winzler, R. J.   In *Methods of Biochemical Analysis*, Vol. II, ed. D. Glick (New York: Interscience, 1955) p 279.
51. Lawrence, S. H., and P. J. Melnick.   Proc. Soc. Exp. Biol. Med. **107**, 998 (1961).
52. Blumberg, B. S., D. Bernacke, and A. C. Allison.   J. Clin. Invest. **41**, 1936 (1962a).
53. Blumberg, B. S., S. Dray, and J. C. Robinson.   Nature **194**, 656 (1962b).
54. Cohen, L., and J. Djordevich.   Lipids **3**, 420 (1968).

55. Seegers, W., K. Hirschhorn, L. Burnett, E. Robson, and H. Harris. Science **149**, 303 (1965).

56. Nichols, A. V., V. Dobbin, and J. W. Gofman. Geriatrics **12**, 7 (1957).

57. Walker, W. J., N. Weiner, and L. J. Milch. Circulation **15**, 31 (1957).

58. Furman, R. H., R. P. Howard, and L. N. Norcia. In *Hormones and Atherosclerosis*, ed. G. Pincus (New York: Academic Press, 1959) p 349.

59. Herbst, F. S. M., and N. A. Hurley. J. Clin. Invest. **33**, 907 (1954).

60. Anderson, J. T., A. Keys, and F. Grande. J. Nutrition **62**, 421 (1957).

61. Linko, E. Acta Med. Scand. **159**, 475 (1957).

62. Lees, R. S., and D. S. Fredrickson. Clin. Res. **13**, 327 (1965).

63. Chin, H. P., L. V. Miller, and D. H. Blankenhorn. Circulation **38**, Suppl. VI, 3 (1968).

64. Oliver, M. F., and G. S. Boyd. Clin. Sci. **14**, 15 (1955).

65. Marmorston, J., F. J. Moore, C. E. Hopkins, O. T. Kuzma, and J. Weiner. Proc. Soc. Exp. Biol. Med. **110**, 400 (1962).

66. Stamler, J., R. Pick, L. N. Katz, A. Pick, B. M. Kaplan, D. M. Berkson, and D. Century. J. Am. Med. Assoc. **183**, 632 (1963).

67. Furman, R. H., R. P. Howard, L. N. Norcia, and E. C. Keaty. Am. J. Med. **24**, 80 (1958).

68. Eder, H. A. In *Hormones and Atherosclerosis*, ed. G. Pincus (New York: Academic Press, 1959) p 335.

69. Hellman, L., H. L. Bradlow, B. Zumoff, D. K. Fukushima, and T. F. Gallagher. J. Clin. Endocrinol. Metab. **19**, 936 (1959).

70. Hellman, L., B. Zumoff, G. Kessler, R. S. Rosenfeld, and T. F. Gallagher. J. Clin. Invest. **41**, 1364 (1962).

71. Cohen, W. D., N. Higano, R. W. Robinson, and R. J. LeBeau. J. Clin. Endocrinol. Metab. **21**, 1208 (1961).

72. Thorp, J. M., and W. S. Waring. Nature **194**, 948 (1962).

73. Strisower, E. H. J. Athero. Res. **3**, 445 (1963).

74. Howard, R. P., P. Alaupovic, O. J. Brusco, and R. H. Furman. J. Athero. Res. **3**, 482 (1963).

75. Hellman, L., E. Kara, I. L. Rubin, and R. S. Rosenfeld. Ann. Intern. Med. **59**, 477 (1963).

76. Strisower, E. H., and B. Strisower. J. Clin. Endocrinol. Metab. **24**, 139 (1964).

77. Strisower, E. H., G. Adamson, and B. Strisower. Am. J. Med. **45**, 488 (1968).

78. Korn, E. D. In *Methods of Biochemical Analysis*, Vol. 7, ed. D. Glick (New York: Interscience, 1959) p 145.

79. Gordon, R. S., Jr., E. Boyle, R. K. Brown, A. Cherkes, and C. B. Anfinsen. Proc. Soc. Exp. Biol. Med. **84**, 168 (1953).

80. Lossow, W. J., S. S. Naidoo, and I. L. Chaikoff. J. Lipid Res. **4**, 419 (1963).
81. Nikkilä, E.   Scand. J. Clin. Lab. Invest. 5, Suppl. 8 (1953).
82. Orvis, H. H., and J. M. Evans. Clin. Res. Proc. **5**, 197 (1957).
83. Kessler, J. I., J. C. Kniffen, and H. P. Janowitz. New Eng. J. Med. **269**, 943 (1963).
84. Klein, E., and W. F. Lever. Proc. Soc. Exp. Biol. Med. **95**, 565 (1957).
85. Havel, R. J., and R. S. Gordon, Jr. J. Clin. Invest. **39**, 1777 (1960).
86. Fredrickson, D. S., K. Ono, and L. L. Davis. J. Lipid Res. **4**, 24 (1963).
87. Losowsky, M. S., D. P. Jones, C. S. Davidson, and C. S. Lieber.   Am. J. Med. **35**, 794 (1963).
88. Furman, R. H., and L. L. Conrad.   J. Clin. Invest. **36**, 713 (1957).
89. Russ, E. M., J. Raymunt, and D. P. Barr.   J. Clin. Invest. **35**, 133 (1956).
90. Rodbell, M.   J. Biol. Chem. **235**, 1613 (1960).
91. Bezman, A., J. M. Felts, and R. J. Havel.   J. Lipid Res. **3**, 427 (1962).
92. Gitlin, D., D. G. Cornwell, D. Nakasato, J. L. Oncley, W. L. Hughes, Jr., and C. A. Janeway.   J. Clin. Invest. **37**, 172 (1958).
93. Nikkilä, E. A., and R. Gräsbeck.   Acta Med. Scand. **150**, 39 (1954).
94. Raynaud, R., J. R. d'Eshougues, P. Pasquet, and S. Di Giovanni. Algérie Méd. **57**, 725 (1953).
95. Lagrue, G., P. Mozziconacci, J. Vialatte.   Ann. Méd. **55**, 196 (1954).
96. Malmros, H., and B. Swahn.   Nord. Med. **48**, 1028 (1952).
97. Malmros, H., and B. Swahn.   Acta Med. Scand. **145**, 361 (1953).
98. Gofman, J. W., O. DeLalla, F. Glazier, N. K. Freeman, F. T. Lindgren, A. V. Nichols, B. Strisower, and A. R. Tamplin.   Plasma **2**, 413 (1954).
99. Olson, R. E., and J. W. Vester.   Physiol. Rev. **40**, 677 (1960).
100. Adlersberg, D., E. T. Bossak, I. H. Sher, and H. Sobotka.   Clin. Chem. **1**, 18 (1955).
101. Harris, L. V. D., M. J. Albrink, W. F. van Eck, E. B. Man, and J. P. Peters.   Metabolism **2**, 120 (1953).
102. Hamwi, G. J., O. Garcia, F. A. Kruger, G. Winup, and D. G. Cornwell.   Metabolism **11**, 850 (1962).
103. Tuller, E. F., G. V. Mann, F. Schertenleib, C. B. Roehrig, and H. F. Root.   Diabetes **3**, 279 (1954).
104. Baker, R. W. R., C. L. Joiner, and J. R. Trounce.   Quart. J. Med. **24**, 295 (1955).
105. Gofman, J. W., F. T. Lindgren, H. Elliott, W. Manz, J. Hewitt, B. Strisower, and V. Herring.   Science **111**, 166 (1950).
106. Lewis, L. A., F. Olmstead, I. H. Page, E. Y. Lawry, G. V. Mann, F. J. Stare, M. Hanig, N. A. Lauffer, and F. E. Moore.   Circulation **14**, 720 (1956).

107. Russ, E. M., H. A. Eder, and D. P. Barr. Am. J. Med. **11**, 468 (1951).
108. Antonini, F. M., G. Piva, L. Salvini, and A. Sordi. Gior. Gerontol., Suppl. 1, 1 (1953).
109. Glomset, J. A., and J. L. Wright. Biochem. Biophys. Acta **89**, 266 (1964).
110. Besterman, E. M. M. Brit. Heart J. **19**, 503 (1957).
111. Fredrickson, D. S. In *Metabolic Basis of Inherited Disease*, eds. J. B. Stanbury, J. B. Wyngaarden, and D. S. Fredrickson (New York: McGraw-Hill, 1960) p 489.
112. Fredrickson, D. S., R. I. Levy, and R. S. Lees. New Eng. J. Med. **276**, 34, 94, 148, 215, 273 (1967).
113. Kinsell, L. W., G. Schlierf, W. Kahlke, and G. Schettler. In *Lipids and Lipidoses*, ed. G. Schettler (New York: Springer-Verlag, 1967) p 446.
114. Schettler, G., W. Kahlke, and G. Schlierf. In *Lipids and Lipidoses*, ed. G. Schettler (New York: Springer-Verlag, 1967) p 412.
115. Lloyd, J. K. Arch. Disease Childhood **43**, 393, 505 (1968).
116. Salt, H. B., O. H. Wolff, J. K. Lloyd, A. S. Fosbrooke, A. H. Cameron, and D. V. Hubble. Lancet **2**, 325 (1960).
117. Bassen, F. A., and A. L. Kornzweig. Blood **5**, 381 (1950).
118. Ways, P., C. F. Reed, and D. J. Hanahan. J. Clin. Invest. **42**, 1248 (1963).
119. Jones, J. W., and P. Ways. J. Clin. Invest. **46**, 1151 (1967).
120. Fredrickson, D. S., P. H. Altrocchi, L. V. Avioli, D. S. Goodman, and H. C. Goodman. Ann. Int. Med. **55**, 1016 (1961).
121. Berg, K. Acta Pathol. et Microbiol. Scand. **59**, 369 (1963).
122. Berg, K. Vox Sang. **10**, 513 (1965).
123. Chin, H. P., and D. H. Blankenhorn. Biochem. Med. **3**, 48 (1969). (1969).
124. Noble, R. P., F. T. Hatch, J. A. Mazrimas, F. T. Lindgren, L. C. Jensen, and G. L. Adamson. Lipids **4**, 55 (1969).
125. Kohn J. Nature **189**, 312 (1961).
126. Farber, E. R., J. G. Batsakis, P. C. Giesen, and M. Thiessen. Am. J. Clin. Pathol. **51**, 523 (1969).
127. Heide, K., and H. Haupt. Behringwerk-Mitt. **43**, 161 (1964)

CHAPTER 8

Hemoglobins

Electrophoresis has played an important role in the discovery and characterization of different types of hemoglobins. Variations in structure and biochemistry of hemoglobins have been actively investigated since Pauling and his colleagues[1] discovered the molecular basis for the disease known as sickle cell anemia.

Hemoglobins are a group of blood proteins responsible for combining reversibly with and transporting oxygen from the lungs to the tissues. Red cells contain about 32% hemoglobin; this translates into approximately 14.5 g of hemoglobin per 100 ml of whole blood. Of this amount, 2% binds iron in the ferric form (methemoglobin) and does not combine with oxygen. Hemoglobin in arterial blood is approximately 98% saturated with oxygen (oxygen tension = 94 mm Hg), while that in venous blood is approximately 75% saturated (oxygen tension = 40 mm Hg).

The prosthetic group (porphyrin-Fe^{++}) is the same for all hemoglobins, and differences among variant forms are due to structural variations in the globin protein. Each molecule has a molecular weight of about 69,000 and contains four iron atoms in the ferrous form which can combine with oxygen. The globin moiety consists of amino acids linked in definite sequences and coiled to give rise to secondary polypeptide structures. The coiled polypeptides are brought together to form tertiary structures of specific size and configuration characteristic of each type of hemoglobin. Individual polypeptide chains are made up of approximately 150 amino acids linked in specific sequences which characterize particular hemoglobins. A change in the amino acid sequence of a single globin chain results in the formation of an abnormal or variant hemoglobin.

Hemoglobin A (Hb-A), the normal type of hemoglobin found in adult blood, is made up of two alpha- and two beta-polypeptide chains. The isoelectric point of Hemoglobin A occurs at pH 6.87. Hemoglobin S, the form found in sickle cell anemia, has an isoelectric point of 7.09. The difference in isoelectric point, brought about by a variation in amino acid composition, causes the two types of hemoglobin to exhibit differences in relative electrical charge in solution and allows them to be separated electrophoretically.

Most variant hemoglobins show a single amino acid substitution at a single locus on either the alpha- or the beta-polypeptide chain of the normal (Hb-A) molecule. The alteration in structure produces a change in net surface charge on the variant hemoglobin and distinguishes it from other hemoglobins. Many of the variants appear to be normal in physiological function, with a few exceptions.

Several hemoglobins have altered oxygen-binding capacity. For example, an abnormally low oxygen affinity of hemoglobin was discovered to be the cause of a mild cyanosis in several members of one family. The total hemoglobin content in these patients was not reduced, but the oxygen affinity of their hemoglobin was below normal. These individuals were later discovered to be heterozygous for a gene governing hemoglobin production.[2] Moreover, mutant hemoglobins have been found in several areas of the world in which familial erythrocytosis (or polycythemia) is associated with an abnormally high affinity of hemoglobin for oxygen.[3, 4, 5]

The exact manner in which the hemoglobin molecule binds oxygen is unknown. However, it has been determined that upon combination with oxygen, the spatial conformation of hemoglobin is altered considerably.[6] The molecule is a tetramer held together by ligand binding. Upon dissociation, it forms symmetrical primary functional units, or dimers. In the case of Hemoglobin A, dissociation yields two identical alpha-beta dimers.[7, 8] It has been postulated that the oxygenation of hemoglobin involves a rapid exchange of oxygen between dimers. This theory suggests that the oxygen affinity of hemoglobin depends upon the rate of dissociation of the tetramer into dimers; hence, the oxygen affinity of hemoglobin would be inversely related to the degree of subunit dissociation.[7] The results of Bunn[9] appear to support the proposed theory.

NORMAL HEMOGLOBINS

Hemoglobins have been described which differ in regard to spectroscopic behavior, immunologic specificity, oxygen dissociation characteristics, isoelectric point, and electrophoretic mobility. The normal hemoglobins and several mutant types have been extensively studied and thoroughly described with respect to physiology and chemistry.[10,11,12] Synthesis of the globin moiety is under genetic control;[13] accordingly, many new variants have been discovered which have frequently been designated by geographical site of origin.

Hemoglobin A is found in normal adults. It has an isoelectric point of 6.87, and it migrates on electrophoretic media with the mobility of human beta globulin. Only one change in the amino acid sequence of its two alpha- and two beta-polypeptide chains is required to transform Hemoglobin A into a mutant type. For example, substitution of valine for glutamic acid at the sixth amino acid from the N-terminal group of the beta polypeptide chain converts normal hemoglobin into the variant responsible for sickle cell anemia.

Hemoglobin A_2, a minor component which comprises about 2.5% of the hemoglobin in normal adults, was first isolated and described by Kunkel and Wallenius.[14] It is made up of alpha and delta chains. Hemoglobin A and Hemoglobin A_2 have identical molecular weights and ultraviolet absorption spectra[15] but can be differentiated electrophoretically. At pH 8.6, Hemoglobin A_2 migrates more slowly than does Hemoglobin A. Hemoglobin A_3 can be differentiated from both of these by virtue of having a higher electrophoretic mobility than Hemoglobin A.

ABNORMAL HEMOGLOBINS

Abnormal hemoglobins are expressions of mutations which are inherited as autosomal genes. Hörlein and Weber[16] reported in 1948 that the hemoglobin of patients with congenital methemoglobinemia exhibited an abnormal absorption spectrum. The disease was transmitted as a dominant factor through several generations. In 1949, Pauling and his colleagues[1] demonstrated that patients with sickle cell anemia had a form of hemoglobin which was electrophoretically distinct from normal hemoglobin. In the same year, Neel[17] reported that the gene responsible for red cell sickling in heterozygous individuals, and for severe sickle cell anemia in individuals homozygous for the factor, was inherited in simple Mendelian fashion. Inheritance of abnormal genes for other variant hemoglobins has also been shown to follow these principles.[18]

All of the abnormal hemoglobins examined by the fingerprint method (electrophoresis followed by chromatography) have shown a single amino acid difference with Hemoglobin A. Since the hemoglobin molecule consists of two identical parts, each having two different peptide chains, substitution of a normal amino acid by one which is more acidic or less acidic will change the structure of both halves of the molecule and thereby change its charge and hence its electrophoretic mobility.[19]

Hemoglobin F has a structure comprising alpha and gamma polypeptide chains and is the principal component of human fetus hemoglobin. It is distinguished from other hemoglobins by its resistance to alkali denaturation.[20] It was first found in umbilical cord blood and separated by means of paper electrophoresis by Smith and Conley.[21] These investigators used a Veronal buffer of pH 8.6 and ionic strength 0.06 to separate Hemoglobin F from Hemoglobin A.

Hemoglobin F comprises from 55–85% of total hemoglobin at birth, but this level falls rapidly and reaches the adult level of approximately 1% at one year of age. As Hemoglobin F falls, it is replaced by Hemoglobin A.[22]

Hemoglobin F is present in some adults affected by hereditary hematological disorders, including sickle cell anemia and thalassemia major and by certain acquired disorders, including pernicious anemia and leukemia. The level of Hemoglobin F in thalassemia major may exceed 90% of the total hemoglobin.[23]

Thalassemia is a hereditary anemia which occurs commonly in the Mediterranean region or in persons of Mediterranean origin. Thalassemia minor, which occurs in individuals heterozygous for the thalassemic gene, is characterized by the presence of target cells and by stippling of erythrocytes. It produces a mild anemia which may be asymptomatic. The level of Hemoglobin A_2 is frequently elevated in these patients. Thalassemia major, or Cooley's anemia, occurs in the homozygous individual and is usually expressed in the first year of life. It is a severe hypochromic anemia characterized by marked changes in red cell morphology accompanied by alterations to the skull and bones due to bone marrow hyperplasia. Affected children usually do not reach adulthood unless given repeated transfusions.

Hemoglobin S, the hemoglobin responsible for sickling of red cells, was discovered by Pauling and associates[1] and is an outstanding example of profound changes in physiologic function which can be brought about by alterations in molecular structure. As with other abnormal hemoglobins, Hemoglobin S is characterized by the substitution of a single amino acid (valine for glutamine) at one locus of the beta-polypeptide chain of normal hemoglobin (Hemoglobin A). Hemoglobin S is occasionally found in association with other abnormal forms of hemoglobin.[24, 25, 26] Individuals homozygous for Hemoglobin

S have severe anemia and experience neurologic and intestinal symptoms. Ulcers are commonly found on the lower extremities, and bone marrow hyperplasia may occur.

Production of Hemoglobin S in affected individuals reaches adult levels approximately 4½ months after birth. Sickling of red cells is found more commonly in adult Negroes than children.[27] The frequency of Hemoglobin S may reach 10–20% in some East African populations. In American Negroes, the incidence of homozygous inheritance is approximately 0.2%; the heterozygous condition occurs with a frequency of approximately 7%.

Hemoglobin C produces a mild form of anemia. It was first isolated by Itano and Neel[28] and is distinguished by a low rate of electrophoretic migration.[29] It is found more frequently in Africa and also becomes more apparent in adults than in the newborn. Hemoglobin C arises from the substitution of lysine for valine of Hemoglobin S. In Ghana, it may reach a 20% frequency; in American Negroes, the incidence of Hemoglobin C is 2–3%. Hemoglobin C is often present in association with Hemoglobin A[30, 31] or with Hemoglobin S.[32]

Hemoglobin D may contain alpha, beta, or gamma polypeptide chains and has the same electrophoretic mobility as does Hemoglobin S on most supporting media. Distinction between Hemoglobin S and Hemoglobin D depends upon a test for red cell sickling and also by the greater solubility of Hemoglobin D. This variant occurs in some parts of India with a frequency of 1%.[24] Differences in peptide amino acid composition of Hemoglobin D among several populations have been observed.[33]

Hemoglobin E migrates to the region of Hemoglobin C, and is more commonly found in Southeast Asia. In Burma, Hemoglobin E has been reported to reach a frequency of more than 10%.[13]

Hemoglobin H is a fast-moving hemoglobin present in patients heterozygous for the thalassemic gene.[17] It is distinguished by having a structure composed of four beta polypeptide chains.[34] It is readily denatured by freezing and thawing. Hemoglobin H has the same electrophoretic mobility as Hemoglobin I which occurs in individuals with no sign of disease. Hemoglobin I is distinguished by the presence of tryptophan.[35, 36, 37]

Hemoglobin M is found in individuals with methemoglobinemia where the prosthetic group contains iron in the ferric form, and the resultant hemoglobin does not combine with oxygen.[38] The occurrence of Hemoglobin M is therefore associated with cyanosis. This variant shows a characteristic absorption peak at 600 mμ[39] and is found near the origin on electrophoresis.

Bart's hemoglobin is a fast-moving form of fetal hemoglobin which is present in thalassemia. It consists entirely of polypeptide chains of gamma configuration.

PROCEDURE FOR ELECTROPHORESIS OF HEMOGLOBINS

The sample for hemoglobin electrophoresis is prepared by collecting whole blood in a tube containing an anticoagulant (*e.g.*, sodium citrate, potassium oxalate, sodium ethylenediaminetetraacetate, heparin, etc.). The contents are mixed and centrifuged at 2000 rpm for approximately 15 minutes, after which plasma is removed and the red cells washed twice with 0.9% saline. Hemoglobin is released into solution by shaking the red cells with approximately two volumes of distilled water for 30 minutes. If desired, the contents may be frozen overnight to ensure complete disruption of red cell membranes. The hemolyzed red cells are shaken with a small volume of chloroform, and cell stroma removed by centrifugation.

An aliquot of the clear hemolysate is applied to the cellulose acetate membrane for electrophoresis in barbital buffer of pH 8.6 or Tris-borate buffer of pH 9.1. The size of sample used depends upon the concentration of hemoglobin in solution, which in turn depends upon the hemoglobin content of the original blood specimen. In many cases

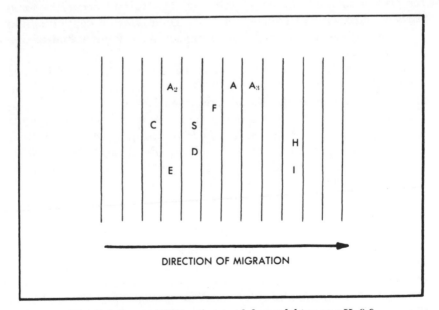

Figure 16. Relative mobilities of several hemoglobins at pH 8.6.

1–5 μl of the hemolysate, prepared according to the above description, are sufficient.

A control, consisting of Hemoglobin C or Hemoglobin A, is usually run along with the unknown in order to establish a point of reference for gauging the mobility of the unknown hemoglobin. Reference hemoglobins are available from a number of suppliers of laboratory chemicals. Use of appropriate control hemoglobins is particularly important because diagnosis of hemoglobin phenotype depends on electrophoretic data. Hemoglobin C is commonly used because it has a relatively low mobility and is far removed from the other hemoglobins on the electrophoretic strip.

Completed electrophoretograms can be examined directly; hemoglobins appear as red bands on the white background of the membrane. In addition, the commonly employed protein stains such as Ponceau S, Amido Black, Nigrosine, Lissamine Green, etc., may be used to stain hemoglobins, provided all traces of stromal or plasma proteins have been removed from the hemolysate. Diagnosis of hemoglobin type and, hence, detection of abnormal variants, is usually made by examination of electrophoretic patterns. Relative mobilities of some hemoglobins are illustrated in Figure 16.

REFERENCES

1. Pauling, L., H. A. Itano, S. J. Singer, and I. C. Wells. Science **110**, 543 (1949).
2. Reissmann, K. R., W. E. Ruth, and T. Nomura. J. Clin. Invest. **40**, 1826 (1961).
3. Charache, S., D. J. Weatherall, and J. B. Clegg. J. Clin. Invest. **45**, 813 (1966).
4. Reed, C. S., R. Hampson, S. Gordon, R. T. Jones, M. J. Novy, B. Brimhall, M. J. Edwards, and R. D. Koler. Blood **31**, 623 (1968).
5. Stamatoyannopoulos, G., A. Yoshida, J. Adamson, and S. Heinenberg. Science **159**, 741 (1968).
6. Muirhead, H., and M. F. Perutz. Nature **199**, 633 (1963).
7. Benesch, R. E., R. Benesch, and G. Macduff. Proc. Nat. Acad. Sci. **54**, 535 (1965).
8. Guidotti, G. J. Biol. Chem. **242**, 3685 (1967).
9. Bunn, H. F. J. Clin. Invest. **48**, 126 (1969).
10. Rhinesmith, H. S., W. A. Schroeder, and N. J. Martin. J. Am. Chem. Soc. **80**, 3358 (1958).
11. Wilson, S., and D. B. Smith. Canad. J. Biochem. Physiol. **37**, 405 (1959).

12. Perutz, M. F., M. G. Rossmann, A. F. Cullis, H. Muirhead, G. Will, and A. C. T. North. Nature **185**, 416 (1960).
13. Ingram, V. M. *Hemoglobin and Its Abnormalities* (Springfield, Illinois: Charles C Thomas, 1961).
14. Kunkel, H. G., and G. Wallenius. Science **122**, 288 (1955).
15. Kunkel, H. G., and A. G. Bearn. Fed. Proc. **16**, 760 (1957).
16. Hörlein, H., and G. Weber. Deut. Med. Wochschr. **73**, 476 (1948).
17. Neel, J. V. Science **110**, 64 (1949).
18. Neel, J. V. Ann. Human Genet. **21**, 1 (1956).
19. Baglioni, C. In *Molecular Genetics*, Part I, ed. J. H. Taylor (New York: Academic Press, 1963) p 405.
20. White, J. C., and G. H. Beaven. Brit. Med. Bull. **15**, 33 (1959).
21. Smith, E. W., and C. L. Conley. Bull. Johns Hopkins Hosp. **93**, 94 (1953).
22. Cook, C. D., H. R. Brodie, and D. W. Allen. Pediatrics **20**, 272 (1957).
23. Rich, A. Proc. Nat. Acad. Sci. **38**, 187 (1952).
24. Lehmann, H. In *Abnormal Hemoglobins*, eds. J. H. P. Jonxis and J. F. Delafresnaye (Oxford: Blackwell Scientific Pubns., 1959).
25. Singer, K., L. Singer, and S. R. Goldberg. Blood **10**, 405 (1955).
26. Sturgeon, P., H. A. Itano, and W. R. Bergren. Blood **10**, 389 (1955).
27. Schneider, R. G., and M. E. Haggard. Proc. Soc. Exp. Biol. Med. **89**, 196 (1955).
28. Itano, H. A., and J. V. Neel. Proc. Nat. Acad. Sci. **36**, 613 (1950).
29. Chernoff, A. I. New Eng. J. Med. **253**, 322 (1955).
30. Singer, K., A. P. Kraus, L. Singer, H. M. Rubenstein, and S. R. Goldberg. Blood **9**, 1032 (1954).
31. Avery, M. E. Bull. Johns Hopkins Hosp. **98**, 184 (1956).
32. Lehmann, H., and G. M. Edington. J. Clin. Pathol. **7**, 171 (1954).
33. Benzer, S., V. M. Ingram, and H. Lehmann. Nature **182**, 852 (1958).
34. Jones, R. T., W. A. Schroeder, J. E. Balog, and J. R. Vinograd. J. Am. Chem. Soc. **81**, 3161 (1959).
35. Rucknagel, D. L., E. B. Page, and W. N. Jensen. Blood **10**, 999 (1955).
36. Schwartz, I. R., J. Atwater, E. Repplinger, and L. M. Tocantins. Fed. Proc. **16**, 115 (1957).
37. Murayama, M., and V. M. Ingram. Nature **183**, 1798 (1959).
38. Gerald, P. S., and P. George. Science **129**, 393 (1959).
39. Gerald, P. S. Blood **13**, 936 (1958).

CHAPTER 9

Haptoglobins

Haptoglobins are a group of carbohydrate-containing proteins which possess the mobility of alpha$_2$ globulins and are unique in their capacity to combine stoichiometrically with hemoglobin. Their presence was first observed in 1938 when Polonovski and Jayle[1] found that serum contained a substance which, when combined with hemoglobin, formed a complex demonstrating peroxidase activity. The name "haptoglobin" is derived from the Greek word "haptein" meaning "to hold."[2]

Initial measurements of haptoglobin content were carried out by direct determination of peroxidase activity. Iodide was oxidized by the complex to iodine in the presence of ethyl hydroperoxide; the iodine formed was titrated with thiosulfate. Using this method of analysis, Jayle[3] showed that free haptoglobin was absent from the urine of patients with hemolytic jaundice. Later it was shown that this occurred because all of the available haptoglobin was bound to hemoglobin and retained in the circulating blood.[4,5] More recent methods employ an indirect approach to determine the amount of haptoglobin present. These make use of the stoichiometric combination of haptoglobin with hemoglobin and the reaction of hemoglobin with suitable staining reagents.

Shortly after its discovery, haptoglobin was found to consist of a group of proteins with very similar chemical properties;[6] this paved the way for subsequent studies.

In 1955, Smithies[7] employed starch gel electrophoresis to demonstrate the molecular heterogeneity of haptoglobins. Smithies and Walker[8] found that the presence of different haptoglobins was controlled by genetic factors. They postulated that the transmission of various haptoglobin types depended upon inheritance of two autosomal allelic genes, Hp^1 and Hp^2. The three combinations of these two genes give rise to the phenotypes known as Hp^{1-1}, Hp^{2-1}, and Hp^{2-2}. Of the three types, Hp^{1-1} has the highest mobility on starch gel, Hp^{2-2} has the lowest mobility, and Hp^{2-1} is intermediate.

The molecular weight of haptoglobin is approximately 80,000.[9] Normal serum contains sufficient free haptoglobin in 100 ml to bind 40–160 mg of hemoglobin.[10] Variations in haptoglobin content have been observed in various pathological conditions, although wide fluctuations may occur under normal circumstances.

The haptoglobin-hemoglobin complex has a different isoelectric point than that of uncombined hemoglobin. Free hemoglobin has an isoelectric point of 6.9, while the haptoglobin-hemoglobin complex becomes isoelectric at pH 5.8 and exhibits a higher rate of electrophoretic mobility at an alkaline pH. In barbital buffer of pH 8.6, haptoglobin has the mobility of alpha$_2$ globulin, while hemoglobin is located close to beta globulin. All of the human types of haptoglobin migrate to the alpha$_2$ globulin region upon electrophoresis on cellulose acetate, paper, agar gel, and in free-boundary systems with a neutral or slightly alkaline buffer. Variations in acetyl neuraminic acid content give rise to differences in isoelectric point of the various haptoglobins which may occasionally be differentiated by starch gel electrophoresis.[11]

PHYSIOLOGY AND METABOLISM

Data are scarce on the rate of turnover of haptoglobin in health and disease. Nyman[12] calculated the half-life of haptoglobin in plasma to be approximately 5.4 days. This is roughly the same as the half-lives observed for fibrinogen and alpha$_1$ globulin. Similar values were found by Jayle and Moretti[13] using radioactive tracers.

Hemoglobin, when administered intravenously, is immediately bound by haptoglobin, after which the complex as a whole is eliminated from the blood stream. The bond between hemoglobin and haptoglobin is so firm that haptoglobin cannot free itself and be reused. The complex is not filtered by the kidneys because of its large molecular size but is destroyed by the reticulo-endothelial system.[14] After saturation of haptoglobin with injected hemoglobin, 5–7 days are required for reestablishment of normal haptoglobin concentrations.[5]

Human haptoglobin can combine *in vitro* with hemoglobin from different animal species.[13] However, polymorphism of haptoglobin appears to be unique in humans since it has not been demonstrated in animals. Haptoglobins in most mammalian species studied are similar to the human type 1–1.[9,15,16]

The biologic function of haptoglobin has not been determined although it has been suggested that the presence of haptoglobin prevents the urinary loss of iron or prevents the formation of methemalbumin. Haptoglobin may therefore operate as a mechanism for conservation of iron stores in the body.

Premature children are anhaptoglobinemic. During the first few days of life, the haptoglobin content is negligible and rises gradually until, at four months of age, it reaches levels found in normal adults.[17,18]

Variations in the concentration of fibrinogen in some diseases have been correlated with changes in haptoglobin content. Nyman[19] found a positive correlation between plasma fibrinogen and haptoglobin. The correlation coefficient of 0.88 indicates that changes in these two factors are usually parallel. In the nephrotic syndrome, no correlation is observed. This may be the case because haptoglobin molecules are more easily lost by glomerular filtration than fibrinogen molecules of considerably larger size (molecular weight 400,000) and hence are eliminated by way of the urine.

Haptoglobin levels are reduced in acute and chronic liver disease and in mononucleosis. This may be due to an increased consumption or a decreased synthesis of haptoglobin.

During pregnancy haptoglobin content is increased but remains stable despite large changes in output of cortisol and estrogens. In nonpregnant women, interference with the balance of these hormones markedly affects the haptoglobin content of plasma.[20,21]

In certain malignant states and in chronic infections and inflammatory conditions, a marked rise in haptoglobin occurs. It has also been reported that serum haptoglobin levels may rise after surgical trauma or myocardial infarction.[22] It is possible that elevations in serum haptoglobin under these conditions are secondary responses elicited by tissue destruction.

In hemolytic jaundice, free haptoglobin is absent from the blood since all of the available haptoglobin is bound by a large excess of hemoglobin. On the other hand, haptoglobin level is normal or slightly elevated in obstructive jaundice, and high values are found in jaundice of neoplastic origin. In this respect, the assay of haptoglobin may be of value in the differential diagnosis of jaundice.

Haptoglobin and alpha globulins are both increased in lipoid nephrosis. In coronary artery disease, haptoglobin is increased and is accompanied by a high level of beta lipoprotein.[23] Diabetic patients with clinical evidence of angiopathy show significant elevations in haptoglobin content which are correlated with a rise in alpha$_2$ globulin.[24]

Studies have shown that different molecular forms of haptoglobin are found more commonly in certain parts of the world. Moullec and

Table VI

Distribution of Haptoglobin in Human Populations*

Country of origin	Percentage of total haptoglobin content		
	Hp 1–1	Hp 2–1	Hp 2–2
Denmark	16	47	37
Finland	15	43	42
France	15	50	35
Sweden	15	50	35
West Africa	53	38	9
American Negroes	40	40	21
China	11	34	54
India	2	14	82
Japan	6	36	58

*Adapted from Moullec and Fine[25] and Kirk *et al.*[26]

Fine[25] and Kirk *et al.*[26] studied the distribution of haptoglobins among various ethnic groups. Table VI presents a summary of some of their findings. Based on these observations, Jayle and Moretti[13] have suggested a possible use for haptoglobin typing in forensic medicine.

ELECTROPHORESIS OF HAPTOGLOBIN

Distinction of the haptoglobin-hemoglobin complex from uncombined hemoglobin can be accomplished by electrophoresis in a pH 8.6 barbital buffer followed by detection with the appropriate dye substance. Haptoglobin has the electrophoretic mobility of an alpha$_2$ globulin, and the haptoglobin-hemoglobin complex migrates with this fraction. Detection of haptoglobin is based on the absence of hemoglobin from plasma under normal conditions. When the normal rate of red cell breakdown is accelerated by intravascular or extravascular hemolysis, free hemoglobin is released into the plasma and combines with the circulating haptoglobin. Electrophoresis is frequently performed on a series of samples containing a standard amount of serum or plasma to which hemoglobin is added in several known concentrations (Method A). Added hemoglobin is immediately bound by haptoglobin, and the end point is selected as the concentration of hemoglobin which just exceeds the binding capacity of haptoglobin, enabling free hemoglobin to become visible as a separate band. The amount of hemoglobin which is bound by haptoglobin is designated as the hemoglobin-binding capacity.

An alternate method (Method B) is to add a concentration of hemoglobin which is known to exceed the available haptoglobin. After electrophoresis the percentage of total hemoglobin bound to haptoglobin is determined, and from this the amount of haptoglobin present can be calculated.

Method A. Known volumes of the sample to be tested are mixed with several known concentrations of hemoglobins. Solutions containing 50, 100, and 200 mg hemoglobin/100 ml are usually sufficient to determine the hemoglobin-binding capacity of haptoglobin. Hemoglobin C is frequently used because it has a low electrophoretic mobility and can easily be distinguished from the haptoglobin-hemoglobin complex which migrates to the alpha$_2$ globulin region. Serum containing no haptoglobin may also be used as a control. For this purpose, umbilical cord blood has been used. The unknown samples are reacted with hemoglobin at 37°C for approximately 30 minutes. Cellulose acetate electrophoresis is carried out in barbital buffer of pH 8.6, as employed for protein electrophoresis. The strips are then stained for 1 minute in a 1–2% solution of benzidine in acetic acid, followed by immersion in 3% hydrogen peroxide in distilled water. The presence of hemoglobin bound by haptoglobin or of free hemoglobin is shown by a red color, and the hemoglobin-binding capacity of haptoglobin is estimated by determining the hemoglobin concentration required to produce a visible band of free hemoglobin.

Method B. For this method, a concentration of hemoglobin known to be in excess of the binding capacity of haptoglobin is added to the unknown sample and incubated at 37°C for 30 minutes. Electrophoresis is carried out as described in Method A. Although benzidine may be used, *o*-dianisidine (3,3′-dimethoxybenzidine) is the preferred stain for this procedure because it produces a stable color for free and bound hemoglobin. *o*-Dianisidine is soluble in organic solvents such as alcohol, benzene, and ether. A procedure employing this staining reagent is described below. Because stained electrophoretic strips can be preserved without fading, immediate inspection as for benzidine-stained strips is not required.

Method B offers an advantage for determination of haptoglobin content because the percentage of total hemoglobin bound to haptoglobin can be determined by photometric scanning of the stained electrophoretic strip. The binding capacity of haptoglobin in the unknown sample is readily derived. This procedure allows results to be expressed in quantitative terms and may be especially useful for studying fluctuations in haptoglobin content.

Three systems have been used to detect the presence of the hemoglobin-haptoglobin complex. All of them are based on the ability of hemoglobin to catalyze the oxidation of the dye substance to its

BENZIDINE

colored derivative in the presence of hydrogen peroxide. Lathem and Worley[27] used a 1–2% solution of benzidine in acetic acid. Electrophoretic strips were placed in this solution for 15–20 seconds followed

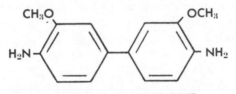

3,3'-DIMETHOXYBENZIDINE

by immersion in 3% peroxide in water for 30 seconds. Maximum color intensity appeared in 5–7 minutes. Owen and Silberman[28] used *o*-dianisidine in ethanol containing acetate buffer of pH 4.7; zones with peroxidase activity developed an intense brown color when stained for 15 minutes in this reagent. Leukomalachite Green was used by

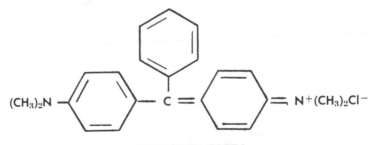

MALACHITE GREEN

Nyman[19] to stain heme-containing proteins. Leukomalachite Green in acid solution in the presence of a catalyst (*e.g.*, iron-porphyrin) is oxidized by peroxide to Malachite Green.

The color produced by oxidation of benzidine develops rapidly, but is transient and fades within a short time. *o*-Dianisidine produces a stable color and can be used with equal ease. The procedure of Valeri *et al.*[29] for cellulose acetate electrophoresis of haptoglobin employs *o*-dianisidine as the staining reagent. Electrophoresis is conducted in phosphate buffer of pH 7.0, ionic strength 0.05, followed by color development in a solution containing 10 ml of 1.5M acetic acid–acetate buffer of pH 4.7, 70 ml of 0.14% *o*-dianisidine in 95% ethanol, 2 ml of 3% hydrogen peroxide, and 18 ml water. The cellulose acetate strips are stained for 10 minutes and rinsed in distilled water. A stable color is produced by the action of hemoglobin or haptoglobin-bound hemoglobin on *o*-dianisidine; therefore, stained strips can be preserved for photometric scanning.

REFERENCES

1. Polonovski, M., and M. F. Jayle.   C. R. Soc. Biol. **129**, 457 (1938).
2. Polonovski, M., and M. F. Jayle.   C. R. Acad. Sci. **211**, 517 (1940).
3. Jayle, M. F.   C. R. Acad. Sci. **211**, 574 (1940).
4. Allison, A. C., and W. Rees.   Brit. Med. J. **2**, 1137 (1957).
5. Laurell, C. B., and M. Nyman.   Blood **12**, 493 (1957).
6. Jayle, M. F., and P. Gillard.   Bull. Soc. Chim. Biol. **29**, 149 (1947).
7. Smithies, O.   Biochem. J. **61**, 629 (1955).
8. Smithies, O., and N. F. Walker.   Nature **178**, 694 (1956).
9. Allison, A. C.   Nature **183**, 1312 (1959).
10. Ratcliff, A. P., and J. Hardwicke.   J. Clin. Pathol. **17**, 676 (1964).
11. Laurell, C. B., and C. Grönwall.   *Advances in Clinical Chemistry,* Vol. V (New York: Academic Press, 1962) p 135.
12. Nyman, M.   Nord. Med. **63**, 540 (1960).
13. Jayle, M. F., and J. Moretti.   In *Progress in Hematology*, Vol. III, ed. L. M. Tocantins (New York: Grune and Stratton, 1962) p 342.
14. Garby, L., and W. D. Noyes.   J. Clin. Invest. **38**, 1479 (1959).
15. Arends, T., and M. L. G. de Rodriguez.   Nature **185**, 325 (1960).
16. Blumberg, B. S.   Proc. Soc. Exp. Biol. Med. **104**, 25 (1960).
17. Hitzig, W. H.   Helv. Paediat. Acta **16**, 46 (1961).
18. Woods, K., B. Yudowitz, and R. Engle, Jr.   Proc. Soc. Exp. Biol. Med. **107**, 616 (1961).
19. Nyman, M.   Scand. J. Clin. Lab. Invest. **11**, Suppl. 39 (1959).
20. Studnitz, W. V., and M. Nyman.   J. Clin. Endocrinol. Metab. **17**, 010 (1057).

21. Borglin, N. E., and M. Nyman.   Scand. J. Clin. Lab. Invest. **13,** 107 (1961).
22. Murray, R. K., and G. E. Connell.   Nature **186,** 86 (1960).
23. Coumel, H., J. P. Farges, H. Baylon, J. F. Dulac, Mme. Dormann, and M. F. Jayle.   Arch Mal. Coeur et Vaisseaux **45,** 328 (1952).
24. Bergstrand, C. G., P. Fürst, Y. Larsson, and G. Sterky.   Scand. J. Clin. Lab. Invest. **14,** 629 (1962).
25. Moullec, J., and J. M. Fine.   Transfusion **2,** 229 (1959).
26. Kirk, R. L., L. Y. C. Lai, S. Mahmood, and R. Singh.   Nature **185,** 185 (1960).
27. Lathem, W., and W. E. Worley.   J. Clin. Invest. **38,** 474 (1959).
28. Owen, J. A., H. J. Silberman, and C. Got.   Nature **182,** 1373 (1958).
29. Valeri, C. R., J. C. Bond, K. Fowler, and J. Sobucki.   Clin. Chem. **11,** 581 (1965).

CHAPTER 10

Glycoproteins

Plasma proteins are known to bind carbohydrate in varying proportions to form glycoproteins. Complexes which belong to this group of substances contain more than 1% carbohydrate usually made up of hexose, hexosamine, and sialic acid. Although the distinction between glycoproteins and mucopolysaccharides is often vague, the two types of protein-carbohydrate complexes differ in chemical composition since glycoproteins do not contain sulfate esters or uronic acids. In addition, the carbohydrate moiety of glycoprotein is firmly bound to the protein portion, and vigorous hydrolytic procedures are required to liberate it. In comparison, mucoproteins or mucopolysaccharides contain uronic acid and sulfate in the carbohydrate moiety (examples are hyaluronic acid, chondroitin sulfate, and heparin) and are readily split into protein and amino polysaccharide components by treatment with mild alkali. Plasma contains a number of glycoproteins which can be separated electrophoretically. Carbohydrate is associated with most of the proteins present in blood plasma including albumin, globulins, transferrin, haptoglobin, ceruloplasmin, and thyroxin-binding globulin. Prothrombin, fibrinogen, and lipoproteins also contain carbohydrate.

CHEMISTRY OF GLYCOPROTEINS

The carbohydrate prosthetic group of glycoprotein is firmly bound to the peptide moiety by means of a covalent bond; therefore, the peptide or amide portion of the glycoprotein molecule cannot be separated from the carbohydrate portion without destructive procedures involving the use of strong hydrolytic reagents.[1]

Glycoprotein or mucoprotein solutions are viscous because of the presence of sialic acid which endows the molecules with a negative charge and causes them to assume a dispersed configuration. Sialic acid is linked to the adjoining sugar, usually galactose or galactosamine; the bond is broken by the action of neuraminidase, an enzyme produced by some bacteria or viruses, or by acid hydrolysis.[2,3] After selective removal of sialic acid residues, the protein assumes a more compact shape with a reduction in viscosity.[4]

The magnitude of negative electrical charge on the glycoprotein molecule appears to be proportional to its content of sialic acid. This difference in electrical charge allows the various glycoproteins to be separated electrophoretically.

Certain serologically specific reactions of blood group substances reside in the carbohydrate portion. An example is the virus hemagglutination reaction which involves agglutination of erythrocytes by heated influenza virus.[5] The reaction is inhibited by several mucoproteins or glycoproteins. This inhibition is abolished by the "receptor-destroying enzyme" of *Vibrio cholerae*, neuraminidase, which splits sialic acid away from the molecules.[6] Sialic acid has also been implicated in the biologic activity of certain hormones. For example, gonadotropins and erythropoietin lose their biologic activity upon removal of their sialic acid residues.[3,7,8]

Studies on the structure of fetuin, a glycoprotein present in fetal plasma, show that the carbohydrate portion of this glycoprotein comprises 22% of the total weight of the molecule, the remainder (78%) being made up of peptide material with amino acid composition similar to that of other proteins. The free carboxyl group of sialic acid confers acidic properties on the molecule. Selective removal of sialic acid residues results in elevation of the isoelectric point of this glycoprotein.[9,10]

ELECTROPHORETIC SEPARATION OF GLYCOPROTEINS

Serum glycoproteins have been studied in ethanol precipitates of whole serum,[11] by electrophoresis on paper strips,[12,13,14] by fractionation on cellulose acetate,[15,16] and in blocks of polyvinyl chloride.[11] Table VII gives the approximate distribution of glycoproteins in normal human serum. It can be seen that the major carbohydrate-bearing fractions migrate with alpha$_2$ and beta globulins.

Electrophoresis of glycoproteins is usually performed in barbital buffer of pH 8.6 and ionic strength varying from 0.06–0.1. Detection of glycoproteins directly on electrophoretic strips is accomplished by

Table VII

Approximate Distribution of Glycoproteins in Normal Human Serum

Protein to which bound	Percentage distribution	
	Average	*Range*
albumin	12.8	6.8–20.9
alpha$_1$	16.6	8.5–23.5
alpha$_2$	28.5	19.9–36.0
beta	25.6	19.9–33.3
gamma	17.1	8.2–22.5

a modification of the method of Köiw and Grönwall.[17] Hydroxyl groups present in the carbohydrate moiety are oxidized by periodic acid to aldehydes; the latter give a purple-red color upon reaction with Schiff's reagent (basic fuchsin decolorized with sulfurous acid). Infante and his colleagues[12] have used a methylated derivative of fuchsin (neo-fuchsin, Ciba)

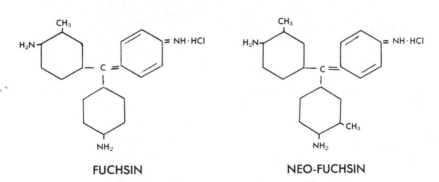

FUCHSIN   NEO-FUCHSIN

which appears to have higher sensitivity than fuchsin when potassium bisulfite is used in place of potassium iodide as the reducing agent.

The same conditions are used for electrophoresis of glycoproteins as for serum or plasma proteins and lipoproteins. Barbital buffer of pH 8.6, ionic strength 0.075 is used. A potential of 150 V (1.5 mA/2.5 cm wide strip) is applied for 90 minutes. These conditions have proved convenient because separation of proteins and lipoproteins can be carried out in the same electrophoresis chamber. Upon completion of electrophoresis, oxidation is carried out in a solution of 0.5% periodic acid (0.5 g of HIO$_4$ in 100 ml water) for 5 minutes. The strip is then placed in periodic acid–Schiff reagent for 10 minutes. Presence of glycoproteins is indicated by a purple-red color; relative mobilities of the glycoproteins usually correspond closely to those of the associated plasma proteins. After staining, the electrophoretic strip is washed several times in 0.5% potassium metabisulfite followed by rinsing in distilled water for 10 minutes. The stained strips are then impregnated with glycerol containing 0.5% potassium metabisulfite (Figure 17) and scanned densitometrically. Glycerol-impregnated strips are preserved in sealed plastic bags. Cleared, dry membranes can also be scanned.[16] Periodic acid oxidation may be preceded by fixation with trichloroacetic acid (0.5%), although this is not a required step. An

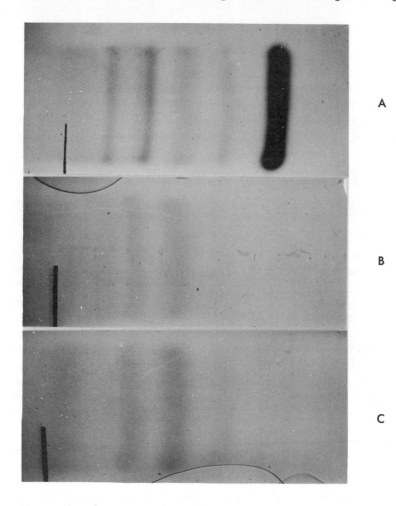

Figure 17. Glycoproteins from plasma (B) and serum (C) matched with plasma protein strip (A) to indicate mobilities of corresponding fractions. Note the predominance of alpha$_2$ glycoprotein. Electrophoresis conducted in barbital buffer, pH 8.6, ionic strength 0.075.

additional rinse with potassium metabisulfite, interposed prior to staining with Schiff's reagent, may be used to reduce the intensity of background staining when necessary.[12]

PHYSIOLOGY OF GLYCOPROTEINS

In normal human serum, the concentration of protein-bound carbohydrate is approximately 270 mg per 100 ml; nearly half of this is made up of hexoses in the form of galactose and mannose. Hexosamine constitutes approximately 30% of the carbohydrate present primarily in the form of N-acetyl glucosamine, with the remainder comprising sialic acid and fucose.[11, 18]

Electrophoretically distinct serum proteins contain bound carbohydrate in varying proportions. Alpha$_1$ glycoproteins are rich in carbohydrate, usually containing about 7.5% hexose compared with normal serum proteins which contain about 1.5% hexose. Of the alpha$_1$ glycoproteins, orosomucoid, also known as alpha$_1$ acid seromucoid, is the most extensively studied. At pH 8.6, orosomucoid migrates to the region of alpha$_1$ globulin; its physiological activity is unknown.[19, 20, 21, 22, 23] The alpha$_1$ glycoproteins include inhibitors of viral hemagglutination and trypsin. In addition, alpha$_1$ lipoproteins and thyroxin-binding protein are associated with measurable amounts of carbohydrate.

The alpha$_2$ glycoproteins in normal serum and plasma have the highest carbohydrate content of any of the electrophoretic fractions and show the largest changes in pathologic conditions. This group includes a number of separate glycoproteins including the haptoglobins, ceruloplasmin, alpha$_2$ macroglobulins, and alpha$_2$ lipoproteins. Haptoglobin is an alpha$_2$ protein with a molecular weight of approximately 80,000[24] which, in nephrotic urine, contains as much as 17% of its mass as hexose and hexosamine.[25] The molecular weight of ceruloplasmin is about 151,000. It is a blue protein containing 0.34% copper and was first isolated by Holmberg and Laurell.[26] This protein contains eight atoms of copper per molecule; on a weight basis, it contains 3% hexose, 1.9% hexosamine, and 2.0% sialic acid.[27]

Beta glycoproteins contain slightly less carbohydrate than the alpha$_2$ glycoproteins. So far two beta glycoproteins have been studied: transferrin and beta$_2$ globulin. Transferrin is the iron-binding serum protein isolated by Holmberg and Laurell in 1945.[28] Beta$_2$ glycoprotein, first isolated by Heremans *et al.*,[29] has a mobility intermediate between that of beta and gamma globulins. It contains 5% hexose and 4% hexosamine.

Fibrinogen contains approximately 3% hexose with 1% hexosamine and less than 1% sialic acid.[27, 30] On electrophoretic media, it migrates between gamma and beta globulins.

The gamma globulins in normal human plasma contain appreciable amounts of carbohydrate. These have been studied by Pappenheimer et al.,[31] Müller-Eberhard et al.,[32] and Rosevear and Smith.[33]

Albumin binds less carbohydrate than the serum globulins and appears to be less closely related to physiological alterations than carbohydrates transported by the globulins. A minor glycoprotein fraction ("tryptophan-rich prealbumin") containing 1.1% hexose was isolated by Schultze et al.[34] This fraction on zone electrophoresis migrated more rapidly than albumin.

The content of serum glycoproteins appears to increase with age. Pearce et al.[14] reported that the important changes occur in $alpha_2$ and beta glycoproteins. These data confirm the observations of Shetlar et al.[35]

Abnormal glycoproteins have occurred in human plasma in certain pathologic states. Waldenström's macroglobulin contains approximately 10% carbohydrate. The rheumatoid factor, isolated by Kunkel et al.,[36] is a high molecular weight gamma globulin with a similar carbohydrate content. The higher electrophoretic mobility observed for certain pathological glycoproteins in plasma may be due to increased amounts of sialic acid which give the molecules a greater negative charge.

In multiple myeloma, increased carbohydrate content accompanies elevations in proteins found to characterize each type of myeloma.[37, 38] $Alpha_2$ glycoprotein is increased in malignant tumors,[39] rheumatic fever, and the active states of rheumatoid arthritis.[40, 41] An increased $alpha_2$ glycoprotein content has also been observed in tuberculosis and other pulmonary diseases[17] and diabetes,[42] while glycoprotein belonging to the gamma globulin fraction is increased in viral hepatitis.[43] In the nephrotic syndrome, an increase in the $alpha_2$ glycoprotein is frequently accompanied by marked elevations in $alpha_2$ globulin and in lipoprotein content.[44, 45, 46] The distributions of serum glycoproteins under normal and some pathologic conditions are illustrated in Figure 18.

The study of serum glycoproteins has acquired additional significance in recent years because of the possible role of glycoproteins in atherosclerosis. Taylor[47] described the subintimal accumulation of mucopolysaccharide in early atheromatous lesions. Serum hexosamine and mucoprotein levels in atherosclerotic patients were shown to be significantly higher than in control individuals of the same age. In addition,

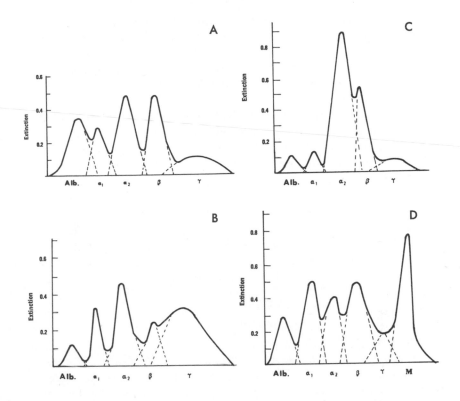

Figure 18. Glycoprotein distributions in normal serum (A); infectious hepatitis (B); lipoid nephrosis (C); and gamma myeloma (D). [Reprinted, by permission, from Clinica Chimica Acta (1960) 672, Figures 1, 5, 6, and 7. © Elsevier Publishing Co.]

a marked rise in serum mucoprotein occurred in rats in company with an elevation of serum hexosamine. These findings confirm Faber's[48] suggestion that increased serum glycoprotein accompanies tissue deposition of cholesterol and is associated with atherosclerosis. Conversely, Schwartz and Gilmore[49] observed that serum glycoprotein levels are lower in Australian aborigines than in urban populations. They suggest that low glycoprotein levels are related to a reduced incidence of atherosclerosis in this nomadic group.

Several recent reports are worthy of note. Schönebeck *et al.*[50] showed that protein-bound carbohydrate in serum was significantly elevated in atherosclerotic patients; this was reflected in an increased content of alpha$_2$ and beta glycoproteins; glycoprotein content in vessel walls was also elevated. At least part of the rise may be ascribed to glyco-

proteins in sclerotic arterial media.[51] Further evidence linking glycoprotein accumulation and atherosclerosis was advanced by Manley
and Mullinger[52] who found that the ratio of sialic acid to uronic acid
was significantly increased in atherosclerotic plaques. The increment
in sialic acid was presumed to be due in large part to an increased
glycoprotein content.

It is clear that much needs to be done to determine the role of
glycoproteins in normal and abnormal physiology. Changes observed
in serum and plasma glycoproteins thus far have not been directly
correlated with specific disease states. Whether alterations in glycoprotein distribution are secondary to physiologic disturbances or reflect
fundamental changes in biochemical mechanisms remains to be seen.
Extensive studies of plasma and tissue glycoproteins, including electrophoretic separation and analysis of individual glycoprotein fractions,
are needed to establish statistical relationships of the protein-carbohydrate complexes to human physiology.

REFERENCES

1. Spiro, R. G.   New Eng. J. Med. **269**, 566 (1963).
2. Gottschalk, A.   *Chemistry and Biology of Sialic Acids and Related
   Substances* (New York: Cambridge University Press, 1960).
3. Gottschalk, A., W. K. Whitten, and E. R. B. Graham.   Biochim. Biophys. Acta **38**, 183 (1960).
4. Gottschalk, A.   Nature **186**, 949 (1960).
5. Burnet, F. M.   Physiol. Rev. **31**, 131 (1951).
6. Gottschalk, A.   In *The Enzymes*, Vol. IV, 2nd ed., eds. P. D. Boyer, H.
   Lardy, and M. Myrbäck (New York: Academic Press, 1960) p 461.
7. Rafelson, M. E., Jr., H. Clauser, and J. Legault-Demare.   Biochim.
   Biophys. Acta **47**, 406 (1961).
8. Rambach, W. A., R. A. Shaw, J. A. D. Cooper, and H. L. Alt.   Proc.
   Soc. Exp. Biol. Med. **99**, 482 (1958).
9. Spiro, R. G.   J. Biol. Chem. **235**, 2860 (1960).
10. Spiro, R. G.   J. Biol. Chem. **237**, 646 (1962).
11. Böttiger, L. E., and L. A. Carlson.   Clin. Chim. Acta **5**, 664, 812
    (1960).
12. Infante, F., S. Juillard, D. Schwartz, and M. Sanz.   Clin. Chim. Acta
    5, 672 (1960).
13. Böttiger, L. E., and G. Sterky.   Acta Med. Scand. **172**, 339 (1962).
14. Pearce, R. H., E. M. Watson, R. Stodolski, J. M. Mathieson, and J. J.
    Theore.   Clin. Chem. **10**, 1066 (1964).
15. Kelsey, R. L., T. P. de Graffenried, and R. C. Donaldson.   Clin. Chem.
    11, 1058 (1965).

16. Klainer, A. S., W. R. Beisel, and W. K. Atkins. Am. J. Clin. Pathol. **50**, 137 (1968).

17. Köiw, E., and A. Grönwall. Scand. J. Clin. Lab. Invest. **4**, 244 (1952).

18. Winzler, R. J. In *Methods of Biochemical Analysis*, Vol. II, ed. D. Glick (New York: Interscience, 1955) p 279.

19. Smith, E. L., D. M. Brown, H. E. Weimer, and R. J. Winzler. J. Biol. Chem. **185**, 569 (1950).

20. Odin, L. Acta Chem. Scand. **9**, 862 (1955).

21. Schultze, H. E., von, I. Gollner, K. Heide, M. Schönenberger, and G. Schwick. Z. Naturforsch. **10b**, 463 (1955).

22. Yamashina, I. Acta Chem. Scand. **10**, 1666 (1956).

23. Popenoe, E. A., and R. M. Drew. J. Biol. Chem. **228**, 673 (1957).

24. Allison, A. C. Nature **183**, 1312 (1959).

25. Jayle, M. F., G. Boussier, and J. Tonnelat. Bull. Soc. Chim. Biol. **38**, 343 (1956).

26. Holmberg, C. G., and C. B. Laurell. Acta Chem. Scand. **2**, 550 (1948).

27. Schultze, H. E. Deut. Med. Wochschr. **83**, 1742 (1958).

28. Holmberg, C. G., and C. B. Laurell. Acta Physiol. Scand. **10**, 307 (1945).

29. Heremans, J. F., M. T. Heremans, and H. E. Schultze. Clin. Chim. Acta **4**, 96 (1959).

30. Blombäck, B. Arkiv Kemi **12**, 99 (1958).

31. Pappenheimer, A. M., Jr., H. P. Lundgren, and J. W. Williams. J. Exptl. Med. **71**, 247 (1940).

32. Müller-Eberhard, H. J., H. G. Kunkel, and E. C. Franklin. Proc. Soc. Exp. Biol. Med. **93**, 146 (1956).

33. Rosevear, J. W., and E. L. Smith. J. Am. Chem. Soc. **80**, 250 (1958).

34. Schultze, H. E., Schönenberger, M., and G. Schwick. Biochem. Z. **328**, 267 (1956).

35. Shetlar, M. R., J. V. Foster, K. H. Kelly, and M. R. Everett. Proc. Soc. Exp. Biol. Med. **69**, 507 (1948).

36. Kunkel, H. G., E. C. Franklin, and H. J. Müller-Eberhard. J. Clin. Invest. **38**, 424 (1959).

37. Sachs, B. A., P. Cady, and G. Ross. Am. J. Med. **17**, 662 (1954).

38. Magalini, S. I., M. Stefanini, and H. M. Marin. Am. J. Med. Sci. **231**, 155 (1956).

39. Roboz, E., W. C. Hess, and F. M. Forster. Arch. Neurol. Psychiat. **73**, 536 (1955).

40. Kuhns, W. J., and J. Crittenden. J. Lab. Clin. Med. **46**, 398 (1955).

41. Südhof, H., J. M. Thum, and H. Kruppa. Klin. Wochschr. **37**, 1181 (1959).

42. Gilliland, I. C., and E. Stanton. J. Clin. Pathol. **7**, 172 (1954).

43. Schaffner, F., A. L. Scheibel, and R. I. Lytle. J. Lab. Clin. Med. **48**, 551 (1956).

44. Raynaud, R., J. R. d'Eshougues, P. Pasquet, and S. Di Giovanni. Algérie Méd. **57**, 725 (1953).

45. Raynaud, R., J. R. d'Eshougues, and P. Pasquet. Semaine Hôp. **30**, 4065 (1954).

46. Wunderly, C., and S. Piller. Klin. Wochschr. **32**, 425 (1954).

47. Taylor, H. E. Am. J. Pathol. **29**, 871 (1953).

48. Faber, M. Arch. Pathol. **48**, 342 (1949).

49. Schwartz, C. J., and H. R. Gilmore. Circulation **18**, 191 (1958).

50. Schönebeck, L., U. Werber, and K. D. Voigt. J. Athero. Res. **2**, 332 (1962).

51. Apostolakis, M., U. Werber, and K. D. Voigt. J. Athero. Res. **8**, 847 (1968).

52. Manley, G., and R. N. Mullinger. Brit. J. Exp. Pathol. **48**, 529 (1967).

CHAPTER 11

Isoenzymes

Most enzymes are intracellular in distribution and are maintained at relatively steady levels of activity. Under normal conditions, they appear in the plasma only in low concentration. Marked changes in activity may result from a combination of factors which reflect a disturbance of the fine balance between cell permeability and tissue metabolism or excretion via normal channels. When an organ is afflicted by disease, cell permeability and/or cell breakdown are accelerated, and enzymes normally present within that organ tend to escape into the circulation, giving rise to increased plasma activity.

Enzyme activity can be determined by various chemical techniques. In recent years, electrophoresis has proved useful for separating and characterizing a number of enzymes. Some of these occur in multiple molecular forms distinguishable by their electrophoretic behavior and are therefore called isoenzymes. Examples can be found among the dehydrogenases, aminotransferases, phosphatases, and peroxidases. In some cases, relationships of considerable biologic significance are believed to exist between electrophoretically distinct forms of certain enzymes and organ function. The following discussion will be centered around the lactate dehydrogenase isoenzymes because the clinical value of variations in their distribution is well established and because procedures used for electrophoresis of lactate dehydrogenase can, with minor modifications, be employed for separation and identification of other enzymes. Methods for examining several other enzymes and isoenzymes of widespread interest will be considered briefly.

101

LACTATE DEHYDROGENASE

Lactate dehydrogenase (LDH) catalyzes the oxidation of lactic acid to pyruvic acid in the body. The reaction requires the presence of the coenzyme, nicotinamide-adenine dinucleotide (NAD):

$$CH_3COCOOH + NADH_2 \overset{LDH}{\rightleftharpoons} CH_3CHOH\ COOH + NAD$$

In 1950, Meister[1] separated two electrophoretically distinct proteins from the crystalline ox-heart enzyme. Each of these was shown to possess enzyme activity.[2] Vesell and Bearn[3] found that human serum contained three distinct components with LDH activity when analyzed by starch block electrophoresis. Similar results were obtained by Sayre and Hill[4] with paper electrophoresis and gradient-elution chromatography. Wieland and Pfleiderer[5] examined a number of organs from several animal species and reported that LDH enzyme activity was found in up to five protein fractions. In recent years, studies of isoenzymes in blood and tissues have been stimulated by the recognition that alterations in isoenzyme content and distribution may have diagnostic value.

LDH isoenzymes differ from each other in electrophoretic and chromatographic behavior, chemical composition, susceptibility to inhibitors, substrate specificity, and immunochemical specificity (*i.e.*, antisera can be prepared which inhibit the activity of a particular isoenzyme without affecting that of the others).

Five molecular forms of LDH have thus far been isolated and identified in humans; each is distinguished by possessing a characteristic electrophoretic mobility. They are numbered 1 through 5 in accordance with their rate of migration. LDH_1, the fastest moving isoenzyme by virtue of its greatest negative electrical charge, migrates farthest toward the anode and is found between albumin and $alpha_1$ globulin; LDH_2 is found with the $alpha_2$ globulin, LDH_3 in the beta region, LDH_4 with the fast gamma, and LDH_5 located close to or at the origin.

All of the isoenzymes have a similar molecular weight of approximately 135,000.[6] By means of extensive hydrolysis with hydrochloric acid followed by amino acid analysis, differences in protein composition of the various isoenzymes have been demonstrated.[7] For example, rat heart LDH_1 contains more acidic amino acids (aspartate) than LDH_5, which contains more basic amino acids (lysine). The aspartic acid content is highest in LDH_1 and declines progressively from LDH_1 to LDH_5. Valine and glutamate content also decline in the same direction.[8] The difference in amino acid composition of the isoenzymes may account for observed differences in electrophoretic mobility; a lower aspartate content in the slower moving fractions results in reduced acidity which produces a fall in negative charge on the molecules when a buffer solution of alkaline pH is employed.

LDH isoenzymes from the same species appear to have the same molecular weight. Each isoenzyme is a tetramer which can be split into four subunits, or monomers, each having a molecular weight of approximately 35,000.[9, 10, 11] LDH_1 is made up of four identical subunits; LDH_5 is also made up of four identical subunits which, however, are different from those in LDH_1. LDH_2, LDH_3, and LDH_4 are hybrid or intermediate forms containing both types of subunits. If LDH_1 and LDH_5 are split by the action of 12M urea or 5M guanidine HCl into their respective subunits, recombination takes place in a manner which gives rise to all five types of isoenzymes. In addition, repeated freezing and thawing causes dissociation of the isoenzymes into subunits. If pure LDH_1 and LDH_5 are mixed and subjected to repeated freezing and thawing, dissociation is followed by recombination into the five tetrameric forms in the ratio 1:4:6:4:1, which is expected when random reassociation occurs.

Each enzyme molecule, moreover, combines with four molecules of coenzyme (nicotinamide-adenine dinucleotide, or NAD). Synthesis of the polypeptide subunits is believed to be under genetic control.[10, 11, 12] A sixth LDH isoenzyme, designated LDH_x, is found in testis and appears to be formed from a different subunit structure.[13]

LDH_1 and LDH_2 predominate in heart muscle; they are also present in high concentration in kidneys and erythrocytes. Skeletal muscle and liver are rich in LDH_4 and LDH_5, while LDH_3 is the principal isoenzyme in pancreas, lung, spleen, adrenal glands, lymph nodes, and white blood cells (Table VIII).

It has been suggested that the specificity of mammalian LDH for L-lactate and inhibition by pyruvate[14, 15, 16, 17] is related to physiologic

Table VIII
Distribution of Lactate Dehydrogenase Isoenzymes

LDH_1, LDH_2	LDH_4, LDH_5	LDH_3
heart	skeletal muscle	lung
erythrocytes	liver	pancreas
kidney		adrenals
brain		spleen
		thymus
		thyroid
		lymph nodes
		leukocytes

function. Certain skeletal muscles, for example, the soleus, exhibit an isoenzyme pattern much like that seen in heart muscle. Red fibers are predominant in this muscle, which is more or less in continuous contraction in order to maintain posture. In contrast, the gastrocnemius, which contains predominantly white fibers and operates periodically in contractile processes associated with locomotion, contains LDH_4 and LDH_5.[18,19,20]

The activity of the heart depends upon aerobic processes. Oxidation of pyruvate via the citric acid cycle provides energy by which the heart can perform its work. Cahn *et al.*[10] have suggested that an increased pyruvate concentration would inhibit LDH of the heart muscle (LDH_1) and force the metabolism of pyruvate to proceed through the citric acid cycle. A tissue such as the heart would consequently not allow lactate to accumulate.

On the other hand, skeletal muscle depends on anaerobic breakdown of carbohydrate for its energy during exercise; this results in the production of lactic acid from pyruvic acid. Since LDH_5 is not inhibited by pyruvate, the presence of moderate amounts of pyruvate would push the equilibrium of the reaction toward the formation of lactate and allow the development of an oxygen debt.

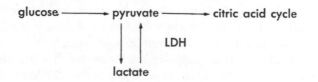

LDH isoenzyme patterns are currently being used to confirm the diagnosis of myocardial infarction. While serum levels of aspartate aminotransferase and creatine kinase may show transient elevation after an episode of myocardial infarction, serum LDH may remain elevated for up to two weeks.[21] The LDH pattern in a patient with myocardial infarction shows a predominance of the isoenzymes characteristic of heart muscle.[22,23,24] These findings have been amply confirmed by other investigators.[25,26,27,28]

The relative organ specificity of LDH isoenzymes makes electrophoretic analysis a particularly useful adjunct to clinical diagnosis of myocardial infarction, especially when equivocal electrocardiographic tracings are obtained due to causes such as arrhythmia, conduction defects, or digitalis therapy.[26] Increased amounts of LDH_1 and LDH_2 can also be detected after cardiac surgery which produces mechanical injury to the heart.[29] In contrast, normal LDH patterns are found in angina pectoris or pericarditis, neither of which involves actual damage to the heart muscle.[26]

The predominant isoenzyme in liver is LDH_5; LDH_4 is also present in high concentration. Increased amounts of serum LDH_5 are found in hepatitis, jaundice, mononucleosis (infiltration of the liver by lymphocytes) and cirrhosis and are characteristic of damage to the liver cells. Elevations of LDH_4 and LDH_5 are also seen in diseases of skeletal muscle. If myocardial infarction is followed by congestive heart failure, interpretation of the LDH isoenzyme pattern may be complicated by a release of LDH_4 and LDH_5 due to secondary liver damage.

Cellulose acetate membranes have been widely used for the clinical investigation of LDH isoenzymes.[30, 31, 32, 33, 34, 35] The procedure for electrophoretic analysis of serum or plasma LDH follows closely those used for the separation of proteins and lipoproteins. Barbital buffer of pH 8.6 is commonly used. An important point to remember is that in order to achieve dependable results, serum or plasma must be fresh and free from hemolysis. Since red blood cells contain 100–150 times as much of LDH as does serum, a slight degree of hemolysis would give rise to grossly elevated serum LDH levels and interfere with interpretation of the electrophoretic pattern. A portion of LDH found in serum may also originate in platelets.[36] It is advisable, whenever possible, to use freshly drawn serum samples for electrophoresis, although overnight storage at 4°C will not produce significant change in the isoenzyme pattern. A single freezing of the sample to be analyzed is also permissible, but repeated freezing and thawing should be avoided because of adverse effects upon the structure of the isoenzyme molecules.

Normally, 10–15 μl of serum are sufficient to obtain a clear LDH isoenzyme pattern. The sample is placed near the cathode bridge of the cellulose acetate membrane by means of a paper transfer strip or wire applicator, and electrophoresis is carried out at 150 V (1.5mA/ strip measuring 2.5×17 cm) for 90 minutes. These conditions have proved satisfactory in actual practice (Figure 19); however, conditions may be adjusted to meet the needs of individual laboratories. Following electrophoresis, the membrane is placed on a glass slide and overlaid with another strip of cellulose acetate soaked with the appropriate mixture including the substrate (lactate), coenzyme (nicotinamide-adenine dinucleotide), hydrogen transferring agent (phenazine methosulfate), and dye (tetrazolium salt). A mixture of these reactants is available in capsule form (Gelman Instrument Company). The contents can be dissolved in distilled water immediately prior to use. Incubation of the electrophoretic strip at 37°C with a reagent mixture-

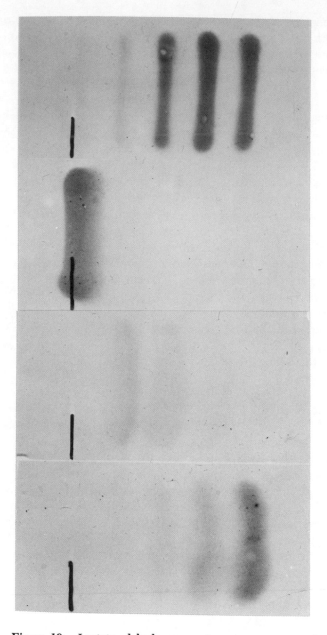

Figure 19. Lactate dehydrogenase isoenzymes separated by cellulose acetate electrophoresis (barbital buffer, pH 8.6, ionic strength 0.075). From the top, extract of heart muscle; liver extract; normal human serum; serum from patient with myocardial infarction.

soaked strip results in appearance of a purple color corresponding to each LDH isoenzyme within 30 minutes. Reagent gels containing the appropriate chemical reagents can also be employed for location of isoenzymes.[37] The course of the staining reaction is illustrated below.

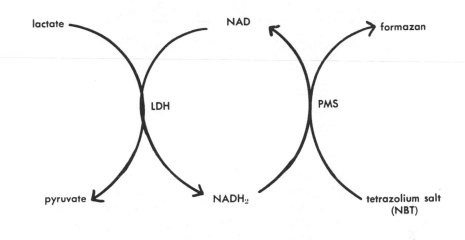

The reaction makes use of the reduction of a tetrazolium salt to a colored formazan by the action of lactate dehydrogenase.[38]

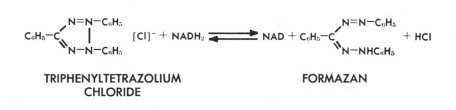

TRIPHENYLTETRAZOLIUM   **FORMAZAN**
CHLORIDE

MTT [2,5-diphenyl-3-(4,5-dimethyl thiazolyl-2)-tetrazolium bromide], a derivative of 2,3,5-triphenyl tetrazolium,

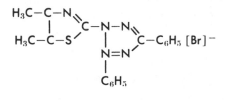

MTT

has been used because of its increased sensitivity.[39, 40, 41] However, the ditetrazolium salt, nitro blue tetrazolium [2,2'-di-p-nitrophenyl-5,5' diphenyl-3,3'-(3-3'dimethoxy-4,4'-diphenylene) dietetrazolium chloride, or NBT],

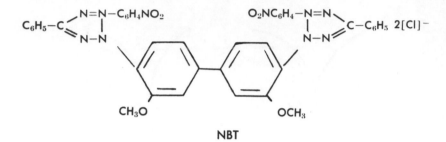

NBT

introduced into use by Tsou *et al.*,[42] exhibits greater sensitivity than MTT and is currently the most widely used tetrazolium salt for reactions involving oxidoreductases.[43, 44, 45, 46, 47] Opher *et al.*[35] employed tetranitro blue tetrazolium while the 2-p-iodophenyl-3-p-nitrophenyl-5-phenyltetrazolium salt has been shown to remain stable and is therefore suitable for standardizing the reaction between the tetrazolium salt and reduced coenzyme.[48] Other derivatives have also been used.

A typical mixture for detecting LDH isoenzymes is one used by Helm *et al.*[49] containing 28.8 mg sodium lactate, 2.2 mg sodium cyanide, 1.1 mg nitro blue tetrazolium, 75.6 mg disodium hydrogen phosphate dihydrate, 10.8 mg potassium dihydrogen phosphate, 0.1 mg phenazine methosulfate, and 4 mg NAD in 4 ml of water. Phenazine methosulfate and NAD are added to the other reagents immediately prior to use. A similar dye reagent has been used by Homer *et al.*[50] Vials containing all of the necessary chemicals for preparing the dye reagent are commercially available. These chemicals can be dissolved in distilled water immediately before use and offer advantages in convenience and avoidance of problems arising from the limited shelf life of chemical solutions. A modification of these mixtures can be used to stain other dehydrogenase isoenzymes, *e.g.*, isocitrate dehydrogenase, glucose-6-phosphodehydrogenase, malate dehydrogenase, etc., when lactate is replaced with the appropriate substrate. In addition, the tetrazolium salt staining procedure can be used to detect other enzymes when coupled with other systems. Aspartate aminotransferases and creatine kinases have been located by incorporating a reaction involving formation of the colored formazan.

MALATE DEHYDROGENASE

Several other oxidoreductases have been shown to exist in multiple molecular forms. Malate dehydrogenase (MDH) catalyzes the oxidation of malic acid to oxaloacetic acid,

$$\text{COOHCH}_2\text{CHOHCOOH} \overset{\text{MDH}}{\rightleftharpoons} \text{COOHCH}_2\text{COCOOH}$$

and is an important enzyme in the citric acid cycle. Vesell and Bearn[51, 52] demonstrated that human serum MDH could be separated into three fractions by starch block electrophoresis. Since that time, various procedures have been used for electrophoretic separation of MDH. The results of cellulose acetate electrophoresis are comparable to those obtained by other methods,[53] and the distribution of MDH isoenzymes in animal and human tissues has been examined by Geyer[54] by means of electrophoresis on cellulose acetate.

The principal component of human heart and liver homogenates and normal blood serum exhibits a mobility similar to that of beta globulin.[55] Yakulis *et al.*[56] found that MDH activity in human organs was concentrated in two bands with mobilities resembling those of LDH$_3$ and LDH$_4$, while Lowenthal *et al.*[57] have found as many as six zones of activity in human and sheep tissues. MDH enzymes from mammalian mitochondria and cytoplasm exhibit differences in electrophoretic mobility[58] and in kinetics of enzyme activity.[59, 60, 61] Furthermore, mitochondria from pig heart have been shown to exhibit four distinct bands on starch gel while the corresponding cytoplasmic enzyme exhibits only one band.[62]

ISOCITRATE DEHYDROGENASE

Isocitrate dehydrogenase (ICD) catalyzes the oxidation of isocitrate to alpha-oxoglutarate. Two distinct types of the enzyme are known. Yeast isocitrate dehydrogenase is dependent upon nicotinamide-adenine dinucleotide phosphate (NADP) and requires 5'-adenosine monophosphate for its action, whereas ICD, which predominates in animal tissue, requires nicotinamide-adenine dinucleotide but not adenosine monophosphate. The NADP-dependent enzyme in animal tissues occurs in multiple molecular forms. Four isocitrate dehydrogenase isoenzymes have been found in human serum.[63, 64] Campbell and Moss,[65] however, found only two peaks of activity in human heart and liver extracts by starch gel electrophoresis. In liver disease, ICD levels in the serum are elevated along with an elevation of LDH and aspartate aminotransferase activity. However, despite the fact that heart muscle is rich in ICD, this enzyme does not appear to be increased after myocardial infarction. Campbell and Moss[65] suggest that this anomalous behavior reflects the labile nature of the electrophoretically slow form which predominates in the heart while the liver enzyme, which migrates more rapidly, remains stable and can therefore be detected after release into the blood stream.

GLUCOSE-6-PHOSPHATE DEHYDROGENASE

Molecular heterogeneity of glucose-6-phosphate dehydrogenase was first reported by Tsao[63] upon electrophoresis of rat tissue extracts in glycylglycine buffer at pH 7.4 on starch gel. Heart muscle and erythrocytes exhibit two distinct bands with an additional band present in kidney and liver homogenates. Cultured cells show two bands of activity on cellulose acetate membranes.[66] The serum level of glucose-6-phosphate dehydrogenase is increased in myocardial infarction, although to a lesser extent than lactate dehydrogenase or aspartate aminotransferase. It is believed that an inherited deficiency of this enzyme in red blood cells causes hemolytic anemia following drug therapy.[67] A rapid procedure for electrophoretic separation of glucose-6-phosphate dehydrogenase has been described by Sparkes *et al.*[68]

6-PHOSPHOGLUCONATE DEHYDROGENASE

6-Phosphogluconate dehydrogenase usually occurs in human erythrocytes as a single band when starch gel electrophoresis is carried out in 0.01M phosphate buffer of pH 7.0 followed by detection of enzyme activity with a mixture containing the substrate, coenzyme, and tetrazolium salt. An additional band may be observed upon occasion in red cell hemolysates; this may be a genetic variant whose expression is governed by Mendelian principles of inheritance.[69]

GLUTAMATE DEHYDROGENASE

Glutamate dehydrogenase from myocardial tissue extracts has been separated into five isoenzymes by means of agar gel electrophoresis in barbital buffer of pH 8.4, ionic strength 0.1.[70] Detection of bands of isoenzyme activity was accomplished by overlaying the electrophoresed sample with a gel containing the appropriate substances to produce the colored formazan.

AMINOTRANSFERASE ISOENZYMES

Aspartate aminotransferase (glutamate-oxaloacetate transaminase, or GOT), which is grossly elevated in the blood of persons shortly after an episode of myocardial infarction, catalyzes the reaction between aspartate and 2-oxoglutarate to form glutamate and oxaloacetate, while alanine aminotransferase (glutamate-pyruvate transaminase, or GPT) catalyzes the reaction of alanine and 2-oxoglutarate to form glutamate and pyruvate.

Heart, liver, skeletal muscle and kidney are rich in aspartate aminotransferase while liver and kidney are rich in alanine aminotransferase. Purified heart and liver aspartate aminotransferase shows two distinct fractions, while the serum enzyme appears to be homogeneous upon electrophoresis.[71, 72] An appreciable portion of the total aspartate aminotransferase activity resides in the mitochondria of rat liver,[73] and the activity in liver mitochondrial homogenates may be 2–4 times that in the supernatant fraction. On the other hand, alanine aminotransferase, which appears to give only one homogeneous band on electrophoresis, appears predominantly in the supernatant fraction of animal tissues.[74, 75]

Detection of aspartate and alanine aminotransferase activity can be accomplished by coupling these enzymes in sequence with oxidoreductase enzymes which reduce tetrazolium salts to their colored formazans. Boyde and Latner[76] detected the presence of aspartate aminotransferase on starch gel by reacting the enzyme with a solution containing L-aspartate, alpha-oxoglutarate, reduced nicotinamide-adenine dinucleotide ($NADH_2$), pyridoxal phosphate, and malate dehydrogenase (MDH) followed by color development with the tetrazolium procedure. Boyd[72, 75] developed a fluorometric procedure for detection of enzyme by reacting the electrophoretic gel layer containing the enzyme fractions with substrate, MDH, and $NADH_2$. The deaminated products are reduced by $NADH_2$ in the presence of MDH; $NADH_2$ is oxidized to give dark bands against a fluorescent background. The reactions are described by the following sequences:

$$\text{L-aspartate} + \alpha\text{-oxoglutarate} \underset{}{\overset{\text{GOT}}{\rightleftharpoons}} \text{L-glutamate} + \text{oxaloacetate}$$

$$\text{oxaloacetate} + NADH_2 \underset{}{\overset{\text{MDH}}{\rightleftharpoons}} \text{malate} + NAD$$

$$\text{L-alanine} + \alpha\text{-oxoglutarate} \underset{}{\overset{\text{GPT}}{\rightleftharpoons}} \text{pyruvate} + \text{L-glutamate}$$

$$\text{pyruvate} + NADH_2 \underset{}{\overset{\text{LDH}}{\rightleftharpoons}} \text{lactate} + NAD$$

CREATINE PHOSPHOKINASE

Three molecular forms of creatine phosphokinase (CPK) have been identified in tissue extracts. Brain CPK consists of one band which migrates in the region of albumin, while skeletal muscle CPK remains at the origin. Heart muscle possesses two distinct isoenzymes; in addition to the form found in skeletal muscle, a fraction of intermediate mobility is seen on electrophoretograms. Erythrocytes appear to lack creatine phosphokinase.

The distribution of creatine phosphokinase isoenzymes may be used to aid in localizing the diseased organ. In muscle diseases, or after myocardial infarction, serum enzyme levels may be grossly elevated. Analysis of the isoenzyme pattern may help to determine the site of tissue damage. Some neurological disturbances are also accompanied by increased creatine phosphokinase levels; however, the predominant isoenzyme is frequently the muscle (slow-migrating) form, suggesting that an increased permeability of muscle cells occurs. Analysis of creatine phosphokinase isoenzyme patterns may be of limited value in such cases.[77]

Rosalki[78] employed cellulose acetate membranes to separate serum and tissue creatine phosphokinase isoenzymes by electrophoresis. A similar method which gives satisfactory separation in only 45 minutes has been described by Trainer and Gruenig.[79] Photometric evaluation can be carried out on the colored formazan formed upon reduction of the tetrazolium salt.

The staining procedure involves the following reaction scheme:

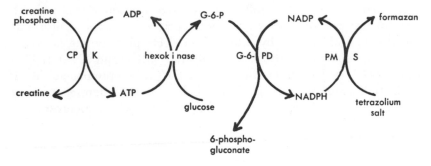

The incubation mixture contains glucose, adenosine diphosphate (ADP), creatine phosphate, hexokinase, nicotinamide-adenine dinucleotide phosphate (NADP), glucose-6-phosphate dehydrogenase (G-6-PDH), phenazine methosulfate (PMS), and nitro blue tetrazolium.

OTHER ENZYMES

Methods have been devised for the electrophoretic separation of amylase,[80, 81] followed by detection utilizing the starch–iodine color reaction. Isoenzymes of serum aminopeptidase[82, 83] and erythrocyte carbonic anhydrase[84] have been separated. Alkaline phosphatase, acid phosphatase, plant peroxidases, and esterases have been separated by agar gel and paper electrophoresis.[85, 86, 87, 88, 89, 90, 91] With minor modifications, these procedures can also be employed for electrophoresis on cellulose acetate to give comparable results with a running time of less than two hours.

REFERENCES

1. Meister, A.   J. Biol. Chem. **184,** 117 (1950).
2. Neilands, J. B.   J. Biol. Chem. **199,** 373 (1952).
3. Vesell, E. S., and A. G. Bearn.   Proc. Soc. Exp. Biol. Med. **94,** 96 (1957).
4. Sayre, F. W., and B. R. Hill.   Proc. Soc. Exp. Biol. Med. **96,** 695 (1957).
5. Wieland, T., and G. Pfleiderer.   Biochem. Z. 329, **112** (1957).
6. Raymond, S., and B. Aurell.   Science **138,** 152 (1962).
7. Wieland, T., and G. Pfleiderer.   Ann. N. Y. Acad. Sci. **94,** 691 (1961).
8. Wachsmuth, E. D., G. Pfleiderer, and T. Wieland.   Biochem. Z. **340,** 80 (1964).
9. Appella, E., and C. L. Market.   Biochem. Biophys. Res. Comm. **6,** 171 (1961).
10. Cahn, R. D., N. O. Kaplan, L. Levine, and E. Zwilling.   Science **136,** 962 (1962).
11. Markert, C. L.   Science **140,** 1329 (1963).
12. Markert, C. L., and H. Ursprung.   Develop. Biol. **5,** 363 (1962).
13. Zinkham, W. H., A. Blanco, and L. Kupchyk.   Science **142,** 1303 (1963).
14. Meyerhof, O., and K. Lohmann.   Biochem. Z. **171,** 421 (1926).
15. Green, D. E., and J. Brosteaux.   Biochem. J. **30,** 1489 (1936).
16. Kubowitz, F., and P. Ott.   Biochem. Z. **314,** 94 (1943).
17. Rosalki, S. B., and J. H. Wilkinson.   Nature **188,** 1110 (1960).
18. Dawson, D. M., T. L. Goodfriend, and N. O. Kaplan.   Science **143,** 929 (1964).
19. Brody, I. A.   Nature **205,** 196 (1965).
20. Rosalki, S. B.   Proc. Assoc. Clin. Biochem. **4,** 200 (1967).
21. Elliott, B. A., and J. H. Wilkinson.   Lancet **2,** 71 (1962).
22. Wieme, R. J.   Clin. Chim. Acta **4,** 46 (1959).

23. Wróblewski, F., C. Ross, and K. Gregory. New Eng. J. Med. **263**, 531 (1960).
24. Latner, A. L., and A. W. Skillen. Lancet **2**, 1286 (1961).
25. Blanchaer, M. C. Clin. Chim. Acta **6**, 272 (1961).
26. Elliott, B. A., E. M. Jepson, and J. H. Wilkinson. Clin. Sci. **23**, 305 (1962).
27. Gonzalez, I. E. Am. J. Clin. Pathol. **42**, 530 (1964).
28. Wright, E. J., L. P. Cawley, and L. Eberhardt. Am. J. Clin. Pathol. **45**, 737 (1966).
29. Pyörälä, K., R. Gordin, A. Konttinen, and L. Telivuo. Acta Med. Scand. **174**, 361 (1963).
30. Pfleiderer, G., and E. D. Wachsmuth. Biochem. Z. **334**, 185 (1961).
31. Barnett, H. Biochem. J. **84**, 83P (1962).
32. Hawkins, D. F., and G. A. Whyley. Lancet **1**, 1126 (1962).
33. Meade, B. W., and S. B. Rosalki. J. Obstet. Gynaecol. Brit. Commonwealth **70**, 862 (1963).
34. Preston, J. A., R. O. Briere, and J. G. Batsakis. Am. J. Clin. Pathol. **43**, 256 (1965).
35. Opher, A. W., C. S. Collier, and J. M. Miller. Clin. Chem. **12**, 308 (1966).
36. Cohen, L., and L. Larson. New Eng. J. Med. **275**, 465 (1966).
37. Myers, R. C., and H. van Remortel. Clin. Chem. **14**, 1131 (1968).
38. Kun, E., and L. G. Abood. Science **109**, 144 (1949).
39. Nineham, A. W. Chem. Rev. **55**, 355 (1955).
40. Pearse, A. G. E. *Histochemistry, Theoretical and Applied*, 2nd ed. (London: Churchill Ltd., 1960).
41. Seligman, A. M. In *Methods in Enzymology*, Vol. VI., eds. S. P. Colowick and N. O. Kaplan (New York: Academic Press, 1963) p 889.
42. Tsou, K. C., C. S. Cheng, M. M. Nachlas, and A. M. Seligman. J. Am. Chem. Soc. **78**, 6139 (1956).
43. Markert, C. L., and F. Moller. Proc. Nat. Acad. Sci. **45**, 753 (1959).
44. Vesell, E. S. Ann. N. Y. Acad. Sci. **94**, 877 (1961).
45. Helm, H. J. van der. Lancet **2**, 108 (1961).
46. Wieme, R. J., M. van Sande, D. Karcher, A. Löwenthal, and H. J. van der Helm. Clin. Chim. Acta **7**, 750 (1962).
47. Gerhardt, W., J. Clausen, E. Christensen, and J. Riishede. Acta Neurol. Scand. **39**, 85 (1963).
48. Whitaker, J. F. Clin. Chim. Acta **24**, 23 (1969).
49. Helm, H. J. van der, H. A. Zondag, H. A. Ph. Hartog, and M. D. van der Kooi. Clin. Chim. Acta **7**, 540 (1962).
50. Homer, G. M., B. Yott, and J. G. Lim. Am. J. Clin. Pathol. **51**, 287 (1969).
51. Vesell, E. S., and A. G. Bearn. J. Clin. Invest. **37**, 672 (1958).
52. Vesell, E. S., and A. G. Bearn. Ann. N.Y. Acad. Sci. **75**, 286 (1958).
53. Wieland, T., G. Pfleiderer, and F. Ortanderl. Biochem. Z. **331**, 103 (1959).

54. Geyer, H. Fres. Z. Anal. Chem. **243**, 578 (1968).
55. Kamarýt, J., and Z. Zazvorka. Clin. Chim. Acta **9**, 559 (1964).
56. Yakulis, V. J., C. W. Gibson, and P. Heller. Am. J. Clin. Pathol. **38**, 378 (1962).
57. Lowenthal, A., M. van Sande, and D. Karcher. Ann. N.Y. Acad. Sci. **94**, 988 (1961).
58. Wieland, T., G. Pfleiderer, I. Haupt, and W. Wörner. Biochem. Z. **332**, 1 (1959).
59. Delbrück, A., H. Schimassek, K. Bartsch, and Th. Büchcr. Biochem. Z. **331**, 297 (1959).
60. Thorne, C. J. R. Biochim. Biophys. Acta **42**, 175 (1960).
61. Siegel, L., and S. Englard. Fed. Proc. **20**, 239 (1961).
62. Thorne, C. J. R., L. I. Grossman, and N. O. Kaplan. Biochim. Biophys. Acta **73**, 193 (1963).
63. Tsao, M. U. Arch. Biochem. Biophys. **90**, 234 (1960).
64. Baron, D. N., and J. L. Bell. Proc. Assoc. Clin. Biochem. **2**, 8 (1962).
65. Campbell, D. M., and D. W. Moss. Proc. Assoc. Clin. Biochem. **2**, 10 (1962).
66. Peterson, W. D., Jr., C. S. Stulberg, N. K. Swanborg, and A. R. Robinson. Proc. Soc. Exp. Biol. Med. **128**, 772 (1968).
67. Carson, P. E., C. L. Flanagan, C. E. Ickes, and A. S. Alving. Science **124**, 484 (1956).
68. Sparkes, R. S., M. Baluda, and D. E. Townsend. J. Lab. Clin. Med. **73**, 531 (1969).
69. Fildes, R. A., and C. W. Parr. Nature **200**, 890 (1963).
70. Helm, H. J. van der. Nature **194**, 773 (1962).
71. Fleisher, G. A., C. S. Potter, and K. G. Wakim. Proc. Soc. Exp. Biol. Med. **103**, 229 (1960).
72. Boyd, J. W. Biochem. J. **81**, 434 (1961).
73. Hird, F. J. R., and E. V. Rowsell. Nature **166**, 517 (1950).
74. Fleisher, G. A. Fed. Proc. **19**, 6 (1960).
75. Boyd, J. W. Clin. Chim. Acta **7**, 424 (1962).
76. Boyde, T. R. C., and A. L. Latner. Biochem. J. **82**, 51P (1962).
77. Cao, A., S. de Virgiliis, C. Lippi, and N. Trabalza. Clin. Chim. Acta **23**, 475 (1969).
78. Rosalki, S. B. Nature **207**, 414 (1965).
79. Trainer, T. D., and D. Gruenig. Clin. Chim. Acta **21**, 151 (1968).
80. Nikkilä, E., K. Ekholm, and H. Silvola. Acta Chem. Scand. **6**, 617 (1952).
81. Kinersley, T. Yale J. Biol. Med. **26**, 211 (1953).
82. Smith, E. E., and A. M. Rutenburg. Nature **197**, 800 (1963).
83. Meade, B. W., and S. B. Rosalki. J. Clin. Pathol. **17**, 61 (1964).
84. Ruiz-Reyes, G., and M. de J. Ramirez-Zorilla. Am. J. Clin. Pathol. **50**, 677 (1968).
85. Baker, B. W. R., and C. Pellegrino. Scand. J. Clin. Lab. Invest. **6**, 94 (1954).

86. Jermyn, M. A., and R. Thomas.   Biochem. J. **56**, 631 (1954).
87. Ahmed, Z., M. A. M. Abul-Fadl, and E. J. King.   Biochim. Biophys. Acta **36**, 228 (1959).
88. Oort, J., and R. G. J. Willighagen.   Nature **190**, 642 (1961).
89. Moss, D. W., D. M. Campbell, E. Anagnostou-Kakaras, and E. J. King.   In *Enzymes in Clinical Chemistry* (Proceedings of 2nd International Symposium on Enzymes in Clinical Chemistry) Ghent, 1961 [London: Butterworths & Co. (Publishers) Ltd., 1962] p 397.
90. Haije, W. G., and M. de Jong.   Clin. Chim. Acta **8**, 620 (1963).
91. Latner, A. L.   In *Enzymes in Clinical Chemistry* (West-European Symposia on Clinical Chemistry, Vol. IV) eds. R. Ruyssen and L. L. Vandenriessche, Ghent, 1964 (Amsterdam: Elsevier Publishing Co., 1965) p 110.

CHAPTER 12

Immunodiffusion and Immunoelectrophoresis

Many naturally occurring substances are antigenic and can induce the formation of antibodies with which they combine to form antigen-antibody complexes. These immunological reactions are of considerable importance because they constitute a mechanism by which the body protects itself against attack from a variety of infectious agents and foreign substances. Immunochemical reactions are also important means for distinguishing differences among proteins from plants and animals and for studying their heterogeneous character. Procedures based on these reactions, namely, immunodiffusion and immunoelectrophoresis, provide possibilities for studying the behavior and composition of many biological substances and for determining their degree of purity.

Antibodies which take part in immunochemical reactions belong to a large class of serum proteins called globulins and are therefore called immunoglobulins. They are produced in response to the introduction of antigenic substances, many of which are present in animal tissues and body fluids. Antibody production is controlled by the presence of chemical determinant groups (haptens) on the antigen molecule (extrinsic heterogeneity) and by the inherited variability of the responding tissue which governs the ability of that tissue to form antibodies (intrinsic heterogeneity). The interaction of these two factors gives rise to a variety of antigen-antibody reactions which characterize individuals and make possible distinction of differences among living organ systems. In most cases, antibody molecules formed in response to antigenic stimuli react specifically with homologous antigens. However, some degree of cross reactivity may occasionally occur which allows antisera to react with a number of antigens from different animal species.

Most antigen-antibody complexes are insoluble in neutral salt solutions. The precipitin test, which is based on the ability of specific antibodies to precipitate the antigens which induced their formation, is the simplest method by which the presence of antibodies in solution can be detected. This reaction constitutes the basis of all immunochemical procedures.

Immunodiffusion and immunoelectrophoresis have become powerful tools for the study of antigenic materials; they have been instrumental in extending the understanding of the nature and reactions of biological systems. Immunodiffusion and immunoelectrophoresis are also used to study the influence of genetic factors in the regulation of protein metabolism and in the clinical diagnosis of some protein abnormalities such as afibrinogenemia, agammaglobulinemia, myelomatosis, and macroglobulinemia. Furthermore, it is frequently desirable to distinguish minute differences in antigenic composition of protein fractions in order to characterize them; immunochemical studies can reveal qualitative and quantitative relationships which lead to differences in biological activity. In addition, impurities present in proteins with or without enzyme activity may give rise to extraneous reactions. Studies of the homogeneity or microheterogeneity of antigenic materials are important to the understanding of basic reaction mechanisms and are necessary to define conditions and causes of variations in behavior which are occasionally encountered.

Several classes of immunoglobulins have been established. These are IgA (γA-globulin), IgG (γG-globulin), IgM (γM-globulin), IgD (γD-globulin), and IgE (γE-globulin). Most immunoglobulins have a molecular weight of approximately 160,000 with the exception of IgM which has a molecular weight of approximately one million. The immunoglobulins appear to be involved primarily with bodily response to infectious agents.

γG-globulins are the most prevalent immunoglobulins in human serum with an average concentration of approximately 1,200 mg/100 ml. They contain the majority of antibacterial, antiviral, and antitoxic substances; in addition, antibodies to insulin and allergens have been reported to be present.[1, 2]

The γA-globulins, with an average serum concentration of approximately 200 mg/100 ml, contain antitoxins and antibacterial agglutinins,[3] antibodies to insulin,[1] and to certain allergens.[4, 5, 6]

γM-globulins have an average concentration of 100 mg/100 ml. They contain the blood group isoantibodies, rheumatoid arthritis factors, and antibodies to thyroglobulin,[7] insulin,[1] and certain types of bacteria.[3]

γD-globulin has an average concentration of 3 mg/100 ml of serum. The physiologic function of γD-globulin is unknown. γE-globulin is present in extremely low concentration and has been shown to be a carrier of reaginic activity.[8]

Use of advanced methods of detection has contributed to the understanding of the role of immunoglobulins in health and disease. Immunoglobulin levels appear to remain quite stable in normal individuals but may change in response to specific diseases. Their concentrations may vary in chronic infections, liver disease, rheumatoid arthritis, and nephrosis. In addition, significant alterations occur in diabetes, neoplastic diseases, collagen disorders, and disturbances in lipid metabolism. Some of the changes have been summarized by Ritzmann and Levin.[9] Differentiation among these various diseases and determination of qualitative and quantitative changes in protein antigens are possible by means of immunodiffusion and immunoelectrophoresis.

Immunodiffusion makes use of the reaction between antigen and antibody in solution to form visible lines of precipitation. The method of single diffusion was introduced by Oudin.[10] Antibody is mixed with heated agar, poured into test tubes, and allowed to gel. A solution containing the antigen or antigens is layered on top of the gel, and diffusion of the antigens into the antibody-containing gel results in the formation of precipitin bands which are clearly visible.

The double diffusion or two-dimensional diffusion technique[11, 12, 13] makes it possible to differentiate between cross-reacting antibodies. By this method antigen and antibody solutions are initially separated by a semisolid gel, and lines of precipitation are formed by their reaction upon diffusion. In Ouchterlony's method, agar is poured into petri dishes and allowed to gel. Solutions of antigen and antibody are placed in wells which are cut in the agar gel. Diffusion of antigen and antibody results in the formation of precipitin lines at the zones of reaction. The presence of cross-reacting antibodies can be detected by examining the lines of precipitation. This method affords a high degree of resolution and allows a series of serological precipitin tests to be carried out simultaneously.

Satisfactory results of immunochemical analyses require that the concentration of antigen be kept at an optimum level since excess antigen will result in solubilization of the antigen-antibody complex. This occurs because antibody molecules in the presence of excess antigen molecules will form small complexes consisting of two mole-

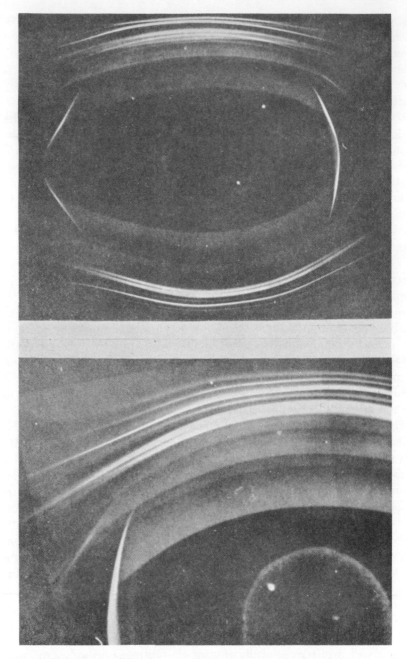

Figure 20.   Immunodiffusion on cellulose acetate. (Reprinted, by permission, from J. Kohn, *Chromatographic and Electrophoretic Techniques*, Vol. II: "Zone Electrophoresis," ed. I. Smith, Figure 3.22. © 1960, Interscience.)

cules of antigen for each antibody molecule. These small complexes interfere competitively with the formation of long chains which normally comprise an alternating array of antigen and antibody molecules.[14]

Immunoelectrophoresis, a combination of immunodiffusion with electrophoresis, was introduced by Grabar and Williams.[15] The protein mixture is first exposed to electrophoresis, after which the separated proteins and antisera are allowed to diffuse and react mutually. Heterogeneity of protein fractions is revealed by the appearance of multiple bands of precipitation. The serum proteins have been separated into many fractions with distinctly different immunologic activities, and numerous protein antigens in normal and pathological blood sera have been detected by use of this method. Techniques involved in immunodiffusion and immunoelectrophoresis have been reviewed by Ouchterlony.[16]

Cellulose acetate membranes can be used for immunodiffusion and immunoelectrophoresis instead of agar gel. Cellulose acetate membranes offer an advantage since completed immunodiffusion and immunoelectrophoretic strips can be dried and preserved permanently after staining (Figures 20 and 21). The procedure for performing immunodiffusion on cellulose acetate is simple, especially since membranes require little preparation.[17, 18] Another possible advantage of cellulose acetate is that soluble antibody fractions may be recovered

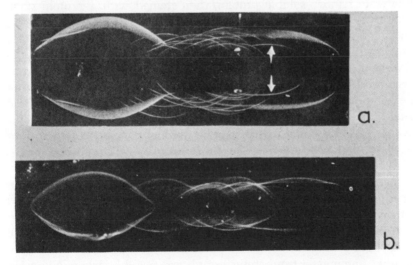

Figure 21. Immunoelectrophoresis on cellulose acetate. (Reprinted, by permission, from J. Kohn, *Chromatographic and Electrophoretic Techniques*, Vol. II: "Zone Electrophoresis," ed. I. Smith, © 1960, Interscience.)

from the membranes, whereas agar gels are partly water-soluble and may contaminate the extract.[14] However, it is possible that certain antigen-antibody reactions which occur rapidly but transiently cannot be visualized on cellulose acetate, whereas the progress of immunodiffusion can be followed constantly when semisolid gels are used.

Methods for immunoelectrophoresis on cellulose acetate have been described by Kohn[19, 20] and by Grunbaum and Dong.[21] Electrophoresis of serum proteins is carried out in the usual manner, after which antiserum is applied in a straight line parallel to the long axis of the strip and 5–10 mm away from the separated protein antigens. Application of antiserum is effected with a capillary pipet or by means of transferance from a narrow (1–2 mm wide) filter paper strip. Frequently, antiserum is applied on both sides of the separated proteins prior to carrying out the immunodiffusion reaction. Antiserum may also be placed at the center of the membrane after completion of electrophoresis, in which case two separate serum samples, each located 5–10 mm away from the center of the strip, may be run simultaneously. The strip containing separated protein antigens and antiserum may be placed in paraffin oil (mineral oil) and left for 16–24 hours to permit diffusion of antigen and antibody. When diffusion is complete, paraffin oil is removed from the strip by gentle wiping and rinsing in a mild detergent solution or by rinsing briefly in methanol or ether. The strip is washed in diluted buffer, saline, or distilled water for 30–60 minutes to remove soluble protein, then stained with a protein stain.

Alternatively, the strip containing separated proteins and antibodies can be left in a moisture chamber for diffusion to take place. Use of a moist incubation chamber avoids the necessity for removing paraffin oil prior to staining. Soluble protein (not the precipitin lines or arcs) is removed by rinsing in buffer, saline, or distilled water, and lines of precipitation are detected by staining for proteins. Ponceau S and Amido Black 10B are commonly used for this purpose, but Nigrosine, because of its great sensitivity, may be used advantageously to discern fine lines of precipitation.

Strips which have been stained and rinsed may be rendered transparent by immersion in glycerol. Transparent strips may also be obtained by drying them after immersion in a mixture of acetic acid and methanol. These procedures are described in the chapter on protein electrophoresis. Results of immunoelectrophoresis on cellulose acetate are generally as good as those obtained with agar gel, and highly sensitive immunoelectrophoretic assays are possible when Nigrosine is employed as the staining reagent. A possible drawback of this method, however, is that precipitin arcs formed only temporarily may not be detected.[22]

The sensitivity of immunoelectrophoresis is increased by the method of crossed electrophoresis.[23, 24, 25] Antigen is allowed to migrate electrophoretically in two dimensions, thus eliminating the necessity for mutual diffusion of antigen and antibody. After unidirectional electrophoresis of antigen proteins in the normal fashion on a 17 cm square sheet of cellulose acetate, the sheet is turned 90° with the separated proteins near the cathode bridge. Antiserum is applied in a narrow band parallel to the separated proteins and approximately one centimeter from them in the anodal direction. When electrophoresis is carried out in the second dimension at right angles to the first, antigens will migrate rapidly into the area containing antiserum. Precipitated antigen-antibody complexes will not migrate; after removal of soluble protein from the membrane by rinsing in distilled water or saline, they can be stained with the appropriate protein stain.

A variation of crossed electrophoresis has been introduced by Zydeck *et al.*[26] This procedure consists of separating gamma globulin from other proteins in the antiserum by means of preliminary electrophoresis, followed by electrophoretic migration of protein antigens in the same direction. Zones of precipitation are formed as the antigens move through the gamma globulin region. This test may be of value in detecting the presence of minute amounts of antigen. Rapid quantitation of protein in a cellulose acetate membrane impregnated with antiserum can be accomplished by the method of immunoelectrophoresis as described by Kroell[27] or by single radial immunodiffusion on membranes sprayed with antiserum.[28]

By means of methods such as those described and by using highly specific antisera prepared against purified protein fractions, the main classes of immunoglobulins which differ in rates of synthesis, concentrations, and distributions in plasma and body fluids have been studied. Data derived from immunoelectrophoresis are valuable for determining the nature of prevailing protein deficiencies, and for identifying proteins involved in the myelomas and paraproteinemias.[9] Immunochemical studies may also be of value in examining mechanisms underlying malignancy and possibly in the design of therapeutic measures to neutralize or reverse the progress of malignant growth.[29]

Immunoelectrophoresis can also be used to detect the presence of soluble complexes of antibody and isotopically labeled radioactive antigen. The position of the labeled antigen-antibody complex is determined and measured by autoradiography. For example, soluble complexes of ^{131}I-insulin with homologous antibody can be differentiated from free ^{131}I-insulin by means of a difference in mobility between free and complexed insulin.[30] Dusanic and Lewert[31] labeled protein extracts of *Schistosoma mansoni* with ^{131}I and were able to differentiate five or six antigen-antibody complexes by cellulose acetate immunoelectrophoresis, compared with 2–5 lines in agar gel precipitin tests with the same sera. In addition, binding of thyroxine by several fractions of human albumins and globulins has been demonstrated by radioimmunoelectrophoresis using labeled thyroxine.[32]

Immunochemical reactions are widely used to study problems of veterinary and human medical importance. Properly used, the techniques can aid in characterizing substances of biological interest. In clinical medicine, they can contribute to the diagnosis of various abnormalities of protein metabolism.[33] Recent reports indicate that certain immunoglobulins may rise with increasing age[34] or in coronary heart disease.[35] Significant conclusions concerning protein metabolism in health and disease will surely arise from systematic study of immunological factors.

It is clear that immunodiffusion and immunoelectrophoresis are important techniques which can be employed to advantage in a large number of diverse applications. They are of proven merit when used to examine certain types of physiological aberrations; they also enable the investigator to perform detailed studies on the nature of proteins and examine reaction mechanisms which characterize the immune responses of humans and other animal species.

REFERENCES

1. Yagi, Y., P. Maier, D. Pressman, C. E. Arbesman, R. E. Reisman, and A. R. Lenzner. J. Immunol. **90**, 760 (1963).
2. Yagi, Y., P. Maier, D. Pressman, C. E. Arbesman, and R. E. Reisman. J. Immunol. **91**, 83 (1963).
3. Heremans, J. F., J. P. Vaerman, and C. Vaerman. J. Immunol. **91**, 11 (1963).
4. Heremans, J. F., and J. P. Vaerman. Nature **193**, 1091 (1962).
5. Rockey, J. H., and H. G. Kunkel. Proc. Soc. Exp. Biol. Med. **110**, 101 (1962).
6. Fireman, P., W. E. Vannier, and H. C. Goodman. J. Exp. Med. **117**, 603 (1963).
7. Fahey, J. L., and H. C. Goodman. J. Clin. Invest. **39**, 1259 (1960).
8. Ishizaka, K., T. Ishizaka, and M. M. Hornbrook. J. Immunol. **97**, 75, 840 (1966).
9. Ritzmann, S. E., and W. C. Levin. In *Lab. Synopsis*, Vol. II (Kansas City, Missouri: Hoechst Pharmaceutical Company, 1967) p 9.
10. Oudin, J. Ann. Inst. Pasteur. **89**, 531 (1955).
11. Ouchterlony, Ö. Arkiv Kemi **1**, 43, 55 (1949).
12. Ouchterlony, Ö. Prog. Allergy **5**, 1 (1958).
13. Oakley, C. L., and A. J. Fulthorpe. J. Pathol. Bacteriol. **65**, 49 (1953).

14. Haurowitz, F. *Immunochemistry and the Biosynthesis of Antibodies* (New York: Interscience, 1968).
15. Grabar, P., and C. A. Williams. Biochim. Biophys. Acta **10**, 193 (1953).
16. Ouchterlony, Ö. *Handbook of Immunodiffusion and Immunolectrophoresis* (Ann Arbor, Michigan: Ann Arbor Science Publishers, Inc., 1968).
17. Consden, R., and J. Kohn. Nature **183**, 1512 (1959).
18. Kohn, J. Nature **217**, 1261 (1968).
19. Kohn, J. Clin. Chim. Acta **3**, 450 (1958).
20. Kohn, J. In Chromatographic and Electrophoretic Techniques, Vol. II: *Zone Electrophoresis* ed. I. Smith (New York: Interscience, 1960) p 56.
21. Grunbaum, B. W., and L. Dong. Nature **194**, 185 (1962).
22. Whitaker, J. R., and G. Zweig. Paper Chromatography and Electrophoresis, Vol. I: *Electrophoresis in Stabilizing Media* (New York: Academic Press, 1967).
23. Nakamura, S., and T. Ueta. Naturwiss. **45**, 569 (1958).
24. Nakamura, S., K. Takeo, I. Sasaki, and M. Murata. Nature **184**, 638 (1959).
25. Laurell, C. B. Anal. Biochem. **10**, 358 (1965).
26. Zydeck, F. A., E. E. Muirhead, and H. Schneider. Am. J. Clin. Pathol. **45**, 323 (1966).
27. Kroell, J. Scand. J. Clin. Lab. Invest. **21**, 187 (1968).
28. Vergani, C., R. Stabilini, and A. Agostoni. Immunochemistry **4**, 233 (1967).
29. Day, E. D. *The Immunochemistry of Cancer* (Springfield, Illinois: Charles C Thomas, 1965).
30. Berson, S. A., and R. S. Yalow. J. Clin. Invest. **38**, 1996, 2017 (1959).
31. Dusanic, D. G., and R. M. Lewert. J. Infect. Diseases **116**, 270 (1966).
32. Gerhards, H. J., K. Joseph, and E. H. Graul. Atompraxis **14**, 21 (1968).
33. Kingdom, L., and E. Shanbrom. J. Amer. Med. Assoc. **200**, 161 (1967).
34. Bert, G., F. Fontana, D. L. Cossano, A. L. Massaro, L. Orecchia, and F. S. Feruglio. Boll. Soc. Ital. Sper. **44**, 297 (1968).
35. Davies, D. F., and A. Clark. J. Athero. Res. **8**, 724 (1968).

CHAPTER 13

Miscellaneous Applications

The previous chapters described techniques and applications of cellulose acetate electrophoretic analysis for a number of substances of well-known importance. Some of the methods are in general use in clinical and research laboratories and have demonstrated their usefulness for studying the development and expression of metabolic disturbances. Many other substances can be separated and examined by electrophoresis when the appropriate buffering solutions and proper operating conditions are selected. Among these are the thyroxin-binding globulins, inorganic ions, amino acids, polysaccharides, viral and bacterial proteins and nucleic acids, and numerous other compounds. The purpose of this final chapter is to point out several types of substances which can be separated electrophoretically; some of these may be of interest to investigators with specialized areas of study.

Most of the electrophoretic procedures which employ filter paper strips or semisolid stabilizing media such as starch, agar, agarose, or polyacrylamide gels can also be performed with cellulose acetate membranes as the supporting medium. As pointed out previously, cellulose acetate membranes offer some advantages over other media because of their uniform structure and composition which make it possible to achieve good resolution. In addition, they require no special preparation for electrophoresis or for immunochemical procedures, a variety of histological stains can readily be used for detection of separated compounds, and quantitative evaluation can be accomplished rapidly and accurately. In many cases results of electrophoresis, immunodiffusion, and immunoelectrophoresis on cellulose acetate are superior to those obtained with other media.

127

Changes in plasma proteins are analyzed in various diseases; in addition, proteins are known to combine chemically with a number of compounds, including carbohydrates, lipids, and hormones. The first two have already been discussed. Hormones occupy a central role in the regulation of metabolism; some are bound to blood proteins and have been examined by electrophoresis. Thyroid extracts labeled with radioactive iodine were separated by electrophoresis on paper by Horst and Schumacher.[1] Although thyroxin may be bound to several serum protein fractions,[2] isotope-labeled thyroxin is mainly associated with serum proteins showing globulin mobility.[3] In clinical medicine, determination of globulin-bound thyroxin may provide useful data to aid in evaluating the metabolic status of patients and following patients under specific therapeutic treatment.

When ^{131}I-labeled free thyroxin is added to serum, it becomes preferentially bound to globulin of alpha$_1$ or alpha$_2$ mobility. Upon saturation of globulin, the excess labeled thyroxin is bound by albumin. Electrophoresis of serum or plasma on cellulose acetate membranes, using procedures employed for electrophoresis of proteins (barbital buffer, pH 8.6), separates globulin-bound thyroxin from thyroxin bound to albumin. Following this, labeled globulin in individual protein fractions is determined by autoradiography or by measuring the radioactivity in segments or eluates of electrophoretograms containing the separated fractions. The percentage distribution of tracer in these fractions can be used to determine the state of a patient's thyroid activity.[4]

The chemistry and structure of the insulin molecule has undergone extensive study.[5, 6, 7] Most samples of insulin comprise several components which can be distinguished by cellulose acetate electrophoresis in phosphate buffer of pH 6.5 containing 7M urea. Insulin and insulin derivatives are stained with Ponceau S, and the amount of each fraction obtained by spectrophotometric measurement at 535 mμ of dye eluted from the electrophoretograms with 0.1N sodium hydroxide.[8]

Protein-bound insulin can be separated from free or unbound insulin by means of electrophoresis.[9, 10] Insulin in blood serum is now most commonly determined by radioimmunoassay.[11, 12] A modification of the radioimmunoassay method makes possible separation of free insulin from antibody-bound insulin and measurement of each, and this modification employs electrophoresis on cellulose acetate membranes. Insulin labeled with radioactive iodine is incubated for 1–2 hours at 37°C with equal volumes of unknown plasma or serum and insulin-binding reagent (rabbit anti-guinea pig serum plus guinea pig anti-bovine insulin serum).

Standards are prepared by substituting insulin solutions of known concentration for the unknown. When electrophoresis is carried out on cellulose acetate strips in barbital buffer of pH 8.6 as employed for protein electrophoresis, free insulin, which migrates to the region of albumin or pre-albumin, is well separated from antibody-bound insulin which remains with the gamma globulin. Radioactivity present in free and bound insulin can be determined by autoradiography or by counting segments of the electrophoretogram.

Determination of free and bound insulin may be carried out by an alternate procedure based on immunoelectrophoresis, which uses a modification of Laurell's[13] method of crossed electrophoresis. Serum or plasma is incubated for 1–2 hours at 37°C with labeled insulin and applied near the cathodal bridge, approximately 6 cm from each edge at the corner of a 17 cm square sheet of cellulose acetate. Electrophoresis in barbital buffer of pH 8.6 is conducted in two dimensions consecutively, the second at right angles to the first. Immediately prior to electrophoresis in the second dimension, insulin-binding reagent is applied in a band 1–2 mm wide, parallel with the direction of migration of the separated proteins and approximately 1 cm distant from the protein fractions. Application of the antiserum can be made with a filter paper or cellulose acetate transfer strip; use of a transfer strip confines the antiserum to the desired area on the membrane. When the second electrophoresis run is carried out, insulin will react with antibody to form a precipitate which will not migrate further. Upon completion of the procedure, the distribution of radioactive insulin on the cellulose acetate sheet can be determined by autoradiography or by sectioning specific areas of the membrane and counting them by conventional methods. This method may be particularly valuable when insulin is known to be present in several forms in blood plasma.

Amino acids and peptides from protein hydrolysates have been separated by means of paper electrophoresis.[14] Basic amino acids can be separated in buffers of alkaline pH and detected by use of a ninhydrin spray.[15] A number of amino acids have been examined with respect to their mobility on paper at different pH values.[16] Derivatives of the proteolytic enzymes chymotrypsin, trypsin, and elastase from pancreas have been fractionated by two-dimensional electrophoresis on cellulose acetate and paper using acidic buffers.[17]

It is interesting to note that amino acid content and distribution may be affected by both genetics and physiology. Thus, Schultz *et al.*[18] found that certain amino acids show characteristic distribution patterns in various animal species, and clinical studies by Cummings and Flynn[19] revealed differences in amino acid composition of human serum

protein in normal and pathological conditions. Excessive amounts of
some amino acids appear in certain pathological blood and urine specimens, and some cases of hereditary aminoaciduria may be associated
with mental retardation. Electrophoresis has been successfully employed for the identification of amino acids in urine;[20, 21] alpha-keto
acids have been separated by paper in barbital buffer of pH 8.6, and
vanilmandelic acid has been isolated from urine by means of cellulose acetate electrophoresis in acetic acid-pyridine buffer of pH 4.2 followed by staining with *p*-nitroaniline.[22] In addition, peptides have
been found in the urine of patients following burns; these ninhydrin-
positive compounds may contribute to the occurrence of shock and
toxemia.[23]

The same procedure is followed for separation of amino acids from
urine or from serum or plasma, with the exception that serum or
plasma samples should first be deproteinized with picric, trichloroacetic, or perchloric acids, and an aliquot of the supernatant used. Electrophoresis is carried out in a buffer of pH 2.0 containing formic acid
and acetic acid (31.2 ml formic acid, 59.2 ml glacial acetic acid, diluted
to 1000 ml). Because amino acids exhibit cathodal migration, samples
should be applied near the anodal bridge. Separated amino acids are
detected by means of a ninhydrin reagent. The procedure has been
described by Scherr.[24]

Adrenal steroids have been examined by paper electrophoresis,[25, 26, 27] and the binding of progesterone to serum albumin and of
hydrocortisone to gamma globulin have been examined by Westphal
et al.[28] In addition, gonadotropic hormone activity has been found
in the alpha$_2$ globulin region.[29]

Cellulose acetate electrophoresis of human gastrointestinal secretions has revealed the presence of several bands, some of which could
be further subdivided into minor peaks. Separation was achieved
with borate buffer of pH 9 and ionic strength 0.12. A large albumin
component appeared in the gastric juice of patients with gastric ulcer
and gastric carcinoma.[30, 31]

The separation of flavin nucleotides, nicotinamide, and pyridoxine
by electrophoresis has been accomplished by Siliprandi *et al.*[32] and
by Peel[33] by means of paper electrophoresis. The separated compounds
were detected by their fluorescence under ultraviolet light.

Complexes containing carbohydrate can be separated by electrophoresis. Using a borate buffer, Consden and Stanier[34] separated
fructose, mannose, galactose, arabinose, and glucose by paper electrophoresis. Mucopolysaccharides and isomers of chondroitin sulfate have
been separated by electrophoresis on paper and by cellulose ace-

tate.[35, 36] Acid mucopolysaccharides of rabbit aorta show changes in specific fractions during early stages of cholesterol-induced atherosclerosis[36] when these fractions are stained with Alcian Blue. Mixtures of colored polysaccharides have been successfully fractionated by electrophoresis on cellulose acetate strips, and results are comparable with undyed polysaccharides separated by free-boundary electrophoresis.[37]

Most purines and pyrimidines are basic, and therefore acid buffers such as citrate–phosphate[38] or formate are used for their separation. Mono-, di-, and tri-nucleotides have been separated by Markham and Smith[39] in ammonium formate buffer of pH 3.5, while an acetate buffer of pH 4 was used by Turba and Enenkel[40] to separate adenosine mono-, di-, and tri-phosphates. Schümmelfeder and Heyer[41] used a Veronal–acetate buffer of pH 2.5 to separate DNA and RNA on paper.

Mononucleotides of cytidine, adenosine, guanine, thymine, and uridine have been separated on cellulose acetate membranes using a sodium citrate buffer of pH 3.15 and proportions of the nucleotides determined by their fluorescence at 254 mμ. Nucleic acids have been separated by means of cellulose acetate electrophoresis in Tris buffer of pH 7.4. Ribosomes migrate as sharp bands when magnesium ions are present in the buffer solution, and they can be visualized by inspection under ultraviolet light of 260 mμ wave length.[43, 44]

Decarboxylation of acetoacetate to acetone by the enzyme from *Clostridium acetobutylicum* forms the basis of the microdiffusion method described by Fridovich.[45] Acetone formed by the action of the decarboxylating enzyme on its substrate reacts with salicylaldehyde to give a red color.

Anodal sample application was found by Mullan *et al.*[46] to give high resolution of soluble liver proteins on cellulose acetate in barbital buffer, while application of the sample near the cathode did not yield a clear separation of the same fractions. This unconventional method of sample application may be employed to advantage for certain analyses where separation of minor components is desired.

When proper compensation is made for the strong electro-osmotic effect of cellulose acetate, these membranes can be used for the determination of isoelectric points of various substances. Kubota and Ueki[47] used the electro-osmotic migration of D-glucose to obtain true values for mobility in determining the isoelectric point of bovine plasma albumin.

The use of electrophoresis to investigate the nature of antibody produced by single antibody-forming cells has been introduced by Marchalonis and Nossal.[48] This type of analytical procedure can prove useful in problems concerned with cell biology since the formation of aberrant proteins in diseases such as myelomatosis and macroglobulinemia can be examined. In addition, immunologic response to antigenic stimuli and vaccines may be studied by use of immunoelectrophoretic methods.[49]

Electrophoretic analysis has been successfully applied to a number of other substances, including human placental proteins,[50] protein extracts of fruit,[51] acetyl choline and related compounds.[52]

Metal ions form complexes with solutions of electrolytes and migrate as complexed ions. Lederer[53] has described procedures and results of the separation of a number of inorganic ions by paper electrophoresis, and separation of metal ions of different valency states has been reported.[54, 55] Aitzetmüller *et al.*[56] employed a cellulose acetate gel to separate mixtures of rare earths which were detected by means of a spray reagent containing Alizarin S and ascorbic acid. Some of the factors concerning electrophoretic separation of inorganic ions have been discussed by Lederer[53] and Whitaker.[57]

REFERENCES

1. Horst, W., and H. H. Schumacher. Klin. Wochschr. **32**, 361 (1954).
2. Gerhards, H. J., K. Joseph, and E. H. Graul. Atompraxis **14**, 21 (1968).
3. Gordon, A. H., J. Gross, D. O'Connor, and R. Pitt-Rivers. Nature **169**, 19 (1952).
4. Berger, S., M. S. Goldstein, and B. E. Metzger. New Eng. J. Med. **267**, 801 (1962).
5. Sanger, F., E. O. P. Thompson, and R. Kitai. Biochem. J. **59**, 509 (1955).
6. Sluyterman, L. A. A. Arch. Intern. Physiol. **62**, 575 (1954).
7. Sluyterman, L. A. A. Biochim. Biophys. Acta **17**, 169 (1955).
8. Carpenter, F. H., and S. L. Hayes. Biochemistry **2**, 1272 (1963).
9. Berson, S. A., R. S. Yalow, A. Bauman, M. A. Rothschild, and K. Newerly. J. Clin. Invest. **35**, 170 (1956).
10. Yalow, R. S., and S. A. Berson. Am. J. Med. **31**, 882 (1961).
11. Hales, C. N., and P. J. Randle. Biochem. J. **88**, 137 (1963).
12. Hales, C. N., and P. J. Randle. Lancet **1**, 200 (1963).
13. Laurell, C. B. Anal. Biochem. **10**, 358 (1965).
14. Durrum, E. L. Rept. Med. Dept. Field Res. Lab., Fort Knox, Ky., Project No. 6–64–12–06, March 1949.
15. Jirgl, V. Anal. Biochem. **8**, 519 (1964).
16. Evered, D. F. Biochim. Biophys. Acta **36**, 14 (1959).
17. Naughton, M. A., F. Sanger, B. S. Hartley, and D. C. Shaw. Biochem. J. **77**, 149 (1960).

18. Schultz, J., G. F. Grannis, H. B. Kimmel, and H. Shay. Federation Proc. **13,** 131 (1954).
19. Cummings, A. J., and F. V. Flynn. J. Clin. Pathol. **8,** 153 (1955).
20. Westall, R. G. Biochem. J. **60,** 247 (1955).
21. Visakorpi, J. K., and A. L. Puranen. Scand. J. Clin. Lab. Invest. **10,** 196 (1958).
22. Butler, T. J. Clin. Chem. **13,** 488 (1967).
23. Goodwin, L. G., C. R. Jones, W. H. G. Richards, and J. Kohn. Brit. J. Exp. Pathol. **44,** 551 (1963).
24. Scherr, G. Anal. Chem. **34,** 777 (1962).
25. Voigt, K. D., and I. Beckmann. Acta Endocrinol. **13,** 19 (1953).
26. Voigt, K. D., and I. Beckmann. Acta Endocrinol. **15,** 251 (1954).
27. McKinley, W. P. Science **121,** 139 (1955).
28. Westphal, U., H. E. Firschein, and E. M. Pearce. Science **121,** 601 (1955).
29. Bourrillon, R., R. Got, and R. Marcy. Bull. Soc. Chim. Biol. **40,** 87 (1958).
30. Piper, D. W., M. C. Stiel, and J. E. Builder. Gut **3,** 349 (1962).
31. Piper, D. W., M. C. Stiel, and J. E. Builder. Gut **4,** 236 (1963).
32. Siliprandi, N., D. Siliprandi, and H. Lis. Biochim. Biophys. Acta **14,** 212 (1954).
33. Peel, J. L. Biochem. J. **69,** 403 (1958).
34. Consden, R., and W. M. Stanier. Nature **169,** 783 (1952).
35. Prout, R. E. S. Biochim. Biophys. Acta **177,** 157 (1969).
36. Saxena, I. D., and J. Nagchaudhuri. Indian J. Med. Res. **57,** 96 (1969).
37. Dudman, W. F., and C. T. Bishop. Can. J. Chem. **46,** 3079 (1968).
38. Burma, D. P. Science **118,** 694 (1953).
39. Markham, R., and J. D. Smith. Biochem. J. **52,** 552 (1952).
40. Turba, F., and H. J. Enenkel. Naturwiss. **38,** 189 (1951).
41. Schümmelfeder, N., and W. Heyer. Naturwiss. **41,** 164 (1954).
42. Cocito, C., and P. Laduron. Anal. Biochem. **7,** 429 (1964).
43. Loening, U. E. Biochem. J. **84,** 28 (1962).
44. Loening, U. E. Nature **195,** 467 (1962).
45. Fridovich, I. Anal. Biochem. **7,** 371 (1964).
46. Mullan, F. A., D. M. Hancock, and D. W. Neill. Nature **194,** 149 (1962).
47. Kubota, Y., and H. Ueki. J. Biochem. **64,** 405 (1968).
48. Marchalonis, J. J., and G. J. V. Nossal. Proc. Nat. Acad. Sci. **61,** 860 (1968).
49. Clark, J. D., and J. W. Foster. Am. J. Vet. Res. **29,** 1293 (1968).
50. Gershbein, L. L., and J. Al-Wattar. J. Chromatog. **34,** 485 (1968).
51. Clements, R. L. Anal. Biochem. **13,** 390 (1965).
52. Potter, L., and W. Murphy. Biochem. Pharmacol. **16,** 1386 (1967).
53. Lederer, M. *An Introduction to Paper Electrophoresis and Related Methods* (Amsterdam: Elsevier Publishing Co., 1955).

54. Lingren, W. E., G. R. Reeck, and R. J. Marson.   Anal. Chem. **40**, 1585 (1968).
55. Facetti, J. F., and M. V. de Santiago.   Anal. Chem. **40**, 1726 (1968).
56. Aitzetmüller, K., K. Buchtela, and F. Grass.   Anal. Chim. Acta **38**, 249 (1967).
57. Whitaker, J. R., and G. Zweig.   Paper Chromatography and Electrophoresis, Vol. I: *Electrophoresis in Stabilizing Media* (New York: Academic Press, 1967).

Index

*The text of this book was typeset at
SSPA Typesetting, Inc., Carmel, Indiana,
in 10-point Caledonia, with 2-point
leading. The chapter headings are in
18-point Square Gothic. The printing
was done by Braun-Brumfield, Inc., Ann Arbor,
Michigan, and the binding by John H. Dekker and Sons,
Grand Rapids, Michigan.*